Ethology and Human Development

John Archer

Department of Psychology
Lancashire Polytechnic

HARVESTER
WHEATSHEAF

NEW YORK LONDON TORONTO SYDNEY TOKYO SINGAPORE

First published 1992 by
Harvester Wheatsheaf
Campus 400, Maylands Avenue
Hemel Hempstead
Hertfordshire, HP2 7EZ
A division of
Simon & Schuster International Group

Typeset in 10/12pt Ehrhardt
by Photoprint, 9–11 Alexandra Lane, Torquay

Printed and bound in Great Britain by
BPCC Wheatons Ltd, Exeter

British Library Cataloguing in Publication Data

A catalogue record for this book is available from the
British Library.

ISBN 0–7450–0916–6 (cased)
    0–7450–0917–4 (pbk)

1 2 3 4 5   95 94 93 92

Ethology and
Human
Development

THE

Series Editor:
Professor George Butterworth, *Department of Psychology, University of Sussex.*

Designed for a broad readership in the English-speaking world, this major series represents the best of contemporary research and theory in the cognitive, social, abnormal and biological areas of development.

Contents

Preface and acknowledgements

Throughout the history of psychology, there have been those who regarded animal behaviour as irrelevant to the study of human psychology. This viewpoint is well represented in the discipline today, at a time when other pressures are being brought to bear on animal research in psychology.

In this book, I shall consider what ethology, the naturalistic study of animal behaviour, can contribute to one area of psychology, that concerned with human development. In doing so, I shall be stating the case for viewing human behaviour in its biological context, and shall argue that this wider perspective can enrich our understanding of human psychological development. I am not denying the influence of learning and culture, but seeking to place these processes into the wider framework achieved by viewing human beings as part of the natural world.

I would like to thank Farrell Burnett of Harvester Wheatsheaf for her support and encouragement; Pat Bateson, Robert Hinde and Peter Slater for their helpful comments on parts of the manuscript and especially Peter K. Smith who read and commented on the whole book. I am grateful to Fred Strayer, Michael Appleby and Frans de Waal for helpful comments and discussion of material in some of the chapters.

I should like to thank the following authors for permission to use material from their work: Michael Appleby; Gerard Baerends; Pat Bateson; Irwin S. Bernstein; Nick Blurton Jones; Kevin Browne; Ivan D. Chase; Charles B. Crawford; Irenäus Eibl-Eibesfeldt; James L. Gould; Robert Hinde; Felicity Huntingford; John Mackintosh; Peter Slater; Peter K. Smith; Sarah Hall Sternglanz; Fred Strayer; Jan A.R.A.M. van Hooff and Glen Weisfeld.

I should like to thank the following publishers for generously allowing me to use material from their publications: Academic Press, Inc. for Figure 4.1; the American Psychological Association for Figure 6.1; Baillière Tindall for Figures 5.2, 5.3, 5.4, 5.8, 5.9, 7.3, 7.4, 7.5 and 9.9; E.J. Brill (Leiden) for Figures 2.9, 7.7 and 8.1; Cambridge University Press for Figures 2.3, 2.6, 2.7,

4.2, 4.3, 4.4, 7.1, 8.4(a) and 9.1–9.5; Garland STPM Press; Karger (Basel) for Figure 4.6; Macmillan Magazines Ltd; McGraw-Hill for Figure 5.10; Methuen; Mouton de Gruyter; Social Science Information; The Society for Research in Child Development, Inc.; Smithsonian Institution Press; John Wiley & Sons for Figures 2.8 and 7.6. Permission to use copyrighted material was also granted by Wayne State University Press.

Chapter 1

Introduction

Ethology and developmental psychology

The developmental origins of human behaviour are often seen as having parallels with the natural world of animals. The gradual development of a complex organism from a single cell was once regarded as retracing its evolutionary history, although it has long been realized that this was based on a misunderstanding of how evolutionary change occurs (Gould, 1977b). Nevertheless, this 'theory of recapitulation' strongly influenced early theorists in developmental psychology, such as Herbert Spencer and G. Stanley Hall (Sants, 1980). Evolutionary theory has continued to influence the study of psychological development in a variety of ways since then (Lickliter and Berry, 1990).

Rather than pursuing such speculative links between evolution and development, Charles Darwin used a background of evolutionary thought for his comparative observations of animal and human behaviour (Darwin, 1872), and for empirical studies of his own children's behavioural development (Darwin, 1877). Although this work contained themes derived from the theory of evolution, such as the mental continuity of animals and humans, empirical observations were foremost. In his approach and his methods, Darwin was the forerunner of later researchers who studied animal behaviour under natural conditions and from an evolutionary perspective. This became known as ethology in the 1930s, and was associated with the observations and concepts of Konrad Lorenz and Niko Tinbergen.

Although influenced by ideas borrowed from the theory of evolution, the psychological study of child development initially travelled along a different path from the ethological tradition. Later there were some well-known points of contact between the two disciplines, notably John Bowlby's use of ethological research on imprinting and motivation to construct a theory of attachment.

The aim of this book is to describe and evaluate ethological research and

1

theory which has influenced, or is applicable to, developmental psychology. In applying approaches derived from studying the natural world of animals to human development, some of the links between research on child development and animal behaviour apparent in Darwin's work are re-evaluated in the light of modern evidence.

Modern ethology – unlike the relatively separate discipline of the 1930s and 1940s – is interlinked with other fields of study, so that it is often difficult to point to influences that travel in only one direction. There are also several different approaches and schools of thought within present-day ethology. Both these considerations complicate any discussion of the influences of ethology on another discipline.

Hinde (1982) has summarized the relations between ethology and the biological and the human sciences. He discussed the importance of ethology for a number of branches of psychology, as well as for anthropology and psychiatry. From Hinde's discussion, it is apparent that apart from comparative psychology, where one would expect the closest links, ethology has had most impact on the psychological study of development. Some of these links were also discussed in two monographs on the contributions of ethology to child development, in volumes of *Carmichael's Manual of Child Psychology*. One (Hess, 1970) is from the viewpoint of the original concepts of ethology, now often referred to as classical or Lorenzian ethology (Chapter 5): here the emphasis is placed upon identifying 'instinctive' patterns of behaviour, which are viewed as being controlled by simple stimuli in the social environment ('releasers'). The other (Hinde, 1983a) reflects later reformulations of ethological thinking, including criticisms of the division of behaviour into innate and learnt aspects, and of simple concepts for explaining behaviour, such as 'releaser' and drive (Chapter 5).

By the 1980s ethology was viewed as an important influence on developmental psychology by authors of introductory textbooks. Some concentrated on classical ethology, leading them to portray the discipline as associated with a set of theoretical views emphasizing the contribution of innate influences on development (e.g. Shaffer, 1989; Miller, 1983, 1989). Others, such as Smith and Cowie (1988), highlighted the importance of ethology for providing an evolutionary perspective on human development. Other texts have emphasized more specific contributions to topics such as morality (Meadows, 1986) and theories of attachment (e.g. Gardner, 1978; Sylva and Lunt, 1981). As indicated below, these accounts provide only restricted portrayals of the range of ethological contributions.

From early on, ethologists have been interested in applying their ideas to human behaviour. Lorenz (1943) used the concept of 'releaser' for a hypothesis that certain exaggerated features found in infants evoke a general parental response in adults. His hypothesis has stimulated empirical research up to the present (Chapter 5). Tinbergen's (1951) classic book summarizing the work of early ethologists and pre-ethologists, *The Study of Instinct*, ended with a section on 'The ethological study of man'. At a later stage, a number of ethologists turned from observing animals to viewing humans from the same perspective and with the same methods. A large part of their research was carried out on children, who, together with some psychiatric patients, provided instances of human behaviour where language could be disregarded in favour of actions.

Nevertheless, the foremost contributions of ethology to developmental psychology have arisen from those ethologists who studied animal behaviour for its intrinsic interest. Some sixty years after the pioneering studies, there is now a detailed body of knowledge and theory which has come to have much to offer to psychologists, and indeed to the other human sciences (Hinde, 1982, 1987). The ethological study of animal behaviour has produced methods which can be used by psychologists, principles of development and motivation, a broad comparative basis for attributes people share with other animals, and – perhaps the most valuable of all – an evolutionary perspective on behaviour.

In the rest of the chapter, I shall outline the historical development of ethology, and then consider its relation to developmental psychology in two ways. The first concerns the common issues they address and the second traces ethological influences from a historical perspective. The chapter ends with a summary of the themes covered in the remainder of the book.

Early naturalists and pre-1955 ethology

As indicated above, Charles Darwin's work combined two characteristics of the later ethological approach, a background of evolutionary thought and careful observation. The second of these links him with early twentieth-century scientific ornithologists such as Oskar Heinroth, Elliot Howard and Julian Huxley, who were the forerunners of the ethologists.

Working in Germany during the first three decades of this century, Heinroth carried out detailed studies of bird behaviour at the Berlin zoo (Sparks, 1982); he hand-reared many birds, and in doing so noticed their attachment to him, a process he referred to as 'Einzuprägen', which is similar to the English term 'imprinting', used by Lorenz in 1937 (Sluckin, 1972). Although experimental investigations of imprinting (and other ethological topics) had been carried out in Britain by Douglas Spalding in the 1870s (Boakes, 1984; Thorpe, 1979), this research was neglected until much later, and was not acknowledged by Heinroth. The term 'ethology', originally used in something approaching its modern meaning by Geoffroy-Saint-Hilaire in 1859 (Jaynes, 1969), was adopted by Heinroth in 1911 to describe his comparative studies of the social behaviour of wildfowl. His general approach, in which the researcher becomes part of the animals' world, was taken up enthusiastically by Konrad Lorenz.

Lorenz followed Heinroth in studying the displays of similar species of birds in order to trace their likely evolutionary relatedness. He also followed Heinroth's interest in imprinting, setting out its characteristic features, thereby laying the foundations for laboratory studies begun in the early 1950s. His work on imprinting also contributed importantly to Bowlby's speculations about the nature of human attachment.

While Lorenz surrounded himself with his animals, the other major pioneer of ethology, Niko Tinbergen, observed animals in their natural habitats. He was a naturalist, albeit one who transformed what this meant to include analysis, experimentation, photography and film. *The Study of Instinct* (Tinbergen, 1951) described many of his earlier field studies and experiments, carried out from the zoology department at Leiden before and after World War II. It also contained a motivational framework for many of these findings, and chapters on the evolution and function of behaviour. *Social Behaviour in Animals* (Tinbergen, 1953) was concerned with social organization and social communication. Tinbergen had, by this time, left Holland for the zoology department at Oxford, where he spent the remainder of his career.

Together with important research by other classical ethologists, such as Baerends, Kortland, Lack and Thorpe, Tinbergen laid the foundation for the following: first, the re-examination and reformulation of classical ethological concepts by zoologists and comparative psychologists in the 1950s; second, the continued interest in the evolution of animal displays, and their motivational control; and third, the renewed interest in the social organization of animals ('social ethology') in the 1960s, which formed the basis for sociobiology in the 1970s. All three were crucially important areas for ethology's later contributions to developmental psychology.

In Tinbergen's early research, questions about development were generally covered within the classical ethological framework of seeking to identify innate patterns of responding to particular environmental stimuli (releasers). Ethological studies of development were more associated with the Cambridge ornithological field station (later known as the sub-department of animal behaviour) at Madingley, established by W. H. Thorpe in 1949. Thorpe had already begun research on the development of song-learning in chaffinches by this time, and he continued this throughout the 1950s (e.g. Thorpe, 1951, 1954, 1958).

The development of modern ethology

After an initial period of relative isolation from psychology, ethology became open to ideas and influences from psychological studies. Critiques of classical ethological concepts such as 'innate' and 'releaser' (see above) provided a dialogue between British ethologists such as Robert Hinde and North

American comparative psychologists such as Lehrman and Schneirla. Developmental issues such as critical or sensitive periods, which had featured in Lorenz's early work on imprinting and in US comparative psychologists' studies of early experience in mammals, provided a link for those interested in development. This was enhanced by both ethologists and comparative psychologists taking up the study of imprinting.

This flexible approach was characteristic of ethology in the Netherlands, Scandinavia and the United Kingdom, where the work of Tinbergen was the dominant influence (Hinde, 1989). In contrast, those adhering to the German or 'classical' approach of Lorenz resisted any attempts to reformulate the original concepts, or to change ethology's nativist emphasis. The classical approach was maintained by some North American ethologists, notably Hess and Barlow, who followed Lorenz rather than Tinbergen (Hinde, 1989). In Germany, Eibl-Eibesfeldt has used the classical approach to study human behaviour. His 'human ethology' consists of the application of Lorenz's concepts to extensive unobtrusive observations of human behaviour (Eibl-Eibesfeldt, 1970, 1979, 1989).

Scrutiny of the framework and concepts of classical ethology began in the early 1950s. The North American comparative psychologist Lehrman (1953, 1970) criticized the concept of instinct as used in Lorenz's work. He argued that it was misleading to transpose the term 'innate' from an evolutionary or selective breeding context to mean unmodifiable through experience. This led to an appreciation of the interactive nature of the developmental process and of the futility of seeking to assign behavioural characters to hereditary or environmental control (Chapter 4).

Thorpe's research on song-learning illustrated the mutual independence of heredity and the environment during development. He examined the process of learning from an ethological perspective (Thorpe, 1951, 1956), emphasizing its complementary nature with 'instinct'. He offered a classification of learning, and he integrated ethological research on topics such as song-learning and imprinting with that of North American psychological research.

Other important papers scrutinized ethological concepts of motivation: for example, it was pointed out that they incorporated ideas of drive and energy similar to those used in psychoanalysis, and which had been discarded by earlier psychologists (Carthy, 1951; Hinde, 1956, 1960). They also contained elements of vitalism and subjectivity (Kennedy, 1954). Hinde (1959b) further examined the shortcomings of supposing that a single drive was responsible for each functional category of behaviour. Such ideas entailed simplified views about the control of behaviour which were not borne out in the detailed studies of birds and fish that were carried out at the time (e.g. Baerends and Baerends-van Roon, 1950; Hinde, 1952, 1953a; Moynihan, 1955; Marler, 1956; Morris, 1958).

One important topic addressed by this empirical research was communication, in particular the courtship and aggressive displays of birds (e.g.

Tinbergen, 1952a, b; Hinde, 1952, 1953a; Moynihan 1955, 1958). The major issues raised in these studies were the derivation of displays from related forms during evolution, the processes underlying evolutionary change and motivational control. As discussed in Chapter 9, similar analyses have been applied to human facial expressions.

Renewed research on imprinting in ducks began at wildfowl stations in the early 1950s, in the United Kingdom and Canada (Sluckin, 1972). In the United States, laboratory studies of imprinting using domestic species began in 1951 (Hess, 1959), and in Britain shortly afterwards at Cambridge (e.g. Hinde *et al.*, 1956). This research led to a revision of the characteristics of imprinting, which Lorenz had described in the 1930s (Thorpe, 1956; Hinde, 1959a).

Another development which departed greatly from classical ethology was the study of social organization, termed 'social ethology' (Crook, 1970a). This began with studies of birds (e.g. Cullen, 1957; Crook, 1960, 1964), and was followed by extensive interest in primate social organization (e.g. Altmann, 1962; Hall, 1965; Crook, 1966). It was based on two earlier research traditions, behavioural ecology (e.g. Darling, 1937; Lack, 1954), and research concerned with the nature of animal societies ('animal sociology': Crook, 1970c; Collias, 1991). By the end of the 1960s, many primate field studies were under way in different parts of the world, and these formed the basis for later theoretical work seeking to synthesize information on social structure and the evolution of animal societies (Clutton-Brock and Harvey, 1976, 1977; Crook, 1970b, 1980; Wilson, 1975).

Social ethology has now blended into the explicitly functional approach called behavioural ecology or sociobiology, which began with theoretical papers by Hamilton (1964), Maynard Smith (1964) and J. L. Brown (1964), culminating in the publication of the book *Sociobiology* (Wilson, 1975). The sociobiological expansion would not, however, have been possible without the social ethology of Crook and the earlier ecologists interested in social behaviour (Hinde, 1989). Sociobiology arose from the integration of social ethology and behavioural ecology with evolutionary biology (Archer, 1986a).

Functional evolutionary thinking has been so influential in providing a fresh approach to animal behaviour that a large proportion of research published in ethological journals over the last 10 or 15 years has adopted a functional framework. However, evolutionary function is only one of the four major types of explanation used by ethologists. Its influence can be said to have a negative side in that it has distracted research from other issues, principally development and motivation. There are, however, signs that a balance is being restored.

The sociobiological approach has been applied to child development by researchers who came to this subject from an ethological background. It has led to fresh ways of looking at issues such as socialization and the influence of father-absence in child-rearing (Chapter 6).

Common themes in ethology and developmental psychology

As indicated above, the term 'ethology' no longer refers to a single orientation or set of aims. The classical approach was maintained by Lorenz and other German ethologists despite reformulations of the earlier concepts. For example, in Eibl-Eibesfeldt's 'human ethology', the aims have been to identify innate patterns of behaviour, and to apply concepts such as releaser (and others, the innate releasing mechanism and fixed action pattern, see Chapter 5) to human behaviour. However, adherence to the framework of classical ethology has prevented theoretical development, and largely confined such investigations to descriptions of behaviour in terms of these classical concepts.

It is widely recognized that the paper that most usefully set out the aims of ethology in a way that opened up the subject for later developments, rather than fossilized it in old issues, was that of Tinbergen (1963). He distinguished four types of explanation which concern ethologists: causation, development (ontogeny), evolution and function (or survival value). The first two are familiar to psychologists, but the other two have been of little interest to them. Evolutionary explanations are concerned with two issues: the change in a behavioural feature through evolutionary history, and how it has been moulded by natural selection during this time. It is important to distinguish (as Tinbergen did) the second of these from the current survival value or present function of a character.

Although much recent ethological research on animals has concentrated on the functional approach, the development of behaviour has continued to attract broad research interest. Topics include the following: the processes of imprinting which underlie, first, the attachment of young to the parent, and second, the choice of a mate during adulthood; the development of play in mammals; song-learning in birds; and parent–infant interactions in primates.

A shared interest in developmental issues provides the obvious common theme linking ethology and developmental psychology. In addition, motivational concepts from ethology have been applied to the behaviour of children: for example, the concept of a behavioural system is central to Bowlby's theory of attachment, a theory of childhood autism has been offered in terms of motivational conflict (Chapter 5). Functional evolutionary explanations have been offered for a variety of topics such as attachment, child-rearing and aggression. The comparative evolutionary approach has been used less frequently, but it has been applied to infant feeding and to the origin of facial expressions.

In addition to Tinbergen's four questions, it is useful to distinguish approaches to the study of social behaviour which concentrate on the group rather than the individual or dyad. Some of the concepts used in social ethology, such as dominance, have been applied to the study of children and adolescents (Chapter 7).

Although there are a number of common issues and interrelations between ethology and developmental psychology, historically they differ not only in the species they study, but also in the methods and approaches adopted when studying development. Ethology traditionally involves a naturalistic, inductive and descriptive phase, which is typically followed by hypothesis-testing, albeit in a more naturalistic context than in psychology (Tinbergen, 1963). Although child development studies of the 1930s and earlier did include much observation (Chapter 2), the 1940s and 1950s were more characterized by theory-driven, laboratory-based, deductive research, which relied more on performance criteria than detailed description. Ethological child observation research of the 1960s reversed this trend by providing a new set of quantitative methods largely derived from field studies of animals.

Major influences of ethology on developmental psychology

From a historical viewpoint, three major influences of ethology on developmental psychology can be identified. The first was Bowlby's application of ethological concepts to the study of human attachment, beginning in the 1950s. The second, from the mid-1960s onwards, occurred when a variety of ethologists used observational methods to study children instead of animals. The third, which is more diffuse, concerned the application of functional evolutionary explanations to child development and to life-span development from the 1970s onwards.

Bowlby (1980a) wrote, 'I first heard of ethology and the names of Konrad Lorenz and Niko Tinbergen in the summer of 1951. I became an instant enthusiast.' Although there was only brief mention of Lorenz's work in *Child Care and the Growth of Love* (Bowlby, 1953a), he was already applying classical ethological concepts to human attachment at that time (Bowlby, 1953b). He further studied ethological principles over the next fifteen years or so, under the guidance of Robert Hinde (Bowlby, 1980a). Lorenz's research on imprinting was initially used as a model for human attachment, in the sense that it showed that a strong and enduring emotional bond to a mother-figure could develop without the intermediary of food during a sensitive period in early life (Chapter 3). Bowlby later came to view the experimental work on early separation in rhesus monkeys by Harlow and Hinde as providing a more useful animal model for guiding research on human attachment.

Bowlby's ideas on the development of attachment were eventually elaborated more fully, in relation to a larger body of ethological work (Bowlby, 1969). In particular, he used the concept of the behavioural system, of each functionally important type of behaviour being organized in a goal-directed fashion (Chapter 5). This was derived from the work of the Dutch ethologists Baerends (1941) and Tinbergen (1942, 1950, 1951). Human attachment was viewed as being a behavioural system, 'a class of social behaviour of an importance equivalent to that of mating behaviour and parental behaviour' (Bowlby, 1969, pp. 223–4).

Bowlby's writings on attachment contain several other influences, notably his own training in psychoanalysis, but also the cognitive approach of Piaget, control theory and to some extent social learning research. Ethology contributed, first, by providing general principles from animal studies which were also applicable to humans; and second, by highlighting the biological significance of attachment through the concept of the behavioural system.

Although many of Bowlby's specific hypotheses, such as the theory of maternal deprivation (Rutter, 1979a, b) and the concept of a single attachment figure – 'monotropism' (Smith, 1979, 1980) – are controversial, the overall influence of his work on the study of human attachment has been enormous. This subject is now a major field of research in developmental psychology, with specific areas concerning the consequences for later development, individual differences in attachment, the developmental course of attachment in older age groups, and extensions of the concepts of attachment and loss to adult relationships and to other forms of attachments.

The second major impact of ethology was to provide a method of study rather than a theoretical approach. The origins of this type of research are diverse. In Germany, Eibl-Eibesfeldt (1967, 1968) and his colleagues (Hass, 1970; Wickler, 1967) began a programme of research following the classical ethological framework (see above). They studied the facial expressions of sensorily deprived children, and made cross-cultural comparisons of adults and children by using qualitative analyses of unobtrusive filming. In Britain, quantitative ethological methods were applied to the study of children in the 1960s. Based on earlier observations carried out in a clinical context (Ounsted, 1955), methods 'similar to those employed by ethologists' (Hutt *et al.*, 1963, p. 243) were used to compare the behaviour of clinical and non-clinical samples of children. More explicitly ethological methods and viewpoints were applied to the study of children by Blurton Jones (1967), an ethologist who had studied bird behaviour under the direction of Tinbergen. Other research followed at several places in the United Kingdom, on topics such as play, aggression and dominance, space and group density, and attachment.

A major impetus for this work was the publication of an edited book by Blurton Jones in 1972, in which he set out the characteristics of the ethological approach to child development. He contrasted these with the traditional methods of psychology, which were viewed as beginning with global concepts such as dependency and aggression, and then setting out to measure them by rating scales and interviews (Blurton Jones, 1972a).

The view that an ethological framework can provide an alternative to traditional psychological methods of studying human social behaviour has continued in the writings of a diverse group of researchers describing their discipline as 'human ethology' (e.g. Dienske, 1984; Eibl-Eibesfeldt, 1979, 1989; Richer, 1979; von Cranach *et al.*, 1979). In contrast, others such as Hinde (1983a, p. 30) and Richards and Bernal (1972), regarded this as a misguided aim, and have used ethological methods in a more integrative way, to complement rather than to replace existing psychological methods (Chapter 2).

Although the ethological approach to child behaviour has been character- ized as different from the methods used in developmental psychology, this is only partially true. Observational studies had been carried out by child psychologists in the United States during the 1920s and 1930s (Fassnacht, 1982; Smith and Connolly, 1972; Smith, 1989). Some observational studies continued, mostly within a social learning framework, during the 1950s and 1960s (Chapter 2).

Although there were some observational studies using methods similar to those of ethologists carried out in the United States in the 1960s (e.g. Freedman, 1964; Gewirtz, 1965), explicitly ethological observations of children began there a little later than in the United Kingdom and Germany. Some, which concerned non-verbal communication, were specifically based on the British ethological research (e.g. Camras, 1977; Ginsburg *et al.*, 1977). Others, on social processes such as dominance, were derived mainly from concepts used in animal studies.

Functional considerations had always formed a part of the application of ethological principles and methods to psychology, but they assumed greater importance following the human sociobiological writings of the late 1970s (Barash, 1977, 1982; Wilson, 1975, 1977). The impact on developmental psychology was at first minimal: the biological determinist flavour of the early contributions tended to preclude consideration of developmental influences. Nevertheless, even these writers did speculate about the functional signific- ance of aspects of child development. Barash (1977, 1982), for example, used a model which set out the conflict of interests between parents and offspring that would result from their different genetic composition and ages (Trivers, 1974). This model has implications for topics such as socialization, weaning conflicts, sibling rivalry and regression (Chapter 6).

Functional thinking has now become less deterministic, and recognizes that development and the environment in which it occurs are part of the adaptive process. Therefore, developmental pathways and their outcomes can be understood in terms of adaptations to different environments (Chapter 6).

Outline of the remaining chapters

In order to consider the specific contributions of ethology in more detail, the remainder of the book is organized under thematic headings. In Chapter 2 the transfer of ethological methods to the study of children's social behaviour is considered in more detail. Some advantages of observational methods are discussed in relation to existing studies of aggression and play. The ways in which ethological and other methods can be integrated are also considered. Chapter 3 describes the use of animal models as a way of simplifying the conditions surrounding human development: this approach is normally associated with developmental psychobiology, but ethology has provided a number of models from more naturalistic sources, and has enabled more subtle influences to be demonstrated.

Chapter 4 considers broad principles of development, specifically the nature–nurture issue, sensitive periods and developmental rules. Many specific examples are considered: for example, it is suggested that there is a sensitive period in human development which parallels the processes involved in sexual imprinting in birds. Chapter 5 concerns the application of motivational concepts, those from classical ethology, such as the fixed action pattern and releaser, and also the behavioural system (see p. 9) and motivational conflict.

Chapter 6 considers the functional or sociobiological approach (see previous section), which is currently having a marked impact on a wide range of human sciences. In this chapter its theoretical concepts are first described, before considering how these have been applied to issues in developmental psychology. The advantages and drawbacks of viewing human behaviour in terms of its evolutionary function are considered. Chapter 7 concerns social ethology, in particular how the concept of dominance has been applied to children's social groups. Its limitations are considered in relation to alternative ways of describing group processes.

The comparative method is considered in Chapter 8. Since comparisons between humans and animals were largely abandoned in comparative psychology, in favour of concentrating on the process of learning in a few species, ethology provided an opportunity to fill this gap. Three topics, the context of development, play and language, are considered in detail to illustrate the application of the comparative method to questions about evolutionary origins. Two further chapters extend the comparative approach by considering, first, non-verbal communication and the expression of emotions; and second, mental processes in animals. Both topics have their roots in Darwin's writings, but have been developed in recent work, particularly the area called 'cognitive ethology', which provides several parallels with research on young children.

Chapter 2

Observational methods

Introduction

In Chapter 1, I described the major influences of ethology on developmental psychology from a historical perspective: these included the transfer of observational methods to studies of child development in the 1960s. Ethology offered a fresh approach to research on children's social behaviour, entailing an evolutionary framework (Chapter 6), less restrained or more naturalistic settings, and methods of observation suitable for these settings. The methods were essentially those which had been used in ethological studies of the social behaviour of primates. They proved suitable because many of the same problems are encountered in trying to observe a group of pre-school children in a nursery or playgroup as are encountered in studying an unrestrained group of primates.

Ethological methods form part of a wider range of observational techniques which have been used in the human sciences. The origins of these are diverse, from developmental, social and clinical research in psychology and from anthropology and sociology. Ethology provides several specific methods of observation, including both qualitative and quantitative varieties.

Qualitative ethological methods

Qualitative methods are derived from the classical ethology of Lorenz, who surrounded himself with the animals he studied, and described their behaviour in individual and anecdotal terms. He relied on verbal description, and rejected experiments, quantification and statistical analysis (Bateson, 1989). These features show a curious parallel with the qualitative methods used in the 'new social psychology' and feminist psychology of the 1980s (e.g. Wilkinson, 1986).

Lorenz's approach was transferred to humans by Eibl-Eibesfeldt and Hans

Hass, who began by filming records of human behaviour in Africa in 1963 (Eibl-Eibesfeldt, 1989). Since then, Eibl-Eibesfeldt has developed a qualitative method based on selecting representative examples from filmed records, to study sensorily deprived infants, and human non-verbal communication in different contexts and cultures (e.g. Eibl-Eibesfeldt, 1967, 1970, 1979, 1989). Reynolds (1982) has used a similar method to study children in the United States, and so have clinical researchers in the United Kingdom (Tinbergen and Tinbergen, 1983; Richer, 1988).

The qualitative ethological approach is, however, open to a number of criticisms, which apply to many other qualitative methods. They often lack validity and reliability checks, thus allowing the possibility of observer bias, selectivity and argument by example. Nevertheless, provided that it is realized that qualitative methods have different aims to quantitative ones, they can provide detailed descriptions which may not be available from quantified results. Eibl-Eibesfeldt (1989) has provided an encyclopaedic account of what this method can achieve in the way of a diversity of examples from many different cultures. The method cannot provide assessments of the frequencies of these examples in the populations studied, nor the answers to questions about causation.

One important contribution of qualitative ethological methods is to provide a preliminary natural history phase before carrying out a more systematic investigation (e.g. Tinbergen, 1963; Tinbergen and Tinbergen, 1983). Such a preliminary phase can be used to generate areas of interest and hypotheses to be followed up in later, more systematic, studies. Tinbergen and Tinbergen (1983) used qualitative observations in this way in their study of childhood autism (Chapter 5).

Quantitative ethological methods

Quantitative ethological methods were introduced into child development, and to a lesser extent clinical, research in the 1960s in the United Kingdom to study topics such as play, aggression, dominance and facial expressions. They involved the sorts of systematic observation which were used in primate field research in the 1960s, and also shared some features with the observational procedures used by child psychologists in the 1920s and 1930s. They produce quantitative results which can be subjected to objective reliability checks, a feature absent from qualitative observational methods.

Nevertheless, the distinguishing features of systematic observational methods, and the limits to their usefulness, are by no means clear-cut. In the case of pre-school children, and certain psychiatric patients, the content of language is not of major importance. Consequently, non-verbal aspects of behaviour can be analysed with methods originally used in ethological studies of animal behaviour. For many researchers this represents the limit of useful systematic observations. Others, however, have sought to extend such methods to include the content of human verbal interactions. Omark (1980), for example, describes as 'holistic human ethologists' researchers who consider the content and meaning of language along with non-verbal behaviour. In a different way, researchers such as Chisholm (1983), Hinde (1983a) and Richards and Bernal (1972) have used ethologically-based observations to supplement other methods which can better cope with the contents and meanings of verbal exchanges (see final section).

In their book entitled *Observing Interaction*, Bakeman and Gottman (1986) concentrated on the analysis of interaction sequences, but did not restrict themselves to *behaviour*: they included analyses of verbal interactions, such as children's conversations and verbal exchanges between marital partners. In these cases, the method used is similar to that for analysing any narrative by means of an explicitly defined coding system which can be subjected to inter-coder reliability checks. The distinction between an observational method and quantitative content analysis becomes blurred in such cases.

Since the present concern is with ethologically-based methods, codings of verbal exchanges will not be covered, although it is realized that they share a number of methodological problems, and that the two methods could be used to complement one another, thus providing one solution to the problem of how to deal with verbal exchanges, referred to above.

Several detailed accounts of systematic observational methods are already available (e.g. Hinde, 1983a; Bakeman and Gottman, 1986; Martin and Bateson, 1986). The discussion in this chapter is therefore restricted to: (1) certain methodological issues, such as the establishment of categories of behaviour, sampling and recording methods, and inter-observer reliabilities; and (2) a discussion of the type of information obtained from observational studies, and its scope and potential uses.

Establishing categories of behaviour

All systematic methods of observation involve a category system, a list of objectively defined categories into which each aspect of behaviour can be placed. The first step is, therefore, to establish the categories, a procedure analogous to designing a coding manual for content analysis. It relies on preliminary unstructured observations, which will usually be qualitative in nature, and represent the 'natural history phase' essential for an ethological study (Tinbergen, 1963).

There are various approaches to devising a category system, and several researchers have sought to characterize the essential features of a distinction between, on the one hand, a small-scale, detailed, wholly ethological approach and, on the other, a larger-scale, more global, interpretative approach. One of the earliest groups of British researchers to be influenced by ethological methods were Corrine Hutt and her colleagues. Hutt *et al.* (1963) commented that the essential difference between ethological categories and those used in observational research from the social learning tradition was that ethological categories did not incorporate the researchers' theoretical assumptions whereas those of the learning tradition did. For example, social learning family interaction researchers who were interested in aggression within the family (e.g. Patterson and Maerov, 1978) specifically chose their categories to fit the clinical and theoretical orientation of their studies. Categories in the 'family interaction coding system' (Patterson *et al.*, 1978) included 'humiliate', 'physical positive' and 'negativism'. The last two in particular involved considerable theoretical interpretation in their definitions. In contrast, the sorts of categories used in an early ethological study of interactions between children (Blurton Jones, 1972c) were 'push', 'hit at', 'wrestle', 'fixate', 'smile' and 'give', all of which can be defined relatively independently of their interpretation.

Distinctions drawn by later researchers (Hinde, 1970; Bakeman and Gottman, 1986) are similar to the one made by Hutt and her colleagues, but they emphasize slightly different criteria. In discussing animal behaviour, Hinde contrasted descriptions based on the pattern of muscular contractions, and those based on the consequences of behaviour. Similarly, Bakeman and Gottman distinguished between category systems based on a physical description, such as movements of specific muscle groups, and those based on social categories, such as 'sadness' or 'distress'.

These distinctions all broadly correspond to different levels of analysis, which are appropriate for answering different types of research questions. For example, if the researcher is concerned with analysing how facial expressions and gestures are used in communication, the descriptive scheme will be at the level of muscular movements. Influenced by the work of Darwin (1872) on emotional expressions (Figures 2.1–2.2), British ethologists such as Grant (1969), Blurton Jones (1971) and Brannigan and Humphries (1972) provided detailed coding-schemes and illustrations of facial expressions (Figures 2.3–2.5). The Facial Action Coding System of Ekman and Friesen (1978) is similar, describing changes in facial expression with reference to specific muscle groups or 'action units'.

These category systems were all intended to provide a foundation for later research, and correspond to the 'ethograms' compiled by some animal ethologists. (An ethogram is a detailed description of the categories of behaviour shown by a particular species.) It was regarded by classical ethologists as being analogous to an anatomical description of the species, and was associated with the classical ethological idea that the behaviour of a species could be broken down into a series of 'fixed action patterns' – forms of behaviour which were constant in form and characteristic of that species. It should be noted, however, that such categories are by no means the fixed entities that classical ethologists have assumed.

Figure 2.1 Human facial expression showing 'terror', from Darwin (1872, Figure 20). This was one of several woodcuts taken from photographs supplied by the French anatomist Duchenne de Boulogne, who induced expressions by stimulating various facial muscles electrically.

Figure 2.2 Photographs of infants crying, obtained from a more natural source, from Darwin (1872, Plate 1).

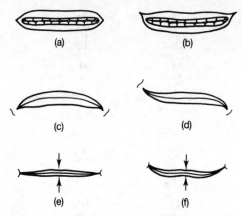

Figure 2.3 Movements of the mouth described by Brannigan and Humphries (1972, Figure 2.4): (a) oblong, viewed as an ambivalent element shown by children who are motivated by aggression and fear; (b) oblong smile, where the previous element is combined with smiling; (c) mouth corners down, indicating doubt or aversion; (d) wry smile, obtained when the previous element is combined with smiling; (e) tight lips, indicating lack of verbal response; (f) compressed smile, when the previous element is combined with smiling.

When a researcher is interested in broader questions about social behaviour, these very detailed categories may not be appropriate. For example, in a study of the development of play, Smith (1978) used only three broad categories – solitary behaviour, parallel play and co-operative play – but these were sufficient to identify broad developmental trends. As Smith and Connolly (1972) have argued, an insistence on using micro-categories of behaviour defined in terms of motor patterns would not only present practical difficulties for this type of analysis, but would lose much of the meaning of social behaviour which is apparent only when it is viewed in more global terms over a longer time-span.

In a study of the effects of crowding on behaviour, Smith and Connolly (1977) used three broad categories: (1) 'group play', which consisted of a variety of possible activities and depended on perceived intentions; (2) 'aggressive behaviour', which relied on perceived intention to hurt; and (3) 'rough-and-tumble play', which was defined in terms of specific actions. Although these were global categories, they were based on a synthesis of more detailed categories used earlier, and were sufficient for the purpose of the study, revealing differences in the frequency of categories of behaviour with manipulations of space, numbers and resources.

Although Smith and Connolly used these global 'social' categories, they nevertheless recognized that by so doing they were introducing more likelihood of the observer's interpretative framework creeping into category

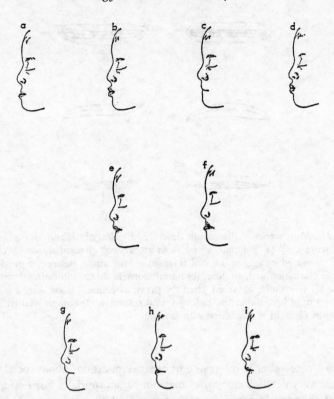

Figure 2.4 Lip positions described by Blurton Jones (1971, Figure 5): (a) lower lip pout; (b) two-lip pout; (c) lips pressed together; (d) lips pressed together with two-lip pout; (e) lower lip bitten; (f) upper lip bitten; (g) both lips rolled in; (h) upper lips rolled in; (i) lower lips rolled in. (Original caption, slightly modified.) (Reprinted from Blurton Jones (1971) by permission of the Wayne State University Press.)

definition. There is therefore likely to be less scope for the transfer of descriptive categories from one study to another than with micro-analytical methods. Bakeman and Gottman (1986) regarded this sort of category system as only suitable for answering the research questions for which it was designed. According to them, at the beginning of each new investigation, a new system has to be designed. While this might apply more to non-ethological methods, such as Patterson's family interaction coding system (see p. 15), the broad categories used in many ethological studies of social behaviour, such as co-operative play, rough-and-tumble play and aggression, are usually transferable from one study to another. There are, however, some studies where Bakeman and Gottman's comment does apply. Savin-Williams (1976) used the category 'dominance', which was widely defined to include verbal commands or orders, verbal ridicules, physical assertiveness, recognizing dominance in the other, physical or object displacement, verbal or physical

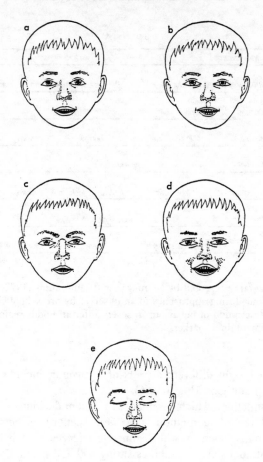

Figure 2.5 Teeth visibility described by Blurton Jones (1971, Figure 7): (a) upper only; (b) upper and lower show equally; (c) lower only; (d) lower only; (e) mostly lower. (Original caption.) (Reprinted from Blurton Jones (1971) by permission of the Wayne State University Press.)

threats and ignoring or refusing to comply with another's request. This inclusive category would be difficult for another researcher to use, and provides a marked contrast to the approach of ethological researchers who seek to provide a basic description or ethogram.

Category systems are often designed to contain mutually exclusive and exhaustive categories, i.e. everything the individual is doing falls into one, and only one, of the categories. This is easier to achieve with broad categories of social behaviour. If every aspect of behaviour is not covered by one system, as may be the case with the micro-level of analysis, it is often useful to have several parallel systems. For example, in Brannigan and Humphries' study of expressions and gestures shown by children in playgroups, they simultan-

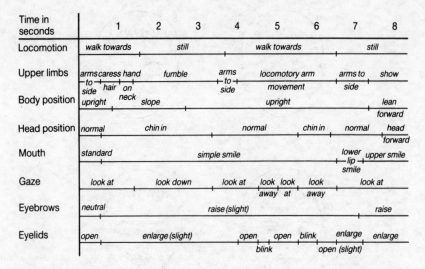

Figure 2.6 Diagram presented by Brannigan and Humphries (1972, Figure 2.1) showing behaviour during approaches to an observer by pre-school children. Simultaneous description of behaviour in seven different bodily regions is presented with an approximate time-marker.

eously recorded eight different aspects of behaviour, including locomotion, mouth position and gaze (Figure 2.6).

A final distinction, which is important when deciding on the type of sampling and recording methods (see next section), is between 'acts' or momentary events, such as when someone sneezes or a baby burps, and 'states' or continuous events, such as sitting still and parallel play. Measures are frequency counts and duration respectively.

Sampling and recording methods

Sampling methods refer to who is observed and when; recording methods refer to how their behaviour is recorded (Martin and Bateson, 1986). The main methods are outlined in Figure 2.7. Sampling methods can be divided into three categories (Figure 2.7): (1) scan sampling; (2) behaviour or event-sampling; and (3) focal sampling.

Scan sampling is the rapid scanning of a whole group of individuals at regular intervals, recording the behaviour of each one at that instant. Abramovitch (1976) used this method to record the spatial positions of pre-school children relative to one another, using 1–1½-minute intervals. From this information, she found that high-ranking children (assessed from dyadic interactions: see Chapter 7) were close neighbours to one another, more than

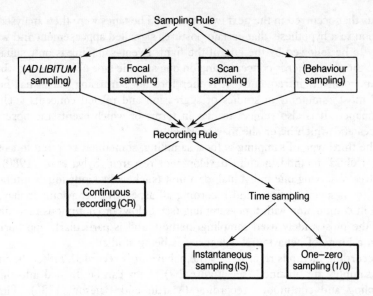

Figure 2.7 Sampling and recording methods, summarised by Martin and Bateson (1986, Figure 4.1).

would be expected by chance. The main drawback of scan sampling is that the observer is usually limited to recording one or two categories, and there is likely to be bias because some individuals will be more conspicuous than others (Martin and Bateson, 1986).

One refinement of this method was used by Strayer and Strayer (1976) whose scan sampling involved videorecording interactions during free play among seventeen pre-school children. The recordings were later analysed in terms of dominance relations between pairs of children (Chapter 7). In cases such as this, problems can arise from the choice of sample lengths and from the temptation to select more interesting interactions.

Behaviour or event-sampling (J. Altmann, 1974) involves observing the whole group and recording all occurrences of a specific type of behaviour, together with a record of which individuals are involved. Savin-Williams (1976) used this method to study dominance behaviour within a group of six 13-year-old boys at a summer camp, by recording all instances of one boy dominating another. (See previous section for the defining features of dominance and for comments about the category system.) Savin-Williams was interested in the relationship between dominance and a variety of other measures, such as athletic ability and popularity (see Chapter 7).

Ginsburg *et al.* (1977) also used event-sampling, in this case to study the outcome of playground fights among 8- to 12-year-old children: whenever an aggressive interaction began, the researchers videorecorded it along with the events that occurred in the next two minutes. The tapes were then analysed in relation to a hypothesis that certain postures signalled appeasement and were likely to be followed by the end of the fight. Event-sampling is only suitable when the researcher is concentrating on one specific type of behaviour, which occurs relatively infrequently. It is therefore not surprising that it has been used most commonly in studies of aggression and related concepts such as dominance. It is also subject to bias in terms of which events the observer notices and which he or she may overlook.

The third type of sampling is focal sampling, sometimes referred to as the 'target child' method in child development research (Sylva *et al.*, 1980). It involves observing one individual, or a unit (such as two individuals interacting), for a specified time, and recording all aspects of behaviour. It may be used in conjunction with time-sampling (see below) or continuous recording. It is the most widely used sampling method, and is particularly appropriate when a range of behavioural categories is being studied.

Recording methods refer to *how* the behaviour is recorded, rather than the way samples are obtained (see Figure 2.7). They can be divided into time-sampling and continuous recording (Martin and Bateson, 1986). Time-sampling, usually combined with the focal sampling method, involves either instantaneous or one-zero sampling (Figure 2.8.). In both cases, the recording session is divided into short periods. For instantaneous sampling, the occurrence or non-occurrence of the behavioural category is noted for each sample point, whereas in one-zero sampling it is recorded for the whole of the preceding time-interval. Previously, the information was most commonly recorded on a check-sheet, with categories providing column headings and time-intervals in successive rows (Hinde, 1973). It can now be processed by a portable microcomputer (Unwin and Martin, 1987).

Both time-sampling methods were originally developed in pre-war child observational research (Goodenough, 1928; Olson, 1930). It was, however, their later re-emergence in social ethological primate field studies (Hinde, 1973; J. Altmann, 1974) that led to their renewed and refined use in ethological observational studies of children beginning in the 1960s.

Both time-sampling methods have their disadvantages: neither provides accurate measures of the frequency of behaviour, nor of its duration, unless a short time-interval is involved (Martin and Bateson, 1986; Pöysä, 1991; Mann *et al.*, 1991). They are unsuitable for analysing sequences of behaviour (i.e. what follows what) unless a very small time period, relative to the duration of behaviour, is used (Bakeman and Gottman, 1986). Nevertheless, time-sampling can in practice provide good estimates of frequency or durations, depending on what is being observed (Tyler, 1979). It also has the practical advantage of condensing information, and can be particularly useful where a large number of categories have to be recorded.

In developmental psychology, time-sampling has been used to observe children in their usual settings, and where broad rather than detailed

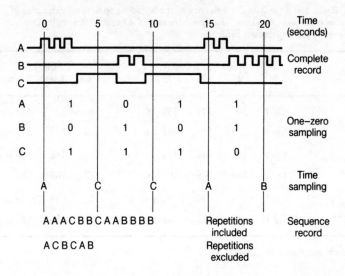

Figure 2.8 Diagram (from Slater, 1978, Figure 1) illustrating the different recording rules shown in Figure 2.8. A, B and C represent three behavioural categories.

categories of behaviour are being used. One-zero sampling has perhaps been used more commonly than instantaneous sampling in observational studies of children. This is reflected in the selection of the following examples.

In a study of the social behaviour of children in day nurseries, Smith and Connolly (1972) used instantaneous sampling, recording from a wide range of behavioural categories every 10 sec. during twelve 5-minute observation periods for each child. Their main interest was to describe the range of normal behaviour in young children, and how this differed with age, sex and setting. In view of the large number of behavioural categories, they used principal components analysis to simplify the information and indicate the main ways in which individuals differed.

In a later study on the effects of crowding (see previous section), Smith and Connolly (1977) used one-zero sampling, involving fairly long time periods (40 sec.) during which a tape-recorded commentary of behaviour, based on a previously established category system, was made. This was then used as the basis for three more global categories (see above), and the results were presented in terms of the number of time periods in which each of these occurred for the different experimental conditions. This is shown in Table 2.1: note that the results are presented as total number of time periods, so that they have to be divided by 24 (the number of children) to obtain the mean number of time periods per child (maximum 24).

Archer *et al.* (1988) also used the one-zero method to sample aggressive

Table 2.1 Results of a study of the influence of space and equipment on categories of social behaviour in pre-school children. The figures refer to the number of samples in which the behaviour occurred (maximum: 576).

| | | Space (sq. ft/child) | | | | Equipment | | |
		25	50	75		1 set	2 sets	3 sets
Group play	Gp I	505	533	555 n.s.		544	526	523 n.s.
	Gp II	526	546	552 n.s.		546	537	541 n.s.
Aggressive behaviour	Gp I	165	146	154 n.s.		179	146	140 $p < .05$
	Gp II	104	108	100 n.s.		122	103	87 $p < .05$
Rough-and-tumble play	Gp I	23	44	46 $p < .05$		40	34	39 n.s.
	Gp II	46	73	67 $p < .05$		77	56	53 $p < .05$

From: Smith and Connolly (1977).

and other activities of 6–11-year-old children in the classroom. The categories, which were recorded on pre-prepared check-sheets, included both broad ones, such as whether the child was alone or with others, whether she or he was moving about, talking and smiling, as well as specific categories indicative of aggression (such as kick, hit and poke). The sampling periods were 15 seconds and each child was observed for eight 5-minute blocks, producing a maximum possible score of 160 per child. The results were expressed as means for the different sex and age categories, producing large scores of around 60–80 for common behaviour such as talk, and scores of no more than 7.8 for categories of verbal or physical aggression.

Davie *et al.* (1984) observed pre-school children in their homes using one-zero sampling of broad categories such as watching television, and playing ball games. The aim of this study was rather different from the two just described. Instead of investigating differences between experimental conditions, age or sex categories, Davie *et al.* sought an estimate of the time-budget of the various activities carried out by pre-school children in their own homes.

In contrast to time-sampling, the aim of continuous recording is to provide a complete record of behaviour, usually accompanied by the time at which each event began and ended, and at which each act occurred (Martin and Bateson, 1986). The importance of the time recording depends on whether frequency and duration are being recorded as well as the sequence of behaviour. If the researcher is only concerned with what follows what (sequential analysis), the time dimension is not, strictly speaking, relevant (Bakeman and Gottman, 1986). Continuous recording is essential in order to carry out such a sequential analysis, since sampling methods will not normally provide information on the transition between one category and the next.

In its simplest form, continuous recording can be achieved through a record – on paper or through a tape recorder – of which category follows the previous one (thus only providing information on sequencing). In this case, there must be no gaps – the categories must be mutually exclusive and exhaustive. By means of lined paper with time markers, or electronic devices (originally a pen recorder), or through filming or videorecording, the time when each category begins and ends can be obtained (Bakeman and Gottman, 1986). More sophisticated devices allow parallel coding of changes in different types of categories, such as those dealing with facial expression, arm movements, or bodily postures (see Figure 2.6). Following earlier computerization of recording methods (Dawkins, 1971), continuous recording can now be achieved by portable microcomputers whose operation is based on the earlier pen recorders (Browne and Madeley, 1985; Guthertz and Field, 1989; Unwin and Martin, 1987).

The software package devised by Browne and Madeley involves, first, establishing a 'library', which contains the category system, and subsequently using this to record behaviour by means of key-presses which correspond to individual categories of behaviour in the library. It can be extended to observe the behaviour of several individuals by having a different key-coding for each one, and recording both the category of behaviour and the individual involved. In a similar way, it can be used for studying interactions between two individuals by assigning a code 'actor' or 'reactor' to them. The data, which will involve the frequency, duration and sequencing of behaviour, can be transferred from the microcomputer to a larger computer for statistical analysis. Guthertz and Field (1989) have described a comparable IBM-compatible lap computer for studying either behaviour of one individual or interactions between individuals. By using such methods, the laborious transcriptions involved in the earlier methods of continuous recording are avoided.

Inter-observer reliabilities

The calculation of 'inter-observer reliabilities' is usually regarded as an essential step in demonstrating the accuracy of the measuring device, i.e. the observer and his/her recording system (Martin and Bateson, 1986). In practice only inter-observer *agreement* is calculated, since there is no absolute standard, as there is with a physical measuring device (Bakeman and Gottman, 1986).

Inter-observer agreement was not a feature of earlier ethological observations of animals, and even of some human ethological studies (Blurton Jones, 1972a). Instead, there was more of an emphasis on obtaining objectively defined behavioural categories and on replicability. However, following the practice of calculating inter-observer agreement in some of the earlier child observation studies (e.g. Olson, 1930), its use was continued by several of the earlier ethological researchers in the 1960s (e.g. McGrew, 1972a, b; Smith and Connolly, 1972).

There are several methods for calculating inter-observer reliabilities, and they have been discussed in detail by Bakeman and Gottman (1986), Martin and Bateson (1986) and by Caro *et al.* (1979). I shall restrict myself to a few general points made in these discussions.

The simplest way to express reliability is by a correlation coefficient measuring the relation between the two observers' scores for the same behaviour pattern over different recording sessions or in different individuals. In this case, the two observers' total frequency scores for each recording session or individual is regarded as sufficient. If it is important for some reason to check each occurrence of a behavioural act or state for agreement or disagreement, or if measurement is on a nominal scale, a simple percentage of agreement is sometimes calculated: this expresses the proportion of samples for which there has been agreement. Unfortunately, it does not take into account agreements resulting from chance. In order to do so, one of the several statistics which correct for chance can be used. Perhaps the most widely used is Cohen's Kappa (Cohen, 1960), which was originally used for assessing reliability of clinical diagnoses.

Ethologists are perhaps more aware of the limitations of relying on inter-observer agreement as method of assessing reliability than psychologists have been (see Caro *et al.*, 1979). This is because they are in general more aware that techniques of observation are a skill learned over a period of time. Thus the correlation between the observations of a skilled and a relatively unskilled observer may be low, but this does not mean that both are inaccurate. This has led researchers such as Blurton Jones (1972a) to put more emphasis on an objectively defined standard in devising the category system, and on the importance of replication, a point also made by Caro *et al.* (1979). A similar problem has arisen with complex observational procedures in psychology. Here emphasis has been placed on the training of new observers. For example, Patterson and his co-workers trained new observers in using a previously established coding system by means of a videotape (Bakeman and Gottman, 1986, Ch. 4), and comparing their observations with those of trained observers.

Scope of observational studies

The first ethological studies of human behaviour involved the social behaviour of pre-school children (e.g. Blurton Jones, 1967; McGrew, 1969), adult psychiatric patients (Grant, 1965a, b, 1968, 1969), and mother–infant interactions (e.g. Richards and Bernall, 1972). In each case, the detailed contribution of language could be overlooked, although categories such as 'talks to infant' and 'talk' were used in these and similar studies. From school age onwards, and in most adults, the content of language is important, thus limiting the scope of purely ethological observational methods.

There is now a division of opinion between researchers such as Eibl-Eibesfeldt (1979, 1989), who seek to preserve the use of ethological methods as a separate 'human ethology', and those who recognize the limitations outlined above, and recommend the integration of ethological with other methods to widen their scope (e.g. Chisholm, 1983; Hinde and Stevenson-Hinde, 1986, 1987). This issue is discussed in the final section.

The settings of ethological observations have been widened since the earlier playgroup and nursery studies to include observations of older children in the classroom and the playground, studies carried out in the home, in US summer camps, and studies of childhood psychiatric conditions in hospitals and clinics. The age range of such studies has also expanded from the earlier concentration on the pre-school age to include infants, middle school children and adolescents. It is apparent that considerable information about social behaviour can be obtained by observation even at ages when language is important. In contexts such as the playground, actions may speak louder – or at least as loud as – words.

Information available from ethological methods of observation

The information potentially available from an ethologically-based study is of two sorts: first, descriptive and second, analytical. Descriptive information may come in different forms, depending on whether the study is qualitative or quantitative. A qualitative analysis emphasizes the benefits of careful observation. It relies on the difference between what a trained observer sees in the world around him or her, and the very selective attention most people pay to their world. It reflects an attitude of mind, not only present in ethologists and the earlier naturalists, but also in anyone who seeks to describe what is around them, irrespective of the form that description takes. The following extract is taken from Hemingway, in which he (reluctantly) gives advice to an aspiring writer:

> Most people never listen. Nor do they observe. You should be able to go into a room and when you come out know everything that you saw there. . . . When you're in town stand outside the theatre and see how the people differ in the way they get out of taxis or motor cars. There are a thousand ways to practise. (Hemingway, 1935)

In most ethological research, qualitative descriptions of behaviour are intended as a basis for later quantitative research. In this context, two criteria for a good qualitative study are that the description is both clear and

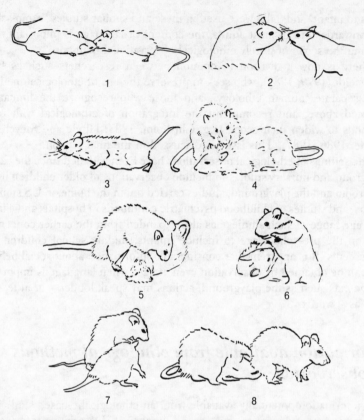

Figure 2.9. Diagrams of some of the acts and postures shown by laboratory
rodents, from the study of Grant and Mackintosh (1963, Figure 1): (1) nosing
(social investigation) in the mouse; (2) nosing in the hamster; (3) stretched attention
(exploratory) in the mouse; (4) aggressive groom in the rat; (5) aggressive and
submissive postures in the rat; (6) offensive and submissive postures in the hamster;
(7) attack in the mouse; (8) sniff and elevated crouch (sexual) postures in the rat.

systematic. The first refers to the detailed acts and postures being described
in such a way that there will be minimum ambiguity when they are used by
other observers. The second refers to an attempt to present them as
something more than a long descriptive list. This may be achieved by grouping
them according to their apparent motivational similarity, although such
groupings would remain hypotheses at this stage. The study by Grant and
Mackintosh (1963) of the social behaviour of several laboratory rodents fits
these criteria. It contains clear descriptions of the behaviour, both verbally and
in drawings (Figure 2.9), and the observers have arranged the behaviour into
the following categories based on apparent motivational similarity: introductory acts, those concerned with flight, aggression, sexual behaviour, ambivalent

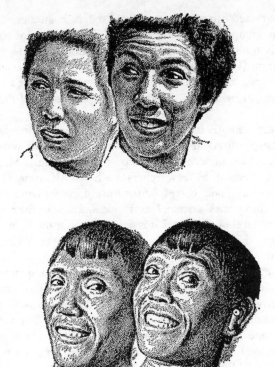

Figure 2.10 Photographs from Eibl-Eibesfeldt (1971, Figure 3), showing greeting expressions using the eyes, in a French woman photographed by Hans Hass, and a Waika man photographed by Eibl-Eibesfeldt.

acts performed at a distance, territorial marking and displacement activities. Mackintosh and Grant's study contains no quantitative information, yet it has proved invaluable for later researchers using these laboratory rodents for quantitative studies of behaviour. The same detailed, systematic approach is also apparent in Grant's (1969) descriptive study of human expressions and gestures, and in similar studies described earlier.

In the classical ethology of Lorenz, qualitative descriptions were an end in themselves, and formed the basis for commentary and theory. As indicated above, this approach has been applied to human studies by Eibl-Eibesfeldt. The outcome is a descriptive commentary illustrated by photographs and drawings taken from the filmed material (Figure 2.10).

In contrast to this method, most ethologists have used qualitative descriptions as a basis for further quantitative description and analysis. The preliminary qualitative phase of observation is nevertheless of crucial importance for assembling the category system.

Where fine-grained categories have been used, as in studies of non-verbal communication, compiling such categories fulfils an important research aim, forming a basis for later analytical studies. Examples include the schemes compiled by Grant (1969), Blurton Jones (1971) and Brannigan and Humphries (1972). Brannigan and Humphries, for example, compiled a list of 136 'units of non-verbal behaviour', covering different regions of the body (e.g. Figure 2.3).

Although these schemes have been used in later quantitative research, the amount of detail involved in the original versions not only poses practical difficulties, but is also unnecessary for many research aims. More inclusive categories were devised by researchers such as McGrew (1972a). For example, his category 'look' corresponds to five different types of looking in Brannigan and Humphries' system. Nevertheless, whatever the research aims, and whatever the level of analysis that is appropriate for them, one of the first outcomes of an ethological study is the construction of a clearly defined category system.

Once this descriptive information is converted into a quantitative form through time-sampling or continuous recording, a variety of other types of information becomes available. One important distinction is between time-budget data (duration and frequency) and sequential data. The former can be *estimated* from time-sampling methods (see Pöysä, 1991; Mann *et al.*, 1991), and can be obtained from sequential data providing there is a time-marker. Such data are crucial for the aims of studies which ask questions such as how children spend their time at home (e.g. Davie *et al.*, 1984), or how particular types of social behaviour differ under different environmental conditions or in different categories of children (e.g. Smith and Connolly, 1977, 1980; Archer *et al.*, 1988). They can also be used to enquire which types of behaviour are associated with which others between individuals (e.g. Archer *et al.*, 1988).

To a limited extent, further analyses aimed at ordering the categories into coherent groupings based on temporal associations can be carried out if there are sufficient observation periods for each individual. Smith and Connolly (1972) used principal components analysis in this way, and Blurton Jones (1972c) used factor analysis (see below). There are limitations to the use of these techniques owing to complications raised by having both within- and between-individual sources of variation.

As indicated earlier, continuous recording is essential for producing sequential data, which enable the researcher to analyse which categories of behaviour are likely to follow which others. The types of sequence which are of interest may be those within a single individual, or those generated from the interaction of two individuals, such as a mother and child. Interest in the statistical techniques necessary for analysing sequences arose in ethology (S. A. Altmann, 1965; Slater, 1973), but they are applicable to similar issues arising from the study of human mother–infant interactions (Schaffer, 1977). An essential problem in dealing with transitions from one type of behaviour to another is to decide whether particular types occur more often than would be expected by chance (Slater, 1973). By identifying those that are highly likely to go together, inferences are made about which behavioural acts are associated within the same individual, i.e. are causally related, or which are associated within a dyadic interaction, i.e. provide evidence of communication.

A common statistical approach used by ethologists to analyse sequences is Markov chain analysis. This determines whether each behavioural act depends only on the immediately preceding one (a first-order Markov chain), or on earlier events (an *r*th-order Markov chain). Most ethological studies involving these sorts of analysis have been concerned with investigating the possibility of a first-order Markov chain, and compare a matrix of observed transition frequencies with that expected by chance assuming independence of all the behavioural categories from one another. However, the conditions of the Markov analysis may be difficult to specify in behavioural data, notably because it is assumed that the probability structure does not change with time, i.e. that the animal remains in a steady motivational state (Slater, 1973).

In this sort of analysis, the researcher examines whether specific types of transition are significantly more common than chance, for example, by comparing the data in the contingency table (showing the number of times each follows or precedes the others) with a random model, using a chi-square or z-score binomial test (Bakeman and Gottman, 1986). In addition to behavioural data commonly violating the assumptions of independence underlying these tests (Slater, 1973), there are problems arising from the construction of the contingency table. One common one is highlighted by the example of Grant's (1968) study of the non-verbal behaviour of psychiatric patients. The contingency table he devised from the sequences of behavioural categories included transitions involving the same act of behaviour: when these are included, the numbers in these categories reflect arbitrary decisions made by the researcher about when to count it as one prolonged sequence, and when to count it as several of the same type following one another. Which strategy the researcher adopts can be shown to influence crucially the outcome, since the expected probability matrix is drastically changed (Slater, 1973).

Similar types of analysis have been applied to sequences of interactions between two individuals (Slater, 1973). The aim of the analysis in this case is to determine whether the behaviour of one animal predicts that of the other to a greater extent than chance, and hence to find evidence of the role of specific acts in communication (see Chapter 8). It is, however, unrealistic to expect only the immediately preceding act of the other animal to be influencing current behaviour. One approach which can potentially overcome this problem is the information theory method of S. A. Altmann (1965). This enabled a calculation to be made of the uncertainty in one animal's behaviour which remained when increasing numbers of preceding acts were taken into account (see Chapter 8). A more recent application of information theory is

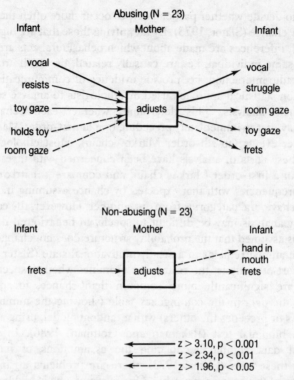

Figure 2.11 Diagrams from Browne and Saqi (1987), showing the probabilities of different acts by an infant preceding and following 'adjusts' by their mother, for mothers suspected of child abuse (left) and control mothers (right). Source: Browne (1989, Figure 8.3).

that by van den Bercken and Cools (1980), who set up several hypothetical models concerning the causation of behavioural sequences in triads of Java monkeys, and tested each one against empirical data from their interactions.

Despite the methodological problems, the general approach of seeking to determine whether certain acts precede or follow others more or less commonly than chance has been widely used to analyse interaction sequences. A form of this type of analysis has been applied to the study of mother–infant interactions between abusing and control mothers and their infants. Browne and Saqi (1987) found that child-abusing mothers would respond to several types of behaviour by their infants with an obtrusive intervention ('adjust'), whereas control mothers would intervene only if their infants fretted. The consequence of adjusting by the abusing mother was often to induce vocalization or struggling in the infant (Figure 2.11). In this study, the researchers were interested in the difference between interactions in two conditions, a rather more restricted aim than establishing whether acts in the sequence function in communication.

Particularly in the study of causation, a further method of analysis has been to look for global patterns in the relations between the activities revealed by the sequential analysis. One approach has been to use factor analysis. In a classic ethological study using this method, Wiepkema (1961) recorded the number of times different acts preceded or followed each other in a large number of observations of the courtship behaviour of thirteen territorial bitterlings, fish which lay their eggs in the gill cavity of the freshwater mussel. These figures were then compared with those expected from a random sequence, and a ratio of observed to expected calculated for preceding and for following for each pair of behavioural acts. The data were then simplified by carrying out a Spearman rank-order correlation separately for preceding and for following. The correlations were factor-analysed to reveal three factors which could explain most of the variance among the original sequences of behaviour for the twelve variables. These three factors corresponded to motivational groupings, and were therefore referred to as major 'tendencies', the term commonly used to refer to motivational systems at that time. The first factor consisted of aggressive acts, the second of non-reproductive movements, and the third of sexual acts.

Wiepkema's study illustrates the way factor analysis has been applied to sequential data to identify motivational groupings. This procedure does, however, contain a number of methodological weaknesses. One is the confounding of within- and between-sources of variation, which is discussed below. Another is the use of derived variables, i.e. ratio scores, which makes the expected scores different from zero, and factor coefficients artificially inflated (Short and Horn, 1984). Several other ethological studies contain the same and other methodological errors in their use of factor analysis (Short and Horn, 1984). This does not necessarily mean their conclusions are incorrect, but it does raise doubts about them. Morgan *et al.* (1976) re-analysed Wiepkema's data using cluster analysis, a technique which makes fewer assumptions and enables a clearer visual representation of the results. They confirmed two of Wiepkema's main groupings, but not the third ('non-reproductive movement').

Although there are no child observation studies using factor analysis on sequential data, Blurton Jones did adapt Wiepkema's method for use with frequency data (Blurton Jones, 1972c; Blurton Jones and Leach, 1972). He calculated the frequency with which twenty-two categories of behaviour occurred in each of fifteen 5-minute observation periods for four groups of children. Blurton Jones then factor-analysed the data for each group. Three of the five resulting factors were consistent across the groups. These were described as rough-and-tumble play, aggression and social activities. In this case, factor analysis was used to examine the association of different categories of behaviour within observation periods, rather than between those preceding or following one another in time.

Although Blurton Jones did not use derived variables as Wiepkema did, both studies confounded within- and between-individual sources of variation ('the pooling fallacy': Machlis *et al.*, 1985). Wiepkema used a large number of observations from thirteen animals, and Blurton Jones used fifteen observation periods from small numbers of children. There is a dilemma when using either multiple sequential observations from the same animals, or using frequency data from several observations carried out on the same animals. The researcher has to choose either to study variations between observation periods carried out on one individual, or examine variations between individuals by collapsing the data for different observation periods.

Blurton Jones (1972c) did recognize this problem, and sought to overcome it by comparing the main factor analysis with one carried out on the total scores for each individual. In doing so, he was able to show that the within-individual source of variation was more important in this case, enabling him to conclude that the factors were based on motivationally distinct groupings of behaviour.

Following Wiepkema's application of factor analysis to sequential data, this technique was used in a number of other studies involving animals (see van der Heijden *et al.*, 1990). However, it is now possible to use correspondence analysis, a method based on the chi-squared distance between activities, to analyse sequential data. This method results in an integrative representation of the structure of the transition matrix, without making the unrealistic assumptions inherent in applying factor analysis to such data (van der Heijden *et al.*, 1990).

The potential uses of observational studies

Observational data have played a part in remedying what critics have seen as the restricted context of psychological inquiries. A call for more naturalistic or ecologically valid research has been made in several branches of psychology (e.g. Bronfenbrenner, 1973; Neisser, 1976), and observational methods provide one way of studying activities occurring outside the confines of the psychological laboratory (although, of course, there are many observational studies which *are* laboratory-based).

A related contribution is to help remedy the lack of a descriptive base apparent in some areas of psychology. Ethologists such as Tinbergen (1963) and Blurton Jones (1972a) have contrasted the emphasis on accumulating descriptive information in ethology with the dominant research strategy in psychology which they saw as testing theories by experimental manipulation. Similar criticisms have been made by some psychologists: writing of research on infancy, White (1969) referred to it as 'an edifice without a foundation', arguing that it had moved straight to an experimental phase without the necessary foundation of a natural history base. The ethological approach, with its emphasis on description, can play a part in building this base.

Systematic observations provide different types of information from other research methods. This may provide either complementary or alternative viewpoints to more traditional psychological methods. For example, the approach of Charlesworth (1979, 1983) to the development of cognitive abilities contrasts with the tradition of investigating cognitive development through specific tests devised by the researcher. Charlesworth carried out observations on young children, concentrating on problems that arose during the course of their spontaneous interactions. A problem was defined as involving a block to ongoing behaviour, and represented a cognitive challenge to the child. Observations focused on the behaviour that was interrupted, the nature of the block, the response, whether or not it removed the block, and whether the previous behaviour was resumed. Charlesworth found that the majority of children successfully removed these blocks, most of which are social in nature, and that there are stable individual differences in how children coped.

Charlesworth's approach is very different from that of traditional cognitive developmental research, which involves tasks which may involve difficulties associated with their unfamiliarity, and with the novel context of testing. However, as Charlesworth pointed out, observations are complementary with, rather than a replacement for, such research. Despite doubts about the generalizability of results from experimenter-designed tests, they do allow experimental manipulation and hence a more thorough investigation of cognitive processes underlying problem-solving. Observational studies, on the other hand, can provide information on the nature and frequency of cognitive challenges in everyday life.

In other cases, ethological research has led to conclusions different from those reached using more traditional psychological methods. Rough-and-tumble play and aggression have been observed in a variety of studies of pre-school children and also in older children (e.g. Humphreys and Smith, 1987; Boulton, 1988, 1991a). Pioneering ethological studies of children, such as those of Blurton Jones (1967, 1972c), emphasized the clear distinction betweeen rough-and-tumble play and aggression: for example, factor analysis revealed high loadings for those acts which had previously been identified as rough-and-tumble play; 'work' was at the other end, with a strong negative loading. Aggressive acts such as fixate, frown, hit, push and take–tug–grab were located on a separate factor. Additional evidence that the two are motivationally distinct is their negative correlation in older children. Later studies of older children (Humphreys and Smith, 1984; Boulton, 1991a) have added to the criteria on which the two types of behaviour can be distinguished: these are discussed in Chapter 5.

Blurton Jones (1972c) argued that his findings had important implications for studies of the imitation of aggression carried out in the experimental tradition of social learning theory. The widely-cited 'Bobo doll' experiment of Bandura *et al.* (1961) involved the learning of 'aggressive' behaviour by children through imitating an adult role-model. Blurton Jones questioned whether these experimental studies *had* involved aggressive behaviour, rather than rough-and-tumble play. As he (and Smith, 1989) pointed out, some of the photographs in the follow-up study (Bandura *et al.*, 1963, p. 8) showed facial expressions indicative of rough-and-tumble play rather than aggressive behaviour. In these studies, the category 'aggression' was not described; we may assume that it was partly or wholly mixed up with rough-and-tumble play. The implications of this confusion are that the children may have been imitating actions in their rough-and-tumble play, rather than in their aggressive acts, as assumed by the researchers. Smith (1989) listed other influential studies of aggression which failed to make this distinction.

This example illustrates the importance of careful observation of behaviour prior to carrying out experimental manipulations, a point recognized by Tinbergen (1963) in his discussion of the ethological approach. It also illustrates the different perspective which careful observation can bring to topics previously studied by other methods, and in this sense could be used to plan later, more meaningful, experimental studies of play and aggression.

The two examples described in this section show how observational methods can provide very different perspectives on issues which have been of interest to developmental psychologists using more traditional methodologies. There is much scope for extending the range of topics to which systematic observations have been applied, with the likelihood of also providing new perspectives and insights on these topics.

Integrating ethological and other methods

In addition to providing methods which are alternatives or complementary to psychological methods, ethological observations can also be combined with other methods in the same study. Such integration provides a contrast with the separate identity sought by the 'human ethologists' (see p. 27). It has occurred when researchers are more interested in focusing on a specific problem than showing that their preferred method is superior to others. Three examples are presented here.

The first is the study of rough-and-tumble play by Smith and his colleagues, referred to above (see also Chapter 5). In order to study both the behavioural details of this form of behaviour and its meaning to the participants, they combined observation with sociometric ratings and inter-views about the meaning of various types of behaviour shown in their videorecordings.

Boulton and Smith (1989) also found that behavioural observations raised issues that could be dealt with by on-the-spot interviews with the participants. On one occasion, they were puzzled by an unusual type of rough-and-tumble play, involving a large number of children of both sexes, lasting for a long time and being particularly boisterous. By asking the participants, they found out the specific meaning of these actions: the children said they were playing a game called 'miners and pigs'. It was based on the violent confrontations between striking miners and police that had occurred at the time of the observations. It is unlikely that observations alone would have revealed the significance of these actions. It is also unlikely that a general interview which was not informed by first-hand observations in the playground would have managed to pinpoint this particular form of rough-and-tumble game.

Two further cases where ethological methods have been combined with other approaches are Chisholm's study of attachment in the Navajo and Hinde's study of relationships. They are both 'ethological' in a broad sense, in that they incorporate approaches derived from ethology rather than simply transposing ethological methods to humans.

Chisholm (1983) viewed his specific research topic, the use of the cradleboard by the Navajo of Arizona, from an evolutionary perspective. Initially, he regarded it as a perturbation which would disrupt mother–infant interaction and the process of attachment. He also recognized the societal context in which the cradleboard was used, primarily as a 'baby-sitting device' rather than for carrying the infant. He carried out detailed observations on Navajo mother–infant pairs, but he also used standardized infant assessment techniques, such as the Brazelton Neonatal Behavioral Assessment Scale (NBAS), and fear of strangers tests administered when the infants were 1–3 months and 3 years old.

Chisholm suggested that the cradleboard would prevent the infant from fully expressing its attachment behaviour, would restrict its ability to perceive behaviour directed towards it, and may also affect its general responsiveness and motivation, in turn lowering its appeal for adult caregivers. Although Ainsworth (1979) found that infants whose mothers were insensitive or unresponsive were more likely to show 'avoidant' or 'ambivalent' attachment (see p. 50), Chisholm (1983, 1987) suggested that there would be alternative pathways to the same end-point of secure attachment, i.e. the development of attachment is canalized (Waddington, 1957) and shows equifinality (Bateson, 1976b; see Chapter 4).

Although the cradleboard was associated with lower levels of infant responsiveness and mother–infant interaction, these effects were restricted to the times when the infant was on the cradleboard, and apparently did not have the long-term consequences which Ainsworth's findings might have predicted. Chisholm identified the following, which might have alleviated or corrected any long-term consequences of the cradleboard: first, it was always placed very near to the mother while she worked; second, crying and fretting led to removal of the infant from the board, and was followed immediately by a period of intense interaction with the mother. He suggested that these provided alternative ways of maintaining attachment which compensated for the restrictions imposed by the cradleboard.

Chisholm's approach is ethological in that it includes an evolutionary framework and observational methods, but he also used methods from developmental psychology, social anthropology and paediatrics, to produce a wider view than would have been possible from a narrowly ethological one.

The third example is Hinde's study of relationships. He argued that the subject required a descriptive base, since most existing studies were concerned with the application of general principles (Hinde, 1979). In ethology, an initial descriptive phase is regarded as essential, but is often lacking in areas of psychology which have been theory-driven and laboratory-based. Hinde offered such a detailed framework for describing relationships. He also emphasized the importance of considering their dialectical nature, every one being embedded in a wider social and societal context, and influencing, and being influenced by, the individual characteristics of the participants. Relationships therefore provide a focal point for integrating studies of societal norms with those of personality. To achieve this integration, behaviour is considered in terms of different levels in a variety of contexts, using several methods of obtaining information.

The emphasis on studying successive yet interrelated levels of complexity, each with their own emergent properties, is 'derived in part from the orienting attitudes of ethologists' (Hinde and Stevenson-Hinde, 1987), presumably from the hierarchical models of Tinbergen and Baerends (see Chapter 1). The emphasis on different contexts is also ethological in a broad sense in that it rejects the laboratory-based methods of much of traditional developmental psychology (Bronfenbrenner, 1973). The methods used by Hinde and his colleagues involved a variety of techniques, some of which (direct observations in the home, playground and classroom) were specifically ethological, whereas others (such as Thomas and Chess's method for assessing infant temperament) were established psychological methods. Hinde's approach again provides a contrast with 'human ethologists' who seek to transfer only the methods (and a limited number of concepts) from ethology to the study of human development.

The results obtained (e.g. Hinde and Stevenson-Hinde, 1986) do not show the simplicity often found in studies addressing more restricted aims. They consist of patterns of correlations describing the relations between characteristics of the mother and child, their relationship, and the child's behaviour in pre-school, and relations with the family context. Factor analysis was rejected because the components were insufficiently replicable across the sexes, ages and situations. Hinde and Stevenson-Hinde specifically chose to preserve the complexity in describing their results, rather than applying global descriptive variables which would allow 'much individual variation to slip through' (Hinde and Stevenson-Hinde, 1986, p. 45).

The examples presented in this section show how both ethological and other methods can be used within a broadly ethological framework to investigate aspects of social development, the complexity of which is not readily addressed by a more traditional psychological approach.

Chapter 3

Animal models

Introduction

An animal model is a simpler version incorporating important properties of the human case, which can be used for experimental investigation. As indicated in Chapter 1, ethological investigations of animal behaviour are not tied to their possible implications for human behaviour. There has therefore not been a tradition of specifically using 'animal models' to illuminate issues in human psychology. Animal models are usually associated with comparative psychology and developmental psychobiology rather than ethology. Nevertheless, ethological findings or ideas were taken up and used to provide 'animal models' for human research, and subsequently some ethologists specifically set out to establish animal models. In this chapter, I shall concentrate on infant–mother relationships, as this is the area of research in which animal models have been most widely used.

Bowlby used two types of animal model in his work on attachment: first, filial imprinting; and second, experimental research on rhesus monkeys by the comparative psychologist Harlow and the ethologist Hinde. In a later article looking back over these developments (Bowlby, 1980a), he listed three advantages of these models for aiding human research: (1) they introduced contemporary biological concepts (presumably principles such as the sensitive period); (2) they enabled research methods to be pioneered; (3) when their findings were broadly similar to less reliable human ones, they added credibility to these. Hinde (1983b) remarked that animal models provide 'harder' data (i.e. there are fewer interacting variables), and consequently findings are more readily replicable than in human studies. This remains their main justification (see final section).

Imprinting as a model of attachment

The initial importance of filial imprinting for Bowlby's approach to human attachment was that it called into question the secondary drive, or social learning, theory of attachment. This held that the adult took on secondary reinforcing properties by dispensing primary reinforcers such as food and warmth. The child was viewed as showing attachment behaviour, such as smiling and approaching, as operant responses. This general view was shared, albeit in a rather different form, by psychoanalysts such as Sigmund and Anna Freud (Rajecki *et al.*, 1978).

Bowlby had become interested in the effects of maternal separation in the 1930s. By the early 1950s, he was dissatisfied with the ability of the secondary drive theory to account for certain features of human attachment. His impression was that infants do not take readily to any adult who feeds them, as the theory implied, but instead develop a more directed response towards their primary caregiver.

When Bowlby read Lorenz's early papers on imprinting, it showed him that a strong emotional bond could develop to a mother-figure without the intermediary of food. The chick follows and becomes attached to the first moving object it sees, even if that object provides no conventional reinforcement. Bowlby (1969) suggested that an imprinting-like process might occur in several other animals whose mother–infant attachment had been studied, such as guinea pigs, sheep, dogs and rhesus monkeys.

In addition to providing an example of attachment in the absence of the usual reinforcers, imprinting provided another principle which Bowlby saw as applicable to the human case. This was the critical or sensitive period (Chapter 4). Lorenz (1937) had correctly seen that the strong tendency to follow and become attached to a moving object would only last for a short period after hatching in the precocial birds he studied. Bowlby transferred the critical period concept to the development of attachment in the human child; however, instead of being a short time at the beginning of independent life, it became much longer, stretching from the first few months after birth to the end of the first year (Bowlby, 1969).

Reed and Leiderman (1983) carried out a study which they regarded as testing aspects of the imprinting model of human attachment. The context of their study was the agricultural Gusii society of Kenya, where the women are subsistence farmers and therefore require additional help in child-rearing. This is provided by older children and other members of the family.

Reed and Leiderman argued that the predictions of the imprinting model were that human attachment should show a sensitive period, with an identifiable beginning and end; individual differences in earlier caregiving experiences should predict differences in later attachments; changes in attachments should be more apparent earlier than later in the supposed sensitive period. Reed and Leiderman made two sets of observations (3 months apart) on each of 28 infants (aged 6–30 months) interacting with his/her mother, a child caregiver and an unfamiliar local adult. The degree of attachment was assessed by observing the behaviour of the infant after each figure had departed for a short time: behaviour such as vocalizing and proximity-seeking was measured. Contrary to the predictions, no particular age for becoming attached to the mother was identified, and there was no particular age at which attachment changed from the mother to the care-giver. Individual differences in the age of attachment were found to be related to the children's level of mental development, as assessed on the Bayley scales.

Reed and Leiderman concluded that the results did not support the predictions they derived from the imprinting model. They are not, however, inconsistent with other interpretations of Bowlby's work, such as that of Sroufe (1988), who stressed the cognitive emphasis (on 'inner working models') found in later writings. Nevertheless, the comparison between principles derived from imprinting and human attachment was clearly made in Bowlby's major book on attachment (Bowlby, 1969).

Reed and Leiderman argued that imprinting is suitable for species in which there is only a small variability in what has to be learned; in humans, more flexibility in attachment formation is necessary in view of the variety of possible caretaking arrangements the infant may encounter. Therefore, the age at which attachments develop is variable, and there is the possibility of a subsequent change in attachment to another caretaker.

The biological context in which attachment develops in precocial birds is indeed very different from the human case. A young chicken or duck is independently mobile soon after hatching, so that it is important that there is a mechanism which ensures that it stays close to its parent from this time onwards. A human baby is incapable of independent locomotion for some time after birth. Instead of a quick-acting mechanism for staying near to its parent, it requires social signals which will make the parent stay near to it. Only much later, and more gradually, will the infant develop attachment to the parent.

This biological context is reflected in the different characteristics of the development of attachment in the two cases. Filial imprinting is confined to a short period after hatching and occurs very rapidly: it is like love at first sight. Human attachment develops some time after birth, and occurs slowly as a result of continued mother–caregiver interaction: it is more like the develop-ment of love after an arranged marriage.

These crucial differences become obscured by attempts to emphasize similarities between the processes of attachment formation in altricial mam-mals and imprinting in precocial birds, for example, by referring to both as 'imprinting . . . in a generic sense' (Bowlby, 1969). Although filial imprinting may share some features with human attachment, and pointed Bowlby in the right direction in his thinking about attachment, it obviously suffers consider-able drawbacks as a realistic model of human attachment.

Attachment in non-human primates as a model of human attachment

Bowlby's attention was attracted to Harlow's experimental studies of rhesus monkeys, since they also demonstrated that attachment was not dependent on food reinforcement as an intermediary (Harlow and Zimmerman, 1958). These studies addressed a number of other issues which were important in relation to the human case, for example, the interactions between mother and infant leading up to attachment, and the short- and long-term effects of maternal separation.

The young rhesus monkey develops a strong and persistent attachment to its mother during the first two weeks of life, and as it becomes older spends a decreasing amount of time with her, and more time with its peers and with other adults. Obviously, the developmental sequence of human attachment is different from this, since the infant is born in a more helpless condition. The human infant only slowly becomes aware of its mother, and only later is able to seek her company in the way that the rhesus monkey can from early in its life. Bowlby (1969) regarded these as superficial differences which overlay a number of principles common to the development of attachment in the two species. He suggested that there has been, within the Primate order, a gradual shift from prosimians – where the infant takes all the initiative in keeping contact with its mother – to the gorilla and human species – where the mother begins by taking all the initiative.

Nevertheless, the main purpose of using the rhesus monkey as an animal model has not been to study the general features of the development of attachment – which can be readily observed in humans – but rather to study the effects of separation once attachment has taken place.

Short-term effects of separation

The short-term effects of separation from the mother or principal caregiver are well known from human studies. Bowlby (1973) has suggested that the reaction can be understood in terms of three phases. The first is active distress, calling and sometimes aggression; the second is a behaviourally more inactive phase termed 'despair'; and the third is referred to as behavioural reorganization, involving detachment from the previous attachment figure. Studies of a variety of animals have shown that these sorts of reaction are common to many young birds and mammals separated from their attachment figures. There is far greater cross-species generality in separation reactions than in the way attachments are formed. Research on this topic comes from a number of different backgrounds – ethology, psychobiology and comparative psychology – and involves birds, rodents and primates.

Most research on filial imprinting has concerned factors affecting its development, rather than the consequences of separation (Sluckin, 1972). Scattered observations and some experimental research show a pattern of distress and increased activity. For example, Hoffman *et al.* (1966) found that ducklings showed distress calling in the absence of their imprinting object. Lamprecht (1977) found that hand-reared goslings (Bar and Canada geese) living in flocks reacted to a short period of separation from their foster-parents (but not their flock companions) with pronounced distress calling and increased locomotion.

Several studies have investigated the effects of separation from the mother in guinea pigs, which were initially used for studies of attachment because they are precocial, and therefore comparable with the birds used for imprinting studies. Sluckin (1968) found that young guinea pigs developed a strong disposition to prefer a moving object after being exposed to it daily in a runway. Sluckin referred to this as imprinting, since it shared many characteristics with the development of preferences in precocial birds. In the guinea pig, however, the development of the preference was superimposed on an already established attachment to the mother. Later studies of these animals did involve attachment to the mother, showing that the young used her as a 'secure base' (Porter *et al.*, 1973) and showed distress calling when separated (Pettijohn, 1979). More recently, Ritchey and Hennessy (1987) showed that young guinea pigs briefly separated from their mothers not only vocalized frequently but also had elevated plasma cortisol levels.

More extensive research has been carried out by Hofer and his colleagues on the behavioural and physiological consequences of maternal separation in rat pups. Reviewing these and related studies, Hofer (1984) argued that there are two separate reactions to separation, differing in antecedents and in behavioural and physiological components. The two reactions correspond to Bowlby's phases. One is an active distress reaction, which Hofer was able to prevent by providing a surrogate companion, even one which was unresponsive. The other is a depressive reaction, which Hofer characterized as slower to develop, and entailing a physiological reaction, different aspects of which are controlled by different aspects of the mother–pup relationship: for example, growth hormone stimulation was found to be controlled by tactile contact with the dorsal surface, and noradrenaline increase by body warmth. These findings are particularly important because they parallel similar findings in primates (see below), and because they have implications for a wider theory of the dual control of separation reactions (Hofer, 1984).

The research of Harlow's group, although primarily concerned with the long-term effects of early separation, also described the immediate reactions of young rhesus monkeys to separation from their mothers. Seay *et al.* (1962) separated four infants from their mothers for a three-week period: they showed emotional disturbances such as high-pitched screeching and crying, accompanied by disoriented attempts to regain proximity. Similar studies carried out by Kaufman and Rosenblum (1967, 1969) on pigtail macaques showed that the immediate reaction of vocalization and frantic activity was replaced after a day or two by an inactive hunched-up posture, suggesting a depressive state. The more usual behaviour pattern gradually emerged thereafter. When the mother was reintroduced after four weeks' absence, a dramatic reassertion of their relationship occurred, with prolonged ventral–ventral contact and close proximity between infant and mother at other times.

A later series of studies undertaken by the ethologist Robert Hinde and his colleagues followed on from these earlier studies, yet was different because it concerned short periods of separation, and contained more detailed behavioural observations. The immediate consequences of separation were investigated by Spencer-Booth and Hinde (1971a) who removed the mothers from nineteen group-living infants at various times between 18 and 32 weeks of age. Some animals were separated twice, approximately 5 and 9 weeks apart. The separation period lasted 6 days, after which the mother was returned. Measures included aspects of the mother–infant relationship, such as contact and proximity, numbers of 'whoo' calls (which are particularly common in separated infants), interactions with companions, tantrums and the total amount of locomotion.

During separation, there was an overall decrease in activity and a large increase in the number of 'whoo' calls (which declined over the 6-day period). On the day the mother was removed, there was no overall reduction in locomotion, because some infants showed initial periods of hyperactivity alternating with sitting still. Within a day of separation, their level of activity became as low as it had been in the other monkeys from the start of separation. The separated infants sought the company of their companions in the pen and sometimes cuddled together. There were marked individual variations in the severity of these reactions.

When reunited with its mother, the separated infant vigorously sought contact, and spent much more time with her than it had done before (as Kaufman and Rosenblum, 1967, had also observed). Tantrums (loud and intense screeching, typically shown by infants rejected by their mothers) were more common, even though the mothers rejected their infants less than before the separation. During the following few weeks, these responses gradually returned to the sort of levels they had shown before separation, but the rate with which this was achieved varied greatly between individuals. Most of the variation could be related to pre-separation characteristics. Hinde and Spencer-Booth (1970) showed that the more stressful the mother–infant relationship was from the infant's viewpoint, the more disrupted the infant would be after separation. Infants who were rejected most by their mothers when seeking ventral contact, and had to make more effort to stay near them, were the ones that were more distressed by separation and its aftermath.

Spencer-Booth and Hinde (1971a) noted that their results were broadly consistent with the first two phases of Bowlby's model of separation reactions, in that distress declined from an initially high level, and some animals showed hyperactivity at first (phase 1), whereas inactivity (phase 2) increased throughout the separation period. Although this is the case, there was considerable overlap between the two types of response – so much so that it is better to view them not as phases but as two interrelated reactions with different time courses, and perhaps with different causes (cf. Hofer, 1984: see p. 43). There was little evidence of Bowlby's third phase (detachment) in Spencer-Booth and Hinde's studies.

Spencer-Booth and Hinde (1971b) found that the reactions of infants to 13-day separation periods were broadly similar to those during six days of separation. The infants' behaviour changed most markedly during the first few days, but remained fairly constant after that, again providing little sign of Bowlby's detachment phase. There were, however, pronounced differences between the two durations of separation when the mothers returned, the longer-separated infants showing more 'whoo' calls and a greater depression of locomotion and play.

Other studies showed that the context of separation was important. When the mother was removed from the familiar social group, as in the studies just described, the infant showed a marked but brief protest reaction, but mainly a depressive response. However, if the infant was removed from its mother and social group and placed in a strange place, it tended to show a much longer 'protest' reaction and to be hyperactive (Hinde and McGinnis, 1977). These infants were less distressed upon reunion than were those whose mothers had been taken from them. These findings may appear counter-intuitive at first sight, because the degree of change imposed on those taken away from their pen is greater, yet their reaction to reunion involves less upset (Hinde, 1974). It is, however, the mothers' behaviour which provides the key to understanding these different reactions. Those mothers who stayed in their home pens were more amenable to their infants' demands upon reunion. There was little rejection, and the infants could maintain proximity more readily than those who had to interact with a previously removed mother who has to readjust all her social relations on returning to the group.

Although the detailed evidence from Hinde's studies provides, at best, only qualified support for Bowlby's phase model, it has nevertheless been widely used in other research on the separation reactions of young primates. In a review of such studies, Mineka and Suomi (1978) identified a phase of active protest followed by withdrawal and despair, but they questioned the evidence for the detachment phase (cf. Kaufman and Rosenblum, 1967, who found a recovery phase in pigtail macaques).

More recent primate studies have included physiological as well as behavioural measures. In squirrel monkeys, Levine *et al.* (1987) found that the depressive reaction to separation was accompanied by elevated adrenocortical secretion. Brief separation produced both high rates of distress calling and elevated cortisol. A longer period of separation was associated with a decline in vocalization, as found for rhesus monkeys, but an increased level of cortisol, producing an inverse relationship between the two. Levine *et al.* also applied the biphasic model of separation reactions to these results, with the active searching phase being represented by the calls, and the depressive phase accompanied by increased adrenocortical secretion, and replacing the first phase if calling does not produce reunification. Again, so long as these responses are viewed as gradually developing and overlapping, the model would seem applicable. These findings also parallel those from rodents, described by Hofer (1984) and others (see above).

Other studies have investigated the response of a wider range of physiological variables to separation. Reite *et al.* (1981) found that, in young pigtail macaques, depressive behaviour was accompanied by decreased heart rate, lower temperature, sleep disturbances and EEG changes when they were separated from their mothers. Reite *et al.* suggested that these physiological changes represent an impairment of autonomic regulating processes, a suggestion reminiscent of Hofer's theory that aspects of the relationship provide physiological regulation. Further research has shown an influence of separation on immune functioning (e.g. Laudenslager *et al.*, 1990).

The various animal models described in this section provide a consistent overall picture of the way a variety of young animals respond to separation from their mothers in the short term. They support, in broad terms, existing descriptions of separation reactions in young children (Bowlby, 1980b), with the possible exception of the lack of evidence for a 'detachment' phase. They therefore add credibility to at least some of the human evidence (Bowlby, 1980a), as well as providing a basis for cross-species comparisons (Chapter 6). As indicated at the beginning of this chapter, the primary use of animal models is to provide data which could not readily be obtained from humans, and to enable more control over the variables involved. Since the broad outline of the immediate effects of separation is well known from human studies (Archer, 1990), animal models would seem to be of lesser importance in this context than, for example, in the investigation of the long-term effects of separation (see below).

Nevertheless, it is possible to point to a number of important detailed findings which are unlikely to have arisen from human studies. These include the effects of different durations of separation experience, the after-effects of separation, and the impact of the context of separation. Animal models allow such topics to be studied with a greater degree of experimental control than in the human case, where the researcher has to make use of whatever unavoidable separations are available.

The psychobiological approach used in recent studies of rodents and primates has introduced a wider perspective on separation reactions. This combines the ethological emphasis on detailed observations of behaviour with physiological measurements, within a functional framework. Although it was always clear from human studies that separation experiences are highly stress-inducing, physiological evidence comes almost entirely from animal models. Comparable human studies – which are possible with modern physiological techniques – have rarely been undertaken (Archer, 1990).

Long-term effects of maternal separation

Harlow's original studies were designed to investigate the long-term behavioural consequences of maternal separation. They involved total or near total social isolation. Earlier studies by comparative psychologists had also investigated the long-term effects of similar extensive periods of isolation in a variety of birds and in dogs (e.g. Kuo, 1967). Such experiences were found to lead to severe disruptions in the animals' social behaviour.

Hinde and his colleagues studied the effects of shorter periods of separation from the mother on later behaviour in young rhesus monkeys. The earlier studies of the immediate effects of separation were extended by testing the monkeys 5 months and 2 years later (Hinde and Spencer-Booth, 1971).

The mother was moved for 6 or 13 days when the young were between 21 and 32 weeks old, and the long-term follow-up was carried out at 12 and 30 months of age. Observations were made in a number of tests which involved confronting the infant with a mildly disturbing or frustrating situation. In familiar surroundings, there were no differences between separated monkeys and those that had not been separated. They both responded similarly to a novel object. However, when a novel object was present in a strange place, the previously separated monkeys approached it to a lesser extent than did the controls. These differences were found at both ages, but were clearer at 5 months after separation, and attenuated 2 years after separation.

A later study (Hinde *et al.*, 1978) which involved 13 days' separation when the infants were 30 days old, provided further evidence that the effects of separation could be detected 5 months and, to a lesser extent, 2 years later. In a novel test cage, mothers who had been separated tended to reject their infants more than those who had not, and infants who had been separated tended to be more dependent than those who had not.

The importance of these findings is that they show that brief separations can produce long-term effects on what human psychologists would call personality (Hinde, 1983b). Such effects are difficult to establish from the human evidence. Since his early work, Bowlby had maintained that early separation from the mother-figure could have long-term consequences. The human evidence was necessarily indirect, because there were so many confounding variables. The evidence for Bowlby's claim was subjected to a number of conceptual and methodological objections (Morgan, 1975; Rutter, 1979a), and it was widely thought that he had overstated his case. The finding of long-term effects of brief separation in rhesus monkeys does at least make

Bowlby's claims about long-term consequences of separation in humans much more likely. In fact, Hinde specifically set up his research as an animal model of whether brief separations could produce long-term effects on what human psychologists call personality (Hinde, 1983b).

More recent research has extended these studies to another species. Capitanio *et al.* (1986) compared adult pigtail macaques who had experienced 10 days of maternal separation during their first year, 2½ to 5 years ago, with matched controls who had not been separated. Their behavioural and plasma cortisol responses were measured in four unfamiliar situations. The previously separated animals showed more behavioural disturbance than did the controls, and the level of disturbance shown to the unfamiliar situations was significantly correlated with the degree of behavioural and physiological disturbance during the original separation. These findings support those of Hinde and Spencer-Booth using a different species and an even longer time since separation.

Animal models of an unresponsive mother

The research described so far has used animal models to guide, and to aid interpretation of, human data on mother–infant separation. Inadequate mothering may also occur as a result of neglect. Field *et al.* (1986) found that the effect of a short period of maternal unresponsiveness was more distressing for a 4-month-old human infant than was a short period of separation. On the basis of this evidence, they suggested that lack of responding or unavailability of the mother for interacting with the infant may be as, or more, disturbing than her absence. In an earlier section, important differences in behaviour after reunion were noted, in rhesus monkeys, between infants that had been removed from their mothers and those whose mothers had been removed from their social group. These differences were due to the relative lack of concern shown after reunion by the mothers who had been removed from the group. Reite (1987) has suggested that this would be an appropriate model for human cases of neglect.

In addition to neglect, unresponsive mothering also occurs when the mother is depressed. In view of the high rates of depression in women with young children (Richman, 1976), it is particularly important to understand the influence of this type of unresponsiveness on the child's development. Maternal depression is associated with behavioural problems in pre-school children (Richman, 1976), but it is difficult to infer causal connections from the correlational evidence.

Other approaches to researching this problem include inducing short periods of unresponsiveness in human mothers who are not depressed, and observing the effects on their infants in the short term (Field *et al.*, 1986). In an earlier study, Cohn and Tronick (1983) had also found that three-month-old infants reacted to a simulated depressed expression by protest, wariness and looking away. As a research method this is useful, but limited by ethical considerations and by the degree to which it simulates aspects of the depressed state.

Studies of interactions between depressed mothers and their infants provide another source of information (Murray and Stein, 1990). These studies show that depressed mothers are less active, emit fewer vocalizations and show fewer positive facial expressions, although some show 'intrusive' interactions, consisting of a high level of anger, pulling at their infants, but still with a low level of positive affect. The infants of depressed mothers typically show protest and discontented behaviour, or else are withdrawn and depressed-looking. Those with intrusive mothers seek to avoid contact with them. These behaviour patterns become generalized to interactions with other adults. Follow-up studies have found that infants from depressed mothers have lower developmental scores on the physical and mental scales of the Bayley tests, and those from severely depressed mothers show insecure or avoidant forms of attachment (based on Ainsworth's classification: see Table 3.1 and section on 'Models of mother–infant relationships').

A study of marmosets by Chalmers and Locke-Haydon (1986) provides an interesting animal model of an unresponsive mother: a tranquillizing drug (Fluphenazine Decanoate) was used to render the mothers less responsive to their infants. This was compared with the effects of separating marmosets of the same age (4 weeks) for the same time (8 days). In both conditions, there were similar changes in the infants' behaviour after separation or during drug treatment. Locomotion was reduced, play was abolished and the time the infants spent with one another was increased. There were, however, differences between the two conditions when the drug was withdrawn or when the mother was returned. Gradual readjustment occurred towards the previously drugged mothers whereas there were marked reunion effects after separation.

One methodological problem with this study is that the possibility of drug transmission via the mothers' milk was not ruled out (Bateson, personal communication). If this problem can be overcome, the method could provide a model of interactions between unresponsive (either neglectful or depressed) mothers and their infants, which could usefully supplement methods used to study its effects in humans. In particular, the long-term effects of periods of maternal unresponsiveness could be investigated, since this is difficult to study in humans.

Chalmers and Locke-Haydon's study provides further evidence that it is the way the caregiver–infant relationship is disrupted, rather than separation itself, that leads to changes in offspring behaviour. This is apparent from the human studies of depressed mothers, Hinde's comparison of infant removal with mother removal, and the relationship between individual differences in attachment and reactions following reunion.

Table 3.1 The three major categories of attachment identified by Ainsworth.

Classification	Descriptor	Classification Criteria (from reunion episodes 5 and 8)[a]				
		Proximity seeking	Contact maintaining	Proximity avoiding	Contact resisting	Crying
A (2 subgroups)	'Avoidant'	Low	Low	High	Low	Low (pre-separation), high or low (separation), low (reunion)
B (4 subgroups)	'Secure'	High	High (if distressed)	Low	Low	Low (pre-separation), high or low (separation), low (reunion)
C (2 subgroups)	'Ambivalent'	High	High (often pre-separation)	Low	High	Occasionally (pre-separation), high (separation), moderate to high (reunion)

[a] Typical of the group as a whole; subgroups differ in non-reunion episodes and to some extent in reunion behaviour. See Ainsworth *et al.* (1978) for detailed classification instructions.
From: Waters (1978, Table 2).

Individual differences

Individual differences have been shown to be important throughout studies of infant attachment and separation. Hinde and Spencer-Booth found marked differences between the reactions of young rhesus monkeys to separation, and, as indicated above, these were related to previous behavioural differences: infants that were more affected by separation had shown more tension in their relationships with their mothers. The long-term effects of separation also showed individual variations, which were related to the amount of disturbance shown during separation. In this research, the emphasis was on the *relationship* with the mother as an influence on reactions to separation. This topic will be discussed in the next section.

Other research has concentrated on the individual characteristics of the infants. Suomi (1989) found that about 20 per cent of rhesus monkeys could be characterized as having a highly reactive temperament. This finding applied to a wide range of circumstances, in the laboratory and under free-living conditions (studies carried out on a Puerto Rican island). Reactive monkeys showed physiological and behavioural arousal to novel events which evoked exploration in the majority of animals. The two reaction styles were discernible early in life and showed stability as the animals matured. In the free-living troop, they were stable from year to year.

The two reaction styles were not readily discernible in the absence of stress, but when the animals were placed in a novel environment, the differences between them became apparent. Heart rate and corticosteroid levels showed more pronounced increases, and habituated more slowly, in the reactive monkeys. These monkeys also explored less and initiated less activity than the majority did.

Under free-living conditions, the mother will be ready to form a consort pair with a male when the young are about one month old. This produces a naturally occurring separation, since the pair may move away for a few days. Infants may try to follow, but the mother will be unresponsive to them. Suomi found that the infants' reactions to these separations paralleled those occurring under experimental conditions, with distress calling being common. There were, however, marked individual variations in behaviour. Some infants became very inactive, huddled and depressed-looking. These features were particularly pronounced in monkeys with the reactive response style. Suomi also found that how the monkey reacted to separations during the first year of life would predict its reactions to later separations.

Suomi argued that these reaction styles show a heritable component, since the infants' ACTH responses to a mild stressor were similar to those of their fathers, even though they were not present during rearing. There was also evidence that rearing conditions could modify reaction style. In cross-fostering experiments, it was found that a reactive infant was rendered less so if it were reared by a nurturant supportive foster-mother. When this social support was removed at 6 months of age, the infants reverted to the reactive response style. This finding suggests that there is a basic stability in responding, which can be overridden – but not removed – by certain rearing experiences.

When cross-fostered infants were placed in an all-male peer group containing an older heterosexual pair, those from the nurturant background sought out the support of the older female, and eventually became the dominant animal in the group (see Chapter 7). Reactive infants which had been cross-fostered to non-nurturant mothers behaved timidly in the peer-groups, avoiding the adults and peers alike.

Although partly concerned with the effects of separation, the main emphasis in Suomi's research was on the reaction styles underlying individual differences in responding to a wide range of environmental changes. Suomi suggested that the reactive monkeys he identified are comparable to shy and anxious human children. The usefulness of an animal model in this context is that it enables such individual differences to be studied under more controlled conditions than is possible in the human case. Suomi's research, although beginning in the laboratory, shows a considerable influence of ethology, in that response styles and separation episodes were studied in free-living animals, and their significance was viewed in relation to the naturally occurring social behaviour of the species. For example, males typically leave their natal troops at around puberty, and subsequently form all-male groups before entering a new troop. Suomi reported that reactive males (as assessed by physiological measures) were likely to leave the natal troop late, and to avoid entering an all-male group. Instead, they go straight to a new troop, where they are located around its edge.

Models of mother-infant relationships

The influence of the mother–infant relationship on the response to separation, and the influence of separation on the mother–infant relationship, were important features of Hinde's research. For example, tension in the relationship before separation predicted more distress upon reunion (see above). In more recent research, Hinde's group have continued to use rhesus monkeys as a model for the development of mother–infant relationships.

Longitudinal studies have shown the importance of the mothers' temperamental characteristics for mediating the relationship and its impact on the offsprings' temperament (Hinde and Stevenson-Hinde, 1986). More confident mothers were found to reject or leave their daughters less and, by one year of age, the daughters themselves tended to be confident. This pattern was not, however, repeated in sons. Confident sons tended to have mothers who were relaxed and slower to react, spending much time with them early in life.

Both types of mother left their infants relatively infrequently, and infants played a small part in maintaining proximity with their mothers. Hinde and Stevenson-Hinde (1986) suggested that this provides a parallel with a type of human attachment characterized as 'securely attached'. This was one of three main categories of human attachment identified by Ainsworth (1979) in her studies of mother–infant interaction (Table 3.1). These were based on home observations, and measures taken in a laboratory playroom, using a standard procedure consisting of eight episodes involving the presence and absence of the mother and an adult stranger ('The strange situation': Table 3.2). The majority of infants were classified as securely attached (category B): the mother is sensitively responsive to her infant and provides a secure base for exploration.

Parallels were also drawn with a second of Ainsworth's categories, the ambivalent form of insecure attachment (category C: Table 3.1). This was identified in excitable infants (of both sexes) whose mothers were overprotective early in life, frequently restricting and approaching their offspring. The sons tended both to approach and leave their mothers, and the daughters to approach them often.

In humans, the pattern of associations between the variables involved in mother–infant relationships and their individual characteristics is very complex. Hinde and Stevenson-Hinde's longitudinal investigations of rhesus monkeys have allowed some of the variables likely to be involved in the human case to be studied under more controlled conditions in a species where the complications of human culture and language are missing. To the extent that comparable temperaments and relationship categories can be identified in rhesus monkeys and in humans, it is justified to draw cautious parallels between them.

Ethical issues raised by animal models

When Harlow's studies were first undertaken in the 1950s, both researchers and public opinion were little concerned about the ethical issues surrounding animal experimentation. The importance of ethical considerations is now widely recognized, particularly among ethologists (e.g. Huntingford, 1984b; Bateson, 1986).

Perhaps the most satisfactory framework for making ethical judgements about animal research is the cost-benefit approach advocated by Bateson (1980b, 1986; Driscoll and Bateson, 1988), and recognized in existing UK legislation on animal experimentation. The value of the research is balanced against the suffering it entails. The usefulness of the specific animal models described in this chapter lies in their ability to generate general principles applicable to humans which could not so readily have been derived from studies of the more complex human case. Additional benefits, such as the

Table 3.2 The eight episodes of the Strange Situation.

Episode	Persons present	Time	Events and procedures
1	M, B	Variable (approx. 1 minute)	M and B are introduced into S/S room by E. If necessary, M interests B in toys before being seated. M does not initiate interaction but is responsive to bids from B.
2	M, B	3 minutes	M remains seated and is responsive to bids for interaction but does not initiate.
3	M, B, S	3 minutes	S enters and is seated; sits silently for 1 minute; talks to M for 1 minute; engages B in interaction and/or toy play for 1 minute.
4	B, S	3 minutes (less if B extremely distressed)	M leaves room, S allows B to play alone but remains responsive to interactive bids. If B is crying, S offers contact and tries to comfort. If B refuses or resists, S does not persist. Terminate episode after 1 minute hard crying or on M's request.
5	M, B	3 minutes	M calls B from outside door and steps inside, pausing at doorway to greet B and to reach and offer contact. If necessary, B is held and comforted then re-interested in toys; otherwise, M is seated and remains responsive to bids from B but does not initiate.
6	B	3 minutes (less if B extremely distressed)	M leaves room; B remains alone. Terminate episode if 1 minute hard crying ensues or on M's request.
7	B, S	3 minutes (less if B extremely distressed)	S returns and is seated. If B is crying or begins to cry without pause, S offers contact and tries to comfort. If B cannot be comforted and crying continues (or on M's request), terminate episode.
8	M, B	3 minutes	M calls B from outside door and steps inside, pausing at doorway to greet B and to reach and offer contact. If necessary, B is held and comforted and then re-interested in toys; otherwise M is seated and remains responsive to bids from B but does not initiate if B is content in toy play.

M = mother; B = baby; S = stranger.
From: Waters (1978, Table 1).

provision of comparative evidence, and adding credibility to existing human evidence, are secondary, and perhaps not sufficient of themselves to justify a specific animal model.

In a brief assessment of ethical issues concerning studies of separation and grief (Archer, 1990), I suggested that because of its cross-species generality, animal models of the immediate response to separation added little to existing human evidence. In retrospect, this failed to recognize the more detailed and subtle contributions of such studies, for example, findings about individual differences, responses after reunion, and the impact of the context of separation. These findings are much more likely to have arisen from animal models – which enable a greater degree of experimental control than do human studies.

These contributions notwithstanding, it is the long-term developmental studies – on the prolonged effects of separation, on individual differences, and how relationships affect temperament – that are likely to have the greatest impact on human research. In these cases, identifying the relevant variables in human studies is particularly difficult.

Considering the other side of the cost-benefit assessment, it is clear that loss and separation cause suffering – distress and a depressive reaction. In his influential book *Animal Liberation*, Singer (1976) devoted several pages to describing the cruelties inflicted by Harlow and his colleagues. However, the procedures used in studies of separation have become less and less drastic since the earlier work of Harlow's group. Suomi, at one time a co-researcher of Harlow, is now concerned with naturally occurring individual differences, and the impact of very mild disturbances on the behaviour of rhesus monkeys. His research has moved from the laboratory to include free-living populations, where the occurrence of short periods of separation was shown to be a natural event when the mother formed a consort pair.

The separation periods used by Hinde and his group were little more than the naturally occurring separations described by Suomi. They were much less drastic than those used in Harlow's research, and less drastic than the separation experiences of human children described in Bowlby's work. In terms of suffering, therefore, these procedures involve disruptions which are similar to those the animal would normally experience under natural conditions. As indicated before, their contribution has been considerable.

One major impact of ethological thinking in the area of animal models has been to encourage the move away from drastic and unnatural procedures towards the study of more subtle disruptions in the infant–mother relationship, and towards longitudinal studies of the development of social relationships and personality in the absence of any disruptions.

Chapter 4

General principles of development

Introduction

The search for general principles of development has concerned both developmental psychologists and ethologists interested in development. Ontogeny was one of the four questions identified by Tinbergen (1963) in his influential paper on the aims and methods of ethology.

In classical ethology, the 'innate' or instinctive nature of many types of behaviour was emphasized. This was partly a reaction against the environmentalist bias in the North American comparative psychology of the time. It was also a consequence of the apparently invariant and automatic nature of many behaviour patterns in the birds, fish and insects which were the subject matter of classical ethology. Innateness was often assumed if behaviour were constant in form, and characteristic of a species. Lorenz advocated an experimental approach to determining whether a character was innate. In the deprivation or isolation experiment (Lorenz, 1965), young animals were isolated from their social companions so as to remove the likely sources of learning and thereby identify aspects of behaviour which were apparently innately controlled.

The concern with identifying 'innate' aspects of behaviour was associated with a view that behaviour emerged at particular ages under the control of internal processes. This view is broadly similar to maturational theory in psychology, with its notion of mental and behavioural 'growth' beginning at conception (e.g. Gesell and Ilg, 1943). Unlike maturational theory, classical ethology was not associated with detailed studies of behavioural ontogeny, or concerned with establishing a developmental timetable. Detailed descriptive studies of the development of behaviour were carried out later, and led to the realization that apparently innate behaviour patterns had complex developmental histories (e.g. Kruijt, 1964; Hailman, 1967).

The nature–nurture issue became the subject of a long-running debate between classical ethologists and British neo-ethologists, together with North

American comparative psychologists who had influenced them. Konrad Lorenz's writings, which involved a defence of the concepts of innate and instinctive, were the main focus of criticism. He in turn defended, with certain provisos, the utility of the deprivation experiment for eliminating the influence of learning, and hence for identifying what is innate (Lorenz, 1965). This approach has been maintained in the human ethology of Eibl-Eibesfeldt (see Chapters 1 and 2). Nevertheless, there is now a consensus among ethologists and developmental psychologists that some form of interactionist approach to development is more realistic than seeking to perpetuate the nature–nurture dichotomy.

Although he was little concerned with studying the ontogeny of behaviour, Lorenz (1937) did identify an important developmental process. This was imprinting, the mechanism through which the offspring-to-parent bond is formed in precocial birds (Chapter 2). Lorenz set out the characteristics of imprinting, which included the concept of the critical (later 'sensitive') period: this described the crucial time in the bird's life when it would follow a moving object. Research on imprinting was revived in the 1950s, when these characteristics were subjected to experimental scrutiny, and it was observed in a range of species (e.g. Ramsay, 1951; Hinde *et al.*, 1956).

Thorpe (1951, 1954, 1958) showed that there was a sensitive period for song-learning in the chaffinch, as well as for imprinting. This occurred several months prior to the bird's ability to produce the song itself. Song-learning was also shown to be constrained: the bird would only learn the song of its own species, or something very similar to it.

Ethologists interested in development have continued to study the processes of imprinting and song-learning, so that there is now considerable information available on these two topics. It is mainly this body of knowledge which informed discussions of the general principles underlying behavioural development, such as the sensitive period, the importance of nature and nurture, and discontinuities in development. These issues have recurred in both ethological research on development and in developmental psychology. However, ethologists have a number of advantages over their colleagues who study human development. They are able to draw on the results of naturalistic observations and experimental studies with animals whose lifespan and range of environmental influences are less than those affecting humans. They have also been able to compare different species, and to view development in the context of natural selection. Ethologists' discussions of general principles can therefore provide a different vantage-point from those of developmental psychologists.

The general principles discussed in this chapter are the nature–nurture dichotomy, the interaction of maturation and experience, sensitive periods and early experience, continuities and discontinuities and, lastly, the rules of development.

The nature–nurture dichotomy

As indicated above, there is still a clear difference on this issue between the classical ethology of Eibl-Eibesfeldt (1979) and research influenced by neo-ethology and comparative psychology. Following Lorenz's use of the deprivation experiment in research on animals, Eibl-Eibesfeldt used evidence from children deprived of sensory feedback, along with cross-cultural comparisons, to make inferences about the innate bases of human behaviour. This approach has its parallels in psychology, for example, in research on infant expressions and gestures (Freedman, 1964, 1965; Trevarthen, 1977), and in discussions of human sex differences (Hutt, 1972; Freedman, 1980).

Many psychology texts of fairly recent origin still characterize ethology as necessarily involving the nativist viewpoint (e.g. Miller, 1983; Shaffer, 1989). However, criticisms of this position began in the 1950s with the work of Lehrman (1953) and Hinde (1959a), and carried on thereafter (Hailman, 1967; Lehrman, 1970; Hinde, 1970; Bateson, 1976a, 1987; Slater, 1983), paralleling the criticisms of psychologists (Hebb, 1953; Anastasi, 1958; Hirsch, 1970; Lerner, 1976; Johnston, 1987, 1988).

Among the points made by these critics are the following. The term 'innate' has been used in two senses and this has led to confusion. One is to describe a form of behaviour which is typical of a species, and which is subject to alteration by selection; the other sense means unaffected by learning during development. The two meanings are very different (Lehrman, 1970). There are many examples of behaviour that is subject to selection but is modifiable by experience during development (Bateson, 1981). This is because selection operates on the *outcome* of the developmental process, which itself arises from the interplay of genetic and environmental influences.

A related point (Lehrman, 1953; Hinde, 1970) is that attempts to classify *behaviour* as either innate or learned are misplaced, since all behaviour must have resulted from a combination of the two sorts of influence, albeit in different ways. This point was made in earlier papers by psychologists criticizing the either–or approach to the nature–nurture issue (Hebb, 1953; Anastasi, 1958). Its acceptance necessarily leads to an interactionist position regarding behavioural development, although, as indicated in the next section, adopting this position does not necessarily dispense with the nature–nurture issue.

Even when the terms inherited and environmental are restricted to describing sources of influence on development rather than behaviour, they still generate problems. In Lorenz's (1965) discussion, he equated environmental influences with learning. But they are far wider than this (Lehrman, 1970; Hinde, 1970; Bateson, 1976a). There must be a certain range of environmental influences to sustain development at all. The deprivation experiment may omit the most obvious and major sources of social learning from the animal's environment, but it does not remove all sources of environmental influence. Temperature, nutrition and light all provide examples of general – as opposed to specific, learned – environmental influences. Lorenz (1965) acknowledges these reservations, and indeed listed a number of rules which need to be followed in carrying out such experiments, and in interpreting the results.

No deprivation experiment can exclude all environmental influences (Hinde, 1970). Because of this, the method is more useful for investigating specific environmental – rather than innate – influences. This has been the way in which comparative psychologists have used it, for example, in Harlow's research on early social restriction (Chapter 3). Thorpe (1961) also used it this way to investigate bird song. He studied its development in chaffinches isolated from the time when they were nestlings. The song they produced as adults, although split into notes, lacked all the detailed structure and characteristics of the usual song. Thorpe used this 'deprivation' experiment as a foundation for examining the impact of specific types of environmental influence. He played adult song to isolated birds at different times during development, and found that there was a sensitive period for song-learning. There were also limits to what could be learnt during the sensitive period, suggesting the existence of a crude neural template at hatching, which guides the bird towards certain types of sounds (see Chapter 8).

The deprivation experiment also raises the issue of general and specific environmental influences, elaborated by Bateson (1976a). General influences affect a wide range of behaviour, and specific ones only one form of behaviour. Both can refer to inherited or to environmental sources of influence. Bateson provided two examples of inherited influences from the behaviour of honeybees: a specific one was a gene affecting a particular form of behaviour such as removing the top of a hive cell containing diseased larvae. A general influence was a gene affecting responsiveness to light, and hence a wide range of behaviour. Specific environmental influences refer to particular learning experiences, whereas general ones refer to more wide-ranging influences, such as nutritional restriction, which affect later behaviour, for example, by impairing learning mechanisms.

Bateson acknowledged that in practice there is a continuum between general and specific influences, and there may be difficulties in classifying individual cases. He argued that behaviour varies in terms of whether it is subject to many or a few specific environmental or inherited influences, illustrating this with a scatter diagram showing four types of behaviour differing in the degree to which they are affected by such influences (Figure 4.1). Thus, hygienic behaviour in the honeybee is affected by a few internal determinants with specific effects but no specific external effects; typewriting in humans is affected by many external determinants with specific effects but by few internal determinants.

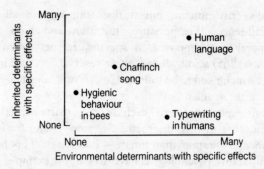

Figure 4.1 Scatter diagram from Bateson (1976a, Figure 3), showing hypothetical points assuming all developmental influences with specific effects were known.

Anastasi (1958) offered a classification of inherited and environmental influences which shows some points of similarity to Bateson's scheme. Anastasi argued that hereditary influences are always in some sense indirect, since their outcome depends on interaction with the specific environment in which development takes place. Nevertheless, there is a continuum of indirectness, from direct effects which are stable across a range of environments, and cannot easily be countered by intervention, to indirect ones which are mediated by social reactions to external appearance, such as physique, sex or skin colour.

Anastasi regarded environmental influences as varying in terms of the pervasiveness of their effects on behaviour, some having broad effects relating to many aspects of behaviour and enduring over long periods of time. Others have narrower, more limited effects. This distinction is similar to Bateson's division into specific and non-specific environmental influences, although the examples given by Anastasi indicate a difference of emphasis.

In discussing the deprivation experiment, Bateson (1981) referred to the possibility that feedback from an animal's own behaviour (for example, vocalizations: Gottlieb, 1991) may form part of the usual developmental environment. The deprivation experiment does not remove such influences. This point is similar to one raised by Scarr and McCartney (1983) and other psychologists. Environmental influences cannot be experimentally separated from the organism itself because the organism *creates* its own environment, both by responding to feedback from its own behaviour, and also (as Scarr and McCartney suggested) by its own behaviour producing characteristic responses in others. Thus an aggressive person will generate an environment laden with conflict (cf. Caspi *et al.*, 1987). A shy person will create a socially impoverished environment (cf. Caspi *et al.*, 1988).

These discussions all concern the complexities which are revealed once researchers begin to think about the multitude of processes which are hidden behind the labels 'hereditary' and 'environmental'. One approach which has sought to perpetuate the distinction between the two sources of influence is that of biometrical genetics. Although there is a recognition of the importance of both sources of influence in development, they are nevertheless quantified separately. This involves asking the question 'How much?' – a strategy that both psychologists (e.g. Anastasi, 1958) and ethologists (e.g. Bateson, 1987) have regarded as misleading.

Biometrical genetics involves the use of quantitative procedures for measuring the variation in a character attributable to genetic and environmental influences. The heritability estimate is a measure of the variability in a population which is attributable to genetic variation as a proportion of the total variability. Its best-known application in psychology has been in relation to racial differences in intelligence (Jensen, 1973).

If a genotype is reared in a limited range of environments, the proportion of the variance attributable to heredity will be high, whereas if it is reared in a wider range of environments, the proportion will be lower, because the environmental contribution is higher. Therefore, it is misleading to use the heritability estimate as a way of dividing an individual's behaviour into hereditary and environmental components, as some researchers have. It refers to a population in a particular range of environments, rather than to individuals (Hirsch, 1970; Bateson, 1983a, 1987).

Heritability estimates also involve the assumption that genetic and environmental components can be added together (Bateson, 1983a, 1987). For example, Mather and Jinks wrote: 'Since, however, the genetical analysis cannot pretend to ascertain the individual effects and properties of genes which are not individually distinguished, we may take the more limited aim of seeking a scale on which the genic and non-heritable effects are additive on the average, as far as the data go' (1971, p. 64). Bateson (1987) questioned the validity of this rescaling of data to eliminate multiplicative interactions. It eliminates important sources of variation, giving a false impression of the way in which hereditary and environmental influences interact.

The term 'norm-of-reaction' is used in behaviour genetics to indicate the limits of the potential outcomes from a particular genome. The exact outcome will depend on environmental influences. Hirsch (1970) argued that this too was misleading, since it implied that the outcome could be assessed in advance from knowledge of heredity and the environment, and perpetuated the nature–nurture dichotomy. Hirsch argued that the interaction between genotype and environment involves processes which are unique to *that particular interaction*, and hence – from the researcher's viewpoint – will be indeterminate. In practice, therefore, the norm-of-reaction is also misleading: even under the most favourable conditions for study, it cannot be predicted from knowledge of the separate hereditary and environmental components. I shall return to the issue of indeterminacy in behavioural development in the next section.

The interaction of maturation and experience

Recognition that the ontogenetic process involves the continued interplay of two sources of influence – the genome and the environment – must lead to some form of interactionist position. It is no longer possible to concentrate entirely on one of the two influences and ignore the other. Or is it? I shall argue that it is possible to hold to an interactionist view of behavioural development and still concentrate on one side of the nature–nurture dichotomy. There are various ways of doing so.

The first and most straightforward was adopted by Lorenz (1965) in response to the critics of his nativist position. He acknowledged that both sorts of influence must interact in development, but maintained that the way they combined was such that they could be separately identified in the resulting behaviour.

Essentially, Lorenz was concerned with the interaction between species-typical behaviour (fixed action patterns: Chapters 2 and 5) and experiential influences in development. He regarded the two sources of influence, or 'information' as he called them, as being still identifiable in the organization of behaviour, innate behaviour being 'intercalated' with that resulting from learning. Learned behaviour was viewed as being slotted into a framework provided by innate behaviour. Several British neo-ethologists have criticized Lorenz's argument. As Bateson (1976a) pointed out, although the two sources of influence may be identifiable at the beginning of the developmental sequence, they thereafter become indistinguishable – like the ingredients of a cake. A similar point also informed Hirsch's criticism of the norm-of-reaction, described in the previous section.

In defence of Lorenz's view, Barlow (1989) argued that the *form* of certain types of behaviour – the fixed action patterns which constitute the consummatory act at the end of a sequence – are affected very little by experience, which influences mainly the timing and organization of such behaviour. This type of behaviour contrasts with that referred to as 'appetitive' (Craig, 1918), and which leads up to the consummatory act. Barlow viewed Lorenz's intercalation as a way of addressing the issue of how these different types of behaviour are organized together. The more stereotyped forms provide a solid landmark around which variable, experientially influenced, types of behaviour are located.

In many ways, the principles used in biometrical genetics represent another way of recognizing the interaction of both heredity and environment in development but nevertheless still maintaining that they can be separated, at least in quantitative terms. This then leads to the position that the one with the larger heritability estimate is of greater importance than the other, which is then neglected. The objections to this view have already been discussed.

Similar reasoning is involved where the interplay of environment and organism in development is recognized, but one is simply viewed as more important than the other, which for practical purposes can be neglected. Although not often made explicit, this is essentially the position of psychologists espousing one side of the nature–nurture issue in areas such as sex differences. Archer and Lloyd (1985, Ch. 9) referred to this as the main effect model because, in terms of an analysis of variance, the main effect of heredity or the environment would be viewed as producing most of the variance. Of course, it would be possible to have both main effects contributing to the variance, in which case it would be similar to the additive model of biometrical genetics. What such approaches omit is the possibility of outcomes which can be attributed neither to heredity nor the environment, but to the unique combination of the two interacting together. This would entail an outcome which would not be readily predictable from knowledge of the two sources of influence, and is what Hirsch suggested in his criticism of the norm-of-reaction.

Hirsch's criticism leads one to ask whether all developmental interactions, involving the continuous interplay of hereditary and environmental influences, are necessarily interactions in this statistical sense, with an indeterminate outcome. Clearly, they are not, or else the course of development would always be unpredictable. Although some outcomes may be unexpected, others appear with great regularity and can be predicted in advance. The crucial difference between the two is that some controlling principle can be identified in the second but not the first case.

Bateson (1976b) outlined a model of the developmental process which incorporated both the principle of developmental interaction and that of control of development. First, he considered the case where there is substantial internal control over development. This will be apparent where the system can survive any environmental perturbation and return to a constant developmental pathway. Waddington's (1957) concept of canalization describes such a process. Bateson used the example of restriction of nutrition in development. If the nutrition of a young rat is restricted for a period, and then given in plentiful supply, the rat is able to catch up to where its weight would have been with *ad lib* feeding (Figure 4.2.). A similar process seems to occur with the growth of children, so that if weight is depressed by malnutrition or illness, gain is subsequently more rapid and usually ends up where it would have been (Tanner, 1970).

The term 'equifinality', derived from systems theory, has been used to describe the convergence of several different routes on the same end-point. Bateson (1976b) outlined a more formal depiction of how this can come about in the case of restricted nutrition. Control is exercised through a negative feedback loop (Figure 4.3). The actual weight is compared with a reference value based on an age-related preferred value. If there is a substantial discrepancy, the animal feeds at a higher rate, which leads to increased weight gain.

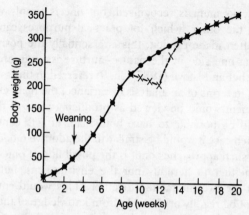

Figure 4.2 Graph showing weight gain plotted against age in rats. The solid line shows normally nourished rats and the dotted line that for rats undernourished between 9 and 12 weeks. At this age, the weight loss was rapidly made up when *ad lib* feeding resumed (from Bateson, 1976b, Figure 2, based on McCance, 1962).

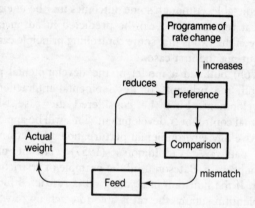

Figure 4.3 Model for weight control in the developing rat, from Bateson (1976b, Figure 3). Actual weight has no influence on preference unless discrepancy between actual and preferred weights is more than a predetermined amount (caption based on original).

There are a number of examples which suggest that the principle of equifinality can operate, at least partially, in behavioural development. ten Cate (1989) has argued that the developing animal plays an active role in the behavioural interactions which lead to song-learning and imprinting. He suggested that if the conditions for effective learning are deficient, the bird will behave so as to increase the relevant stimulation. Young male zebra finches learn song from an adult male during a sensitive period. If they are exposed instead to adult males from the related Bengalese finch species, they show active listening. This occurs, ten Cate suggested, because Bengalese finch males sing less than zebra finch males. The young zebra finch is therefore actively compensating for a lack of appropriate stimulation.

Another example is the restriction of the human infant's movements by the use of a cradleboard (see Chapter 2). Chisholm (1983, 1987) found that although it led to lower levels of infant responsiveness and interaction with the mother, the infants still became securely attached to their mothers. Chisholm suggested that locating the baby near to its mother and her rapid responding when it cried or fretted combined to provide alternative ways of maintaining attachment which compensated for the restrictions imposed by the cradle-board.

In this example, compensation arose from the environment in the form of additional maternal responsiveness. The same principle would operate whenever children are required to reach a specific level of competence at the end of training irrespective of their initial ability. In an account of their New York Longitudinal Study, Thomas *et al.* (1970) referred to a process whereby basic temperament becomes subject to a routine: for example, most children come to accept taking a bath whatever their initial reaction was. In these cases, performance would be monitored from the outside until it satisfied the criterion. Essentially, this conforms to an environmentalist view of socialization. It applies to instances where, for practical purposes, individual differences can be overlooked.

The principles outlined so far apply to cases where the outcome of the developmental process is largely predictable. They account for consistency. Absence of such control mechanisms, either within the organism or in the environment, would account for cases where the outcome of development is unpredictable.

Bateson described a further possibility, where the control mechanism itself arises from the interaction of organism and environment early in life. Usually this results in a predictable outcome, but outside the usual environment the developmental process may take one of a number of different courses. Bateson used imprinting as an example, but the same principles are likely to apply to other behavioural systems, for example, the development of responsiveness to the maternal call in the mallard: this is dependent upon hearing their own contact calls before hatching (Gottlieb, 1991). If this does not occur, they become susceptible to developing a preference for the maternal calls of other species.

In the case of the following response involved in imprinting, the chick begins with a search for an object matching a range of preferred properties (resembling those of an adult hen). Once a match has been achieved, the

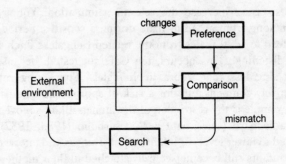

Figure 4.4 Model for imprinting, from Bateson (1976b, Figure 5): a negative feedback loop in which the preferred value is changed by external stimulation.

reference value will be altered so as to correspond more closely to the specific imprinted object (Figure 4.4). This new modified value will come to direct subsequent behaviour.

This sort of depiction of the developmental process allows a reconciliation between the principles of control and flexibility. It can be applied to cases where there is an initial search for a widely specified class of objects or individuals during a sensitive period, the results of which produce a narrower specification which controls the subsequent course of development. The development of human sexual orientation may be one example which fits this general model. So might gender development (Archer and Lloyd, 1985, Ch. 9). In this case, the potential for classifying and acting on the basis of the categories male and female is present early in life, but only after interaction with a gender-differentiated social environment does a gender-related self-concept develop. This then directs the child's actions along gender-role consistent lines.

Another variation on this model might apply to cases where the internal controlling mechanism is elaborated gradually during development. Arguing against human young-to-parent attachment developing during a single critical period (cf. Chapter 3), Sroufe (1988) described 'inner working models' as gradually being elaborated over a period of time, although they become 'somewhat firm' early in childhood. Sroufe was concerned with how earlier experiences with attachment relationships were internalized so as to provide a consistent guide based on representations of the self, others and relationships.

The discussion in this section shows that adopting an interactionist position regarding behavioural development does not necessarily entail the view that there is no overriding control for any character either from within the organism or from the environment. Stability in the outcome of development must involve control, and I have outlined various ways in which it can come about, derived from the work of Bateson (1976b). This will still leave cases where the outcome in a particular case remains uncertain, where control cannot be said to reside in one or the other source of influence.

Sensitive periods

The concept of the sensitive period became an important one in both ethology and in developmental psychology, where it was associated with the issue of whether early experiences necessarily exert disproportionate effects on development. The original term was 'critical period' (e.g. Scott, 1962; Scott and Marston, 1950), which had its origins in the study of embryological development (Bateson, 1979; Lerner, 1976; Oyama, 1979), with the notion that there is a fixed timetable for the developmental process. Thus part of the embryo which is the focus of development at the moment will be particularly sensitive to potentially disruptive or facilitating influences. If that part does not develop within its critical period, the focus of development will shift elsewhere.

The concept became transferred to psychological and behavioural development. Within psychoanalytic theory, it influenced the notion of stages, with the focus of psychosexual development changing at different times during development. In ethology, it was reflected in Lorenz's description of imprinting (e.g. Lorenz, 1937) and in studies of bird song-learning (e.g. Thorpe, 1961). In comparative psychology it was introduced into studies of the formation of affectional bonds, the development of learning and effects of early stimulation (e.g. Scott, 1962; Scott and Marston, 1950). Its impact can also be seen in other areas such as language development and the development of the visual pathways (Bateson, 1979, 1983b; Bornstein, 1989).

Lorenz (1937) originally characterized the time during which the following response (filial imprinting) occurred as a fixed 'critical period'. Later experiments (e.g. Guiton, 1959; Salzen and Meyer, 1967) have shown that the period when a young bird is susceptible to following a moving object can be varied (within limits) by manipulation of the sensory input, and is not necessarily irreversible (Bateson, 1979). Such results led to a consensus that the term 'sensitive period' was more appropriate, since 'critical period' implied that the boundaries were fixed from within.

Similarly, the period during which some birds learn adult song can be varied as a result of experience (e.g. Eales, 1985, 1987; Kroodsma and Pickert, 1980; Petrinovich and Baptista, 1987). For example, Eales (1985) found that young male zebra finches learn adult song between the time of independence from their parents and sexual maturity. However, this period may be extended beyond sexual maturity if they do not encounter an appropriate 'song tutor' (an adult male). Thus male zebra finches raised by females retain the ability to learn song from an adult tutor made available to them after the end of the normal sensitive period. This later learning overrides learning of song from 'unsuitable' tutors (i.e. females) encountered during the sensitive period (Eales, 1987). ten Cate (1989) has suggested that these and similar findings for white-crowned sparrows indicate some degree of self-termination in ending the sensitive period, as opposed to control by some form of internal clock.

The concept of the sensitive period, based on the assumption of an imprinting-like process, has been applied to several aspects of human behavioural development. In addition to infant-to-mother attachment (Bowlby, 1953b, 1969; see Chapter 3), it has also been applied to the development of gender identity (Kohlberg, 1966; Money and Ehrhardt, 1972; Money *et al.*, 1957), sexual relationships at adolescence (Money and Ehrhardt, 1972, p. 189), musical preferences (Holbrook and Schindler, 1989) and the formation of mother-to-infant attachment (Klaus and Kennell, 1976).

In Chapter 3, I pointed out that the imprinting model applied to human infant-to-mother attachment was misleading, not only because it implied that there was a fixed critical period, but also because it suggested that attachment occurs rapidly, when in fact it develops over a longer time period. Some of the other applications of an imprinting-like sensitive period to human behaviour may also prove to be based on misleading analogies. They usually entail the assumption of a fixed critical period, and are derived from the older research on imprinting.

Perhaps the best-known example is 'maternal bonding'. Klaus and Kennell (1976) and subsequent studies found that mothers who were given extra contact with their babies in the period immediately after birth showed a number of later indications of closer attachments and lower incidences of child abuse. Despite methodological flaws in some of the most widely cited studies, inconsistencies in the behaviour supposedly affected by 'bonding' and several negative findings (Herbert *et al.*, 1982; Myers, 1984), the evidence was readily accepted as supporting the view that the mother is susceptible to forming a bond with her infant shortly after birth. One reason for this acceptance was the belief in a critical period, based on an analogy with imprinting (Sluckin *et al.*, 1983).

Arguing against rejecting the notion of maternal bonding altogether, Daly and Wilson (1988a) suggested that there was some directional consistency in the findings, particularly those showing increased risk of child abuse when the baby had been separated from its mother immediately following birth. They suggested that a more complex process is involved. It begins with an assessment phase, when the mother shows apparent indifference to the baby. This is followed by the establishment of 'individualized love' and, during the succeeding months and years, by a gradual deepening of this feeling. Therefore the establishment of the bond is not an automatic process and can occur to a variable degree depending on the result of the assessment. Bonding can also occur after the sensitive period, but there is an advantage in establishing the initial bond. This would seem a sensible view which involves none of the drawbacks of the imprinting model, yet still retains the idea of a sensitive period, linked to an assessment process derived from evolutionary thinking (Chapter 6). It also fits ten Cate's (1989) suggestion that a high quality stimulus encountered during the sensitive period results in rapid learning, whereas a low quality stimulus results in the sensitive period being prolonged.

The belief that there are sensitive periods during human development is a widely held one, and most of the examples considered so far were based on rather general analogies with the following response of young precocial birds. In his original characterization of imprinting, Lorenz (1937) did not distinguish between this process, which occurs just after hatching, and sexual imprinting, which occurs during a later sensitive period (Immelmann, 1972; Bateson, 1979), and on which later mate choice is based. More recent studies suggest that closer parallels with human development may be found by examining sexual imprinting.

Sexual imprinting can be illustrated by describing Immelmann's (1972) research which involved cross-fostering eggs between two related and interbreeding species of birds, the zebra finch and the Bengalese finch. Males from one species (e.g. the zebra finch) were hatched in the nest of the other one (in this case the Bengalese finch), and were subsequently isolated until they were sexually mature in order to rule out later influences. These zebra finch males preferred to mate with Bengalese finch females when given the choice of the two species. This occurred even though the female of the native species was more receptive. The preference proved to be resilient in the face of considerable sexual experience with females different from the imprinted ones (Immelmann, 1972). As Lorenz (1937) had noted, it is the preference rather than the behaviour that is resilient. An animal may mate with a less preferred partner because it is the only one available, yet the preference is not diminished. The sensitive period for sexual imprinting in zebra and Bengalese finches lasted from 13 to 40 days after hatching, some time before sexual maturity, but only a few days' exposure within this period was necessary for establishing the preference.

More recent studies (Bischof and Clayton, 1991; Immelmann *et al.*, 1991) have shown that sexual imprinting is also affected by the first sexual encounter, which normally acts to stabilize the learnt preference. If conflicting information is given at these two stages, the outcome depends on the intensity of interactions the bird shows to its parents and to its first sexual partner.

Other studies, involving preferences for different varieties within the same species (Gallagher, 1976), or individuals with different plumage (Bateson, 1979, 1980a, 1982) have also shown a sensitive period for learning the characteristics of related individuals or close kin some time after that for filial imprinting. Bateson showed that mate choice in Japanese quail was based on the following mechanism. Sibling characteristics are learned during a sensitive period when juvenile characteristics have been replaced by adult ones. During

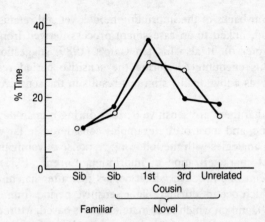

Figure 4.5 Time spent by adult Japanese quail near member of opposite sex according to relatedness and familiarity. Clear circles are data for 22 males, shaded circles data for 13 females (from Bateson, 1982, Figure 2).

adulthood, this learning is used as a standard, preference being shown towards opposite sex individuals whose plumage is slightly discrepant from the standard (Figure 4.5). This mechanism results in optimal outbreeding (Bateson, 1978a; see Chapter 6).

Bateson (1978b, 1979) has speculated that a similar mechanism underlies the learning of sexual preferences in humans. This is based on two sorts of evidence. The first is that people choose sexual partners similar to themselves on a wide range of characteristics. The second is that individuals of the opposite sex who have spent their childhood together find one another sexually unattractive, even when there are strong social pressures favouring a bond between them. This had been referred to by Westermarck (1891, 1922) in his book on human marriage as an innate aversion to sexual intercourse between persons living very closely together from early youth: he described cases where a girl betrothed in childhood and taken into the future husband's family was treated as a sister, making later sexual relations problematic. Bateson referred to more recent studies confirming these observations for Taiwanese arranged marriages. In a study of Kibbutz rearing, Shepher (1971) found that there was an absence of sexual activity and marriage between individuals who had been reared together. He suggested that a process of 'negative imprinting' occurs in those who are brought up together. This rearing produces an internal representation of the rearing group, and later choice of sexual partner is based on the principle of slight novelty. This suggested mechanism is very similar to that proposed by Bateson in his research on Japanese quail.

A similar process may underlie the development of human sexual orientation, the establishment of homosexual or heterosexual preferences. A variety of sources indicate that such sexual preferences originate before puberty, and are stable throughout adult life. For example, Havelock Ellis (1926) stated that in 88 per cent of a sample of 64 homosexuals, their preference began early in life, without previous attraction to the opposite sex, and in most cases it pre-dated puberty, between the ages of 5 and 11 years.

More recent studies have identified a pattern of cross-gender role behaviour during childhood in male (and possibly female) homosexuals. In a cross-national study, Whitam and Zent (1984) found that male homosexuals showed a consistent pattern of an early interest in dolls, playing with girls and cross-dressing, and were regarded as 'sissies'. The longitudinal study of Green *et al.* (1987) found that boyhood doll-play and feminine role-playing were specifically associated with later homosexual orientation in boys who originally showed various types of cross-gender behaviour.

Van Wyk and Geist (1984) investigated the association between adult homosexual behaviour and a range of variables in a sample of over 10,000 American men and women. Again, the male homosexuals were shown to have had a preference for playing with girls before puberty, and homosexual women had reported fewer female companions.

In accounting for their results, Van Wyk and Geist suggested an initial role for biological disposition, controlled by prenatal androgens, which results in individual differences in susceptibility to social influences. This can be linked with the idea of negative imprinting as follows. Most children mix predominantly with their own sex peers before puberty (Maccoby, 1988; Archer, 1992). According to the negative imprinting hypothesis, this experience will result in a marked reduction in the later attractiveness of same-sex individuals as sexual partners (on a principle similar to that occurring with opposite-sex siblings). On the other hand, those children who do mix predominantly with the opposite sex during childhood will tend to prefer their own sex as a sexual partner, since negative imprinting will in their case have occurred to the opposite sex. On this view, a broad range of potential sexual preferences becomes narrowed down as a result of childhood social experiences.

If this theory is correct, the parallels between the development of human sexual orientation and sexual imprinting in birds are striking. Preferences are influenced by social experience in a sensitive period prior to puberty, they are not dependent on reinforcement from sexual experiences at this time, they are long-lasting and they resist change in the face of alternative sexual experiences. There are also parallels in the variation found between individuals in susceptibility to imprinting.

A further similarity concerns the impact of the first sexual experience. Normally this has a consolidating effect on the preference derived from sexual imprinting, since it would be in accord with that preference (Immelmann, 1981). However, when a bird's first sexual experience is with a non-preferred variety, such experience modifies the preference in the direction of this variety

(Immmelmann, 1981; Immelmann *et al.*, 1991; Bischof and Clayton, 1991; Kruijt and Meeuwissen, 1991). Sexual imprinting appears to be a two-stage process, depending not only on information learnt in the sensitive period, but also on testing the validity of this information during the first sexual encounters (Bischof and Clayton, 1991). In their large-scale study, Van Wyk and Geist (1984) found that adult homosexual preference was associated with the first masturbatory experience being with a same-sex individual. They viewed early sexual experience as being particularly important in consolidating preferences, so that once a pattern of sexual preference had been established shortly after puberty, it soon became resistant to change. These findings indicate that at this time of development, close confinement with the same sex would make a homosexual orientation more rather than less likely.

In addition to providing parallels with human behaviour, ethological research involving sensitive periods can also help to understand the principles underlying their control, and complement similar endeavours by psychologists (e.g. Bornstein, 1989). Bateson (1979) argued that although the process of imprinting can be generalized to other sensitive periods in humans (e.g. language and visual pathway development), some important general points about sensitive periods can still be derived from considering experimental studies of imprinting.

He was concerned with reconciling the apparent contradiction between two viewpoints, one which emphasized the establishment of preferences and dispositions during sensitive periods, and a second which emphasized the scope for change in adulthood. This issue was central to the debate on the impact of early experiences on later development in humans (Clarke and Clarke, 1976; Rutter, 1979a). Bateson concluded that the end of the sensitive period for filial imprinting arose more from an 'unwillingness' to learn new features than from an inability to do so. By this he meant that there are mechanisms which protect the dispositions learned during the sensitive period from being replaced by others later in life. Such protective mechanisms may be susceptible to removal by later influences such as habituation or stressful conditions (Bateson, 1983b, 1987), thus introducing the possibility of modifying early dispositions under some circumstances (cf. Kagan, 1976).

Bateson (1983b) considered the circumstances under which previously stable dispositions could be changed during adulthood in humans, following experiences generating strong emotions or stress, such as brainwashing techniques, religious conversions or emotionally charged therapies. Looked at this way, the interesting issue is the nature of the mechanisms that normally protect a behavioural disposition which has originated during a sensitive period, from being affected by later experiences.

This throws a different perspective on aspects of human development which have been characterized as involving early learning during a sensitive period, the effects of which are then irreversible. For example, Money *et al.* (1957) and Money and Ehrhardt (1972) viewed gender identity (self-categorization according to perceived sex) as involving such an imprinting-like process, the effects of which were irreversible. In characterizing gender identity thus, they leaned heavily on earlier views of filial imprinting. Although Diamond (1965) challenged the irreversible nature of human gender identity, and pointed out the dissimilarities with classical descriptions of imprinting, the analogy still persisted. Imperato-McGuinley *et al.* (1976) later showed that at least in some circumstances, gender identity could be more flexible than originally supposed. Money and his colleagues nevertheless used the imprinting analogy to support a particular approach to therapy for transsexual patients. They argued that since gender identity is irreversible, it is better to change the person's anatomical sex so that this coincides with gender identity.

Adopting Bateson's more flexible notion of filial imprinting involving protective mechanisms blocking off the potential for later change, it is possible to acknowledge an imprinting-like process and yet leave the way open at least to consider possible alternative forms of therapeutic intervention, based on the prospect of psychological rather than anatomical change. This may in the end prove too difficult, but what I am arguing is that it should not be excluded from consideration through adherence to an outdated model based on earlier imprinting research.

Continuity and discontinuity in development

In both developmental psychology and ethology, researchers have debated the extent to which the developmental process can be characterized as continuous or discontinuous. Although this is, like the nature–nurture issue, a false dichotomy in absolute terms (Hinde, 1983a; Hinde and Bateson, 1984; Lerner, 1976), there has been a long-running debate about where to place most emphasis.

The term 'discontinuity' can be used in several different senses (Kagan, 1976; Bateson, 1978c). The first concerns a change in rank-order of an attribute relative to a reference group, such as peers or a group of animals: for example, changes in the ordering of marks from a school class from one year to the next, or changes in the dominance order of individuals over time (Figure 4.6), would be of this sort. Lerner (1976) used the term 'stability' to distinguish this case from 'discontinuity', which he defined as involving a change in the laws controlling behaviour from one time to another within a single individual. Rank-order changes may reflect the consequences of interpersonal processes such as aggressive interactions, in the case of changes in dominance. They can also arise from other causes, which are trivial in the sense that they are concerned more with the particular measurements used (Bateson, 1978c), for example, because they reach a floor or ceiling value, or the same behavioural category comes to be used in a different way.

As Hinde and Bateson (1984) remarked, the case for discontinuities in

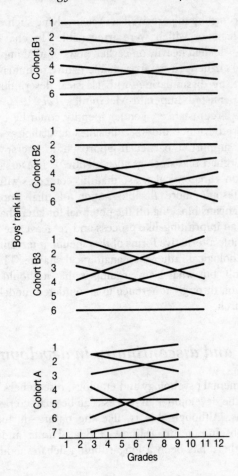

Figure 4.6 Stability of dominance over time-intervals in the longitudinal study of Weisfeld *et al.* (1987: Figure 2). Measures are other boys' ratings.

development commonly rests on such changes in the rank-order of individuals over time, rather than on evidence of discontinuity in the sense used by Lerner. They outlined four further types of evidence which are relevant to discontinuity in this sense. First, a qualitatively new pattern of behaviour appears or an old one disappears: the emergence of adult sexual behaviour at adolescence, or the disappearance of suckling after weaning are obvious examples. Secondly, the rate of behaviour suddenly changes with age: play may not entirely disappear with age, but its rate generally declines. Thirdly, the links between certain forms of behaviour, as shown by correlations between them, change with age: for example, in a longitudinal study of American boys, Weisfeld *et al.* (1980) found that dominance and leadership were unrelated to perceived intelligence at earlier ages, but by 16 to 18 years of age these attributes were positively correlated, reflecting developmental changes in the male role (Archer, 1984, 1989, 1992). Fourthly, there may be a change in the rank-order of the frequencies of certain activities compared to others within an individual: after a traumatic life-event, a person may change from being outgoing with a predominantly positive mood to being withdrawn and hostile. These different types of evidence refer to different forms of discontinuity.

In psychology, the continuity–discontinuity debate has been connected with several other issues, including the nature–nurture issue and the influence of early experience. If we are concerned with a psychological attribute which can be measured at different ages, such as intelligence or aggression, and it is held to be subject to strong internal control, it would follow that such an attribute would show developmental continuity. We would expect an individual who was described as aggressive early in life to be aggressive during adulthood. Rushton and Erdle (1987) used evidence from correlations between measures of aggressiveness taken from ages 8 and 30 years to support the case for the heritability of this trait. Researchers who have argued for a strong hereditary influence on other aspects of personality, such as emotionality, sociability and impulsiveness, have also emphasized their stability throughout childhood (e.g. Buss *et al.*, 1973). It should be noted that the sort of data used in these cases involves stability in the rank-order of individuals across time, and is therefore subject to the reservations outlined above.

If we are concerned with a psychological attribute which is subject to the strong influence of an early experience, as in the case of sexual imprinting in birds, and (as argued above) sexual orientation in humans, we should again expect this attribute to show developmental continuity. One of the four characteristics of imprinting set out by Lorenz was that its effects would be irreversible. This term has now been replaced by 'stable' or 'long-lasting' (see previous section), but its implications for later behaviour are still that we should expect stability of behavioural tendencies over time. In this case, we are concerned with the stability of an individual's behaviour over time, rather than their behaviour as compared to some reference group.

In these cases, developmental continuity can be viewed as arising from consistent internal control of the developmental process, as outlined in an earlier section. Control of behaviour is viewed as arising from heredity, in the case of temperament, or from an interaction between the organism and a part of the environment at a crucial phase of development, as in the case of sexual imprinting (Bateson, 1976b).

Developmental stability may also arise in other ways. A consistent influence from the social environment may produce consistency over time, again as shown in the section on the interaction of nature and nurture. Thus, many social learning theorists have also emphasized continuity in development (Kagan, 1976, 1978).

There are also more subtle ways in which developmental continuity may arise. I referred earlier to Scarr and McCartney's argument that people's temperament influences the sorts of environment they evoke and select for themselves, thereby enhancing continuity through feedback from the consequences of behaviour.

Caspi *et al.* (1987) carried out an investigation, based on the Berkeley Guidance longitudinal study begun in 1928, on the association between temper-tantrums assessed at 8–10 years (in 1936–8) and adult assessment at age 30 and at 40 years. Interview assessment showed that the previously ill-tempered boys were more under-controlled, moody and irritable than their even-tempered peers as adults. Path analysis revealed a direct link between being ill-tempered as a child and an erratic work life during adulthood. Ill-tempered boys also showed lower educational attainment, which in middle-class men led to lower socio-economic status than for their more even-tempered counterparts. They were also less likely to have an intact first marriage at the age of 40 years.

For women, Caspi *et al.* found no apparent association between childhood temper-tantrums and adult disposition, based on interviews with them. But they were perceived both by their husbands and by their children as less adequate and more bad-tempered as mothers than were women who had been even-tempered as children. The husbands of the ill-tempered women were also of lower socio-economic status than those of their even-tempered counterparts, and there were more marital conflicts.

These findings show long-term continuity in both the behaviour itself and a number of variables which are presumably either the direct or indirect consequences of that behaviour. Caspi *et al.* distinguished between two mechanisms underlying this continuity. The first is longer-term and occurs, for example, when an ill-tempered boy ceases education, thereby limiting future career opportunities and selecting more frustrating circumstances, which evoke further aggressive behaviour. The second is short-term, and occurs when an ill-tempered boy coerces others into providing immediate reinforcement and thereby learns an interactional style which is maintained under similar circumstances even though it is, in the long term, counterproductive. This distinction corresponds to that made by Scarr and McCartney between genotypes selecting different types of environment, and eliciting different kinds of responses from others.

The examples discussed so far indicate the wide range of mechanisms that can produce continuity in development. It is not surprising that there has been a general assumption that development is essentially a continuous process in the most influential theoretical orientations of psychology, such as psychoanalysis, individual differences and even behaviourism (Kagan, 1976, 1978; Clarke and Clarke, 1976, 1984). One notable exception has been the cognitive developmental approach, as described by Kohlberg (1966), who questioned the long-term influences of early experiences. His accounts of the development of the understanding of gender and moral development (Kohlberg, 1976) emphasize qualitative differences in the understanding of gender role concepts at successive stages of development. The concept of developmental stages presupposes discontinuities in development (although it is not necessarily incompatible with the assumption of some fundamental degree of stability, as in the case of psychoanalytic or maturational stage theories).

Kagan (1976, 1978) and Clarke and Clarke (1976) have also put the case for the existence of discontinuities, and argued against the widespread assumption of behavioural continuity in development. They argued that this assumption has had many ramifications, including the following. First, it led to undue emphasis being placed on the irreversible nature of early experiences (see previous section). Second, it led to the neglect of resilience and catch-up effects in development, for which Kagan (1976, 1978) argued that there is more evidence than is usually recognized. Third, childhood behaviour such as play was viewed only in terms of its consequences for later development (see Chapter 8).

A major way that ethology has contributed to this debate is in questioning this last assumption from a functional perspective (Chapter 6). This highlights the view that many features found in young animals are not precursors of adult ones, but serve to aid survival at that point in development. In addition, as Bateson (1987) pointed out, juvenile behaviour may also be necessary for the process of development: it may enable the animal to learn about particular aspects of the environment, but once this has taken place, the mechanisms underlying the learning will no longer be necessary (see also Hinde, 1983a). From this perspective, it can readily be appreciated that there may be discontinuities in psychological development associated with the occurrence of features that function only at one stage of development. In the animal kingdom there are many examples. Metamorphosis is, of course, the most striking, although even in this case, experiences in the larval phase may have influences on the adult (Hinde and Bateson, 1984). Specific features possessed by juvenile forms may only occur at that time in their life history, and be discarded thereafter. Among the immature forms of the parasitic wasp, *Collyria calcitrator*, there is one specialized for fighting. It possesses a sclerotized head and large mandibles, which are only present at this stage of development (the end of the first instar; Clausen, 1940). Similarly, suckling pigs possess short, sharp but temporary canine teeth while they are in competition to determine which position they will occupy on the maternal teats (Geist, 1978). Milk teeth provide a further example from human development.

Nevertheless, partially in response to what they viewed as an overstatement of Kagan's position, Hinde and Bateson (1984) have urged caution when assessing the evidence for radical discontinuities. They argued that undue emphasis on uncovering examples of discontinuities, and contrasting these with the assumption of continuity, may impede understanding of the *process* of development. They point to a number of other reasons why the dichotomy may obscure rather than help understanding of development. These include the heterogeneous criteria on which discontinuities have been assessed, the equivocal nature of evidence for suggested radical reorganizations of behaviour, and the lack of correspondence between discontinuities in behaviour and underlying psychological mechanisms.

Rules of development

Hinde and Bateson argued that too great an emphasis on looking for discontinuities may hinder the understanding of processes involved in development. Similarly, Chalmers (1987) argued that gradual change is characteristic of most aspects of behavioural development. He went on to discuss the rules which govern or direct the course of development. In doing so, he assumed that current or past behaviour would influence the developmental process, i.e. that behaviour is not simply the by-product of physical development, but that feedback from existing behaviour is crucial for understanding behavioural development. There is much evidence to support this assumption (e.g. ten Cate, 1989; Gottlieb, 1991).

For *directing* the course of behavioural development, Chalmers assumed that the animal monitors some aspect of its own behaviour as it develops, either cumulatively, or in the short term, and that the results are matched to a template which is either independent of age or age-dependent (cf. Bateson, 1976a). This produces four possibilities, generating four different predictions about the consequences of experimentally depressing the quantity of behaviour the animal performs. For example, if assessment is instantaneous and the set-point age-dependent, the effect of depressing behaviour will be to produce a simple rebound to the normal trajectory when the perturbation is removed. Examples of this case are rare, but include the ultrasound distress calls of rats. More common, Chalmers suggested, is the case where the set-point is age-dependent but assessment of behaviour is cumulative, for example, when the performance of behaviour is monitored over a period of time. Examples include suckling in rats and the rate of pecking in jungle fowl. The consequences of a perturbation will be to produce a rebound effect followed by a return to the normal trajectory.

In the case of play, the evidence suggests the amount shown at a given age is sensitive to environmental conditions, and Chalmers suggested that there are probably no optimal age-dependent schedules of play, i.e. the set-point is age-independent in this case. A perturbation would depress the behavioural curve laterally. For example, this occurs when social play and mobility are depressed in marmosets (Chalmers and Locke-Haydon, 1986). Another example would be when a male zebra finch encounters a sub-optimal 'song tutor' during the sensitive period (ten Cate, 1989).

Chalmers also considered stopping rules, whether behaviour ceases as a result of some external event or as a result of performance criteria, and he discussed the adaptive aspects of these behavioural rules.

The search for developmental rules, and the mechanisms underlying them, is a fundamental aim for developmental psychologists as well as for ethologists. Chalmers' discussion, which was based largely on ethological examples, obviously has a general applicability, and the examples he used were widespread, including infant feeding, mother–infant interactions, play and language development.

Conclusions

The discussion of general principles of development was presented in terms of three broad areas: (1) nature, nurture and their interaction; (2) sensitive periods and early experience; (3) continuity, discontinuity, and the rules of development. I showed that ethological theory has progressed considerably from the nativist position characteristic of its early days. Yet discussions of ethology in psychological texts and journals often appear unaware of its progression. For example, Johnston (1987) considered the interaction of nature and nurture in development largely in terms of Lehrman's critique of Lorenz's division of the 'information' controlling behaviour into genetic and environmental sources.

Once researchers progress beyond the nature–nurture issue, to consider the processes involved in the interaction of environmental and hereditary sources of influence, the following conclusions can be drawn:

1. There are two different uses of the term 'interaction', to denote first a process and secondly an outcome.
2. The issue of whether innate and environmental sources of influence can be identified in behaviour is still strongly disputed: Lorenz's concept of intercalation, and the assumptions made in calculating heritability estimates, both seek to separate the two sources, but the consensus is that such exercises are misleading.
3. Feedback from the consequences of behaviour is an important environmental influence in the short term; it should also be acknowledged as an important contribution to developmental stability.
4. It is important to identify whether or not the developmental process is subject to control, and if it is, to specify the nature of the control. Principles such as canalization and equifinality can be associated with behavioural development whose outcome is subject to control. It is also possible to identify ways in which development may be both flexible and subject to control.

Sensitive periods were first introduced into ethology in Lorenz's research on imprinting. His early description of imprinting has remained influential for providing analogies with processes involving sensitive periods in human development. However, there have been many theoretical and empirical advances made since then, so that most of these applications now appear inappropriate. One example I highlighted was the imprinting model of gender identity. More recent ethological discussions have focused on the nature of the changes induced by early experience within a sensitive period, and what protects the mechanisms from being affected by later environmental influences.

Early research on imprinting did not sufficiently distinguish between filial and sexual imprinting. Models transferring the concept of imprinting to humans have generally only made use of the former. Yet it seems clear that sexual imprinting has interesting parallels with the development of human sexual preferences.

Continuity in behavioural development has been linked with the impact of early experience, or with stable temperamental dispositions controlled by hereditary influences. In psychology, critics have argued that the assumption of widespread continuity in development is unwarranted. The implications of this view are that psychological attributes are more flexible and open to change during the course of development than is usually assumed.

Ethologists have contributed to this debate by identifying the different ways in which the term continuity has been used, and by pointing out that discontinuities in development are matters of degree. They have also provided a fresh viewpoint by introducing functional considerations: juvenile behaviour may have its own function, rather than always being the precursor of adult features. Finally, assuming that much of behavioural development is continuous, it is possible to view it in terms of control by the consequences of behaviour. This is achieved through different types of set-points, which are either cumulative or short-term, and either age-dependent or not.

It is apparent that many of the discussions of general principles of development in the psychological literature (e.g. Lerner, 1976; Johnston, 1987) could have been enriched by consideration of these ethological discussions of similar issues.

Chapter 5

Motivational concepts

Introduction

The study of motivation (or 'causation') was one of the four aims of ethology outlined by Tinbergen (1963). It involves the analysis (by detailed observation and experimentation) of the immediate internal and external factors controlling behaviour. From the beginning of classical ethology in the 1930s, motivational analysis involved a set of concepts and theoretical models to guide understanding of the empirical findings. These ideas reached an English-speaking audience in the writings of Tinbergen (1942, 1951) and Lorenz (1950a, b).

Foremost among these motivational concepts was the fixed action pattern, which referred to a stereotyped behavioural response typical of the species. The stimuli which elicited fixed action patterns were also investigated, and where these had specifically evolved for a signalling function, they were termed releasers, or social releasers (Tinbergen, 1951). Research identified many examples of releasers in the behaviour of insects, fishes and birds. They were studied by constructing a series of model stimuli in which aspects of the natural stimulus were isolated and emphasized. Lorenz's earliest theorizing involved the elaboration of a hypothetical mechanism which was viewed as controlling these stereotyped responses to biologically significant stimuli (Lorenz, 1950a, b).

The Dutch ethologists Tinbergen and Baerends were concerned with constructing theoretical models underlying more complex forms of behaviour. Baerends (1941, 1976) used a theoretical scheme involving hierarchical control to depict the organization of nest-provisioning behaviour by the digger-wasp (Figure 5.8). Hierarchical control was also used by Baerends (1970, 1976) in a model derived from his research on incubation in the herring gull (Figure 5.9), by Tinbergen (1942, 1950, 1951) in his general model of instinctive behaviour, and by Hinde (1953b) in research on the behaviour of the great tit.

The idea that there is a series of hierarchically organized systems, each controlling functionally-specific types of behaviour, had several implications which influenced the thinking of later ethologists. First, it involved the concept of a separate behavioural or motivational control system for each biologically significant form of behaviour. Second, it led to investigations of motivational conflict or competition, when two or more of these systems were activated simultaneously. This involved the study of 'derived activities', for example, displacement activities (Tinbergen and van Iersel, 1948; Tinbergen, 1952a), and social displays (e.g. Hinde, 1953a; see Chapter 9). Research on these motivational issues was a very active area in the 1950s and 1960s, but dwindled thereafter, except in Holland where it was kept alive by Baerends and his colleagues (e.g. Wiepkema, 1977; Vodegel, 1978; Carlstead, 1981; Baerends, 1985; Groothius, 1989a, b).

There has only been a limited transfer of ethological motivational concepts and models to psychology. Within developmental psychology there are a few specific examples. Lorenz himself applied the concept of social releaser to some human cases, notably the response of adults to infantile features. This example has been investigated more recently in empirical studies. The concept of fixed action pattern (FAP) has stimulated a comparative study of stereotyped behaviour in human infants. Although these stereotypes are not the same as FAPs, the two types of behaviour do share some common principles of motivational control.

Central to Bowlby's theory of infant-to-parent attachment was his view of attachment as a behavioural system in the sense used by Baerends and Tinbergen. The concept of the behavioural system was also implicit in the work of Blurton Jones (1967, 1972c), who used methods derived from ethological motivational analysis to distinguish between rough-and-tumble play and aggression. This research has more recently been extended by Smith, Boulton and Fry.

Ethological ideas concerning motivational conflict have been applied to two issues in developmental psychology. One was in the research by Tinbergen and Tinbergen on childhood autism, which, they suggested, involved an imbalance between tendencies to approach and to withdraw. Another involved an approach to the motivational basis of childhood aggression by Attili and Hinde (1986).

In this chapter I consider these – albeit limited – examples of the transfer of ethological motivational principles to topics in developmental psychology.

Social releasers: Lorenz's baby characters

As indicated in the previous section, many classical ethological studies were concerned with identifying stimuli to which another animal would respond selectively by showing a specific and stereotyped reaction. The term social releaser was originally associated with a hypothetical motivational mechanism, the innate releasing mechanism or IRM (Lorenz, 1950a; Tinbergen, 1951), on which the specific releaser acted. The analogy used by Lorenz was of the releaser acting like a key in a lock (the IRM) to produce a stereotyped behaviour pattern, the fixed action pattern.

Tinbergen was more interested in hypothetical brain mechanisms than with providing such analogies. He used the following reasoning. If there is an 'innate' (i.e. stereotyped) reaction to a specific releaser, this implies that there is a neurophysiological mechanism controlling both stimulus selectivity and the specific nature of the response. Both Lorenz (1950b) and Tinbergen (1951) incorporated these features into models containing notions of energy and drive controlling behaviour, although Lorenz's model was couched in very different terms, again being on the level of analogy.

There followed in the 1950s and 1960s a number of detailed examinations of classical ethological concepts, some concerned with the nature–nurture issue (Chapter 4), and others with the concepts of drive and energy in motivational models (e.g. Hinde, 1956, 1959b, 1960, 1970). Energy models were viewed as being based on misleading analogies formed from superficial impressions of how some behaviour appeared to be controlled. These concepts were not able to cope with the new experimental evidence on the control of behaviour which arose during this period.

Discussing the concept of innate releasing mechanism, Hinde (1959b) regarded the term 'releaser' as misleading, since such stimuli may have one or more of a number of diverse effects, such as changing the readiness to respond to this or another stimulus, a long-term motivating influence or a decrease in response strength. The notion of a centre in the brain which corresponds to the specific releaser was likewise regarded as misleading, in view of the range of different ways in which selective responding can be mediated. In addition, the conceptual model did not consider the control of behaviour once it has started, nor the factors leading to its cessation. Hinde also questioned the assumption that releasing mechanisms were necessarily innate in specific instances.

Long before these critiques were made of the theoretical underpinning of the social releaser concept, Lorenz (1943, 1950a) had applied it to human behaviour. He suggested that adult nurturance and affection are evoked by certain facial and bodily characteristics found in human infants, and in the young of other birds and mammals. These include a large forehead, large and low-lying eyes, bulging cheeks, short and thick limbs, together with clumsy movements. His original examples, from a young human and three adult animals that show these features, are shown in Figure 5.1.

Lorenz's suggestion has received considerable support since it was first made, despite the conceptual difficulties with the IRM concept referred to above. In the introduction to their cross-cultural study of social behaviour in childhood, Whiting and Edwards (1988, p. 7) wrote: 'In interpreting the

Figure 5.1 Lorenz's diagrams of the 'releasing schema' of young birds and mammals. The figures on the left (child, jeroba, Pekinese dog and robin) contain these features, whereas those on the right (man, hare, hound and golden oriole) do not (from Lorenz, 1950a).

obvious and distinctive eliciting power of infants, we have found Konrad Lorenz's description (1943) of "releasing features" of the infants' appearance to be persuasive'.

Lorenz's suggestion has also received support from experimental studies of adults' preferences. The first of these was reported in a doctoral thesis in 1953 (Cann, 1953, cited in Hess, 1970). Male and female respondents, married and single, parents and non-parents, rated their preferences for pictures of the young and adults of a variety of animal species. Childless women (both married and single) preferred the young rather than the adult pictures to a greater extent than did the childless men. Fathers showed much higher levels of preferences for the young, but these were still lower than those shown by mothers.

A slightly different pattern of sex differences was reported by Fullard and Reiling (1976), who presented adults and children (of various ages) with pairs of slides depicting adults and infants of several species including humans. The female respondents showed a striking preference for the infants, which began at 12 to 14 years of age. The males also showed some evidence of an age-related shift in preference towards the infants, but it was not so dramatic and occurred at least two years later.

Although these studies demonstrate preferences for infants over adults, they did not specifically isolate the features Lorenz identified as releasers. Hückstedt (1965) used one aspect of these features, the forehead arch and its height, in a partial test of Lorenz's hypothesis. She found that when these cranial features were emphasized, they were preferred by 10–13-year-old girls and by 18–21-year-old boys. Girls preferred a 'supernormal' head – one in which these features had been exaggerated beyond the normal range – more than male respondents did. Gardner and Wallach (1965) also investigated the influence of manipulating forehead height, so as to exaggerate either adult or baby profiles. Pairs of such profiles were presented to a mainly female sample, who were asked to judge which one was more babyish (rather than preference as in other studies). Heads in which the forehead arch had been exaggerated were rated as more babyish than naturally occurring baby profiles.

Following an earlier exploratory study by Hess and Polt (1960), which showed increased pupil size by young women in response to pictures of a baby and of a mother and baby, Hess (1967) measured pupil size in response to a series of stylized pictures incorporating to varying degrees Lorenz's baby features. As predicted, he found greater pupilary responses to the baby features.

A third type of reaction was investigated by Alley (1983), who asked young adults to rate how compelled they would feel to defend that individual if they saw someone striking it. He was therefore measuring the capacity of baby features to evoke protective aggression (Archer, 1988a) from adults. The stimuli he used involved one of Lorenz's baby features, cranial height, which was varied in drawings and in profile outlines taken from human heads at various stages of growth from infancy to adulthood. In four separate experiments, higher ratings were obtained for the more immature forms, as predicted. There was also some indication that being female and having experience with children increased the relative ratings given to the immature forms, thus supporting earlier findings (Cann, 1953, cited in Hess, 1970).

Sternglanz *et al.* (1977) set out to investigate the effect of systematically varying the baby features in line drawings on ratings along a seven-point attractiveness scale by American college students. They varied the vertical position of the face (i.e. the relative length of the forehead and chin), the width of the eyes, their height and the size of the iris, all along a graded series involving several steps. Examples are shown in Figure 5.2, which is taken from Sternglanz *et al.* (1977).

Each respondent rated twenty slides, which contained complete sets of two of the four features. The ratings showed that larger eyes were more attractive than smaller ones, and that faces with large foreheads and small chins were preferred. Both of these were among the features described by Lorenz.

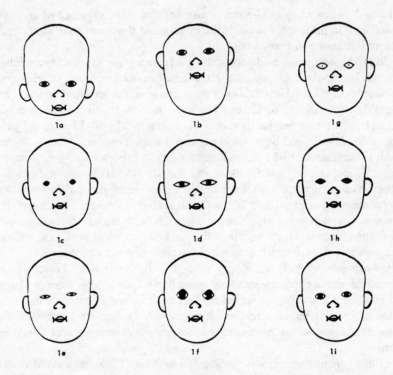

Figure 5.2 Examples of the facial drawings used by Sternglanz *et al.* (1977, Figure 1). 1a has the smallest chin, 1b the largest; 1c has the narrowest width eyes, 1d the widest; 1e has the smallest height eyes, 1f the largest; 1g has the smallest iris, 1h the largest; 1i is a standard infant face.

Pooling the most attractive features together in one face produced a face with a large forehead and large eyes, shown in Figure 5.3.

Another line of evidence concerning Lorenz's baby features comes from the examination of toys and cartoon characters, which are supposed to have incorporated these features so as to be appealing to the mass market for which they are designed. Gould (1980) showed that the cartoon character 'Mickey Mouse' began as a more realistic-looking mouse and gradually 'evolved' into a more cute and appealing figure. His head proportions changed in accordance with those set out by Lorenz (1943), so that Mickey progressed the 'ontogenetic pathway in reverse during his fifty years among us' (Gould, 1980, p. 83). Gould also noted that less positive Disney characters, such as Mortimer and Goofy, have retained adult characteristics such as a long snout and a smaller head relative to body height.

Hinde and Barden (1985) set out to examine whether similar changes could be found in specimens of teddy bears exhibited in a historical collection. They

Figure 5.3 Composite picture incorporating features with highest attractiveness ratings (from Sternglanz *et al.*, 1977, Figure 7).

did indeed show a progression from more lifelike forms with low foreheads and long muzzled snouts, to more modern specimens with larger foreheads and shorter snouts. Hinde and Barden used two sets of measurements (Figure 5.4). The first was the distance from the eyes to the crown compared to that from the eyes to the base of the head, i.e. the positioning of eyes down the face. The second was the distance from the snout to the back of the head compared to that from the crown to the base of the head, i.e. the length of the snout. Figure 5.5 shows one of E. H. Shepard's illustrations for *Winnie-the-Pooh*, first published in 1926 (Milne and Shepard, 1926), indicating a much longer snout than is apparent in present-day teddy bears.

The use of infantile forms of behaviour is prominent in human courtship, for example, in childish forms of endearment and the whispering of 'sweet nothings'. The term 'baby' is often used in North American blues and popular songs to denote a sexual partner, as in 'Baby, please don't go', 'Baby, let me follow you down' and 'I'll be your baby tonight'. The one most directly related to infantile facial features is 'Baby face', which begins with the line 'you've got the cutest little baby face'.

Research on adult faces which incorporate babyish features has been concerned with their impact on judgements by others of features such as dominance and submissiveness or weakness, as well as sexual attraction. In a series of studies on facial cues which signified dominance or submissiveness, Keating (1985) incorporated aspects of Lorenz's baby features into adult Identi-Kit pictures. The features used were large eyes, large lips, thin eyebrows and a rounded jaw, all viewed as immature, and contrasted with opposing mature ones. Keating suggested that, when portrayed by adults, baby features signified lack of threat and subordination. Dominance, on the other hand, was signified by features associated with maturity and strength,

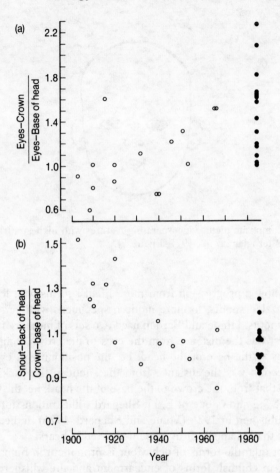

Figure 5.4 Scatter plots showing changes over time in two features related to Lorenz's baby features, in a sample of teddy bears from the Cambridge Folk Museum. The dots on the right are specimens from a shop. A shows the relative proportions of the forehead to the face, and B the snout relative to the head height (i.e. lower values represent a flat face). From: Hinde and Barden (1985, Figure 1).

such as a square jaw and thick eyebrows. In her study, Keating asked American college students to rate pictures of faces incorporating these features on a seven-point scale of dominance. Mature features were, as predicted, rated the most dominant and immature ones the most subordinate.

Other research on baby features in adults has shown that they are rated as indicating that the person shows physical weakness, naivety and social submissiveness (McArthur and Apatow, 1983–4; McArthur and Berry, 1987). This applies to photographs and to videotaped moving faces. McArthur and Montepare (1989) suggested that these judgements represent an overgeneralization of the adaptive reactions to the same features on real infants and children.

Keating (1985) also investigated ratings of attractiveness, and found that, on a female face, baby features were perceived as attractive by men. On a male face, mature (i.e. dominant) features were rated as most attractive. This was also found by McArthur and Apatow (1983–4), who concluded that baby features are appealing on a female but not a male adult face.

Does this indicate that the song 'Baby face' refers to a woman? Cunningham *et al.* (1990) pointed out that in McArthur and Apatow's study, men with the baby features of large eyes were rated as more handsome than those with small eyes, and that in another study (Berry and McArthur, 1985), there was a significant correlation between baby features and perceived attractiveness for men. Cunningham *et al.* carried out three experiments which help to resolve the apparent contradiction. Female college students rated photographs of young males with a variety of different facialmetric features. These were then analysed quantitatively. The baby features of larger eyes and smaller noses were rated as more attractive, but so were the mature features of a large chin and prominent cheekbones, and also smiling and high-status clothing. Although overall there was a negative correlation between the perceived 'babyishness' of the face and its rated attractiveness, this overall correlation hid a curvilinear relationship: women preferred men who possessed a moderate degree of baby features. Cunningham *et al.* concluded that their

Figure 5.5 E. H. Shepard's illustration for A. A. Milne's *Winnie-the-Pooh*, published in 1926, showing a much longer snout than is apparent in present-day teddy bears. In this drawing Pooh also has a low forehead, suggesting that he really is 'a bear of no brain at all' (from Milne and Shepard, 1926, p. 110).

results supported the view that women show multiple motives in assessing men's attractiveness, a combination of mature and childlike features being preferred.

All this research originated from a simple idea based on the classical ethological concept of social releaser. Important aspects of the original concept have survived, despite the abandonment of the theorizing associated with it. It has been shown that isolated parts of a biologically important stimulus configuration can elicit a motivationally-specific type of response across a wide range of individuals. This suggests that there is a generalized reaction to features depicting immaturity among people from different backgrounds (e.g. Sternglanz *et al.*, 1977) and cultures (McArthur and Berry, 1987). Furthermore, this reaction generalizes so as to influence human judgements of young animals, children's toys and adults with 'baby faces'.

The importance of Lorenz's baby features lies in the identification of a simple reaction to a set of stimuli which underlies one aspect of parental responding in humans. It provides a contrast to the view that humans are subject only to learning processes in the development of parental behaviour. However, it is important to recognize the limitations of the releaser concept. As Hinde (1982) pointed out, it does not address the question of the mechanism underlying the selectivity in responding. Careful investigations of cases of social releasers in animals have revealed complexities which go far beyond the original IRM analogy. Identification of baby features as a social releaser in humans still begs the question of the mechanism underlying this selective responsiveness, and its developmental origin. These questions will provide interesting topics for future study.

The fixed action pattern: rhythmical stereotypes in infants

In Chapter 2, I referred to the classical ethological view that the behavioural repertoire of any species could be divided into a number of discrete units or 'fixed action patterns'. There I was concerned with how the concept influenced approaches to the description of behaviour. In this section, its motivational implications are considered in relation to the behaviour of human infants.

Fixed action patterns, or FAPs, were seen as discrete units of behaviour (Lorenz, 1950a; Tinbergen, 1951). The concept was particularly useful for comparing the behaviour of different species. The term also implied several other properties (M. S. Dawkins, 1986): that the whole act is controlled by a discrete set of internally generated instructions, that it results from the release of 'action specific energy' (Lorenz, 1950a, b), and that the form is completely fixed. All three are now viewed as misleading diagnostic features (M. S. Dawkins, 1986). The first two were connected with Lorenz's much-criticized

Figure 5.6 Egg retrieval by the grey lag goose (from Tinbergen, 1951, Figure 69).

energy model of motivation, and the third has been questioned on empirical grounds. For example, both Schleidt (1974) and Barlow (1977) showed that some variability was apparent even in the most clear-cut examples of FAPs.

Schleidt (1974) commented that stereotypy, i.e. a low degree of variability in the behaviour, had become the most important diagnostic feature for the FAP, particularly after Lorenz's motivational model ceased to be credible. Schleidt described various ways in which stereotypy could be quantified, since the earlier ethologists had judged the existence of the FAP with the unaided eye. Although he commented that a degree of variability was present in FAPs, Schleidt nevertheless regarded the term as still being useful provided the variability is recognized. Barlow (1977) also outlined ways in which behavioural variation could be measured, and suggested replacing the term FAP with the more accurate 'Modal Action Pattern', which designated variability around a modal response.

As indicated above, stereotypy was originally one of the main criteria of an FAP. Many of the classic FAPs appeared to continue once they had begun, irrespective of changes in the stimuli which initiated them. The best-known example of this was egg retrieval in the grey lag goose (Tinbergen, 1951). This ground-nesting bird reacts to an egg which has rolled out of its nest by stretching out its neck beyond the egg and rolling it back to the nest, controlling it with a sideways balancing movement (Figure 5.6). If the egg slips away, the retrieving movement is completed without the egg, albeit in the absence of the sideways balancing movement. In this case, feedback from the consequences of the behaviour does not affect the main course of action. But in many other examples of fixed action patterns, such feedback does affect the continuation and direction of the behaviour (Barlow, 1977). As Hinde (1982) commented, it seems arbitrary to divide up FAPs according to whether or not they are affected by their consequences.

Despite these reservations about the term, it has nevertheless been applied to the behaviour of human infants. Several researchers have regarded the human smile as an example of a fixed action pattern (e.g. Ambrose, 1966; Eibl-Eibesfeldt, 1972; see Chapter 6). Bowlby (1969) also described the baby's smile as an FAP. Initially, it is given to simple 'sign stimuli' associated with the human face (Bowlby, 1953b). At around the age of 4 months it predictably leads to greater proximity by the mother. However, he pointed out that this reaction is stereotyped, since it does not vary according to whether the mother is seen to be approaching or not. Bowlby therefore included both the stereotyped nature of the smile and its relative lack of control by environmental consequences as criteria for the FAP in this case.

Thelen (1979) also concentrated on the stereotyped nature of FAPs in enquiring whether comparable responses could be found in mammals. The animals used in early ethological studies were usually insects, fish and birds, whose behaviour contains more apparently stereotyped responses than that of mammals. Thelen pointed out that stereotyped behaviour is particularly common in human infants, but had not been systematically studied up to that point.

Thelen's own study was longitudinal in design, and involved detailed observations on twenty infants while they were awake in their own homes. Rhythmical and stereotyped behaviour was common, and it could involve limb, head or body movements. A total of forty-seven behavioural acts were identified. These showed clear developmental sequences: for example, some, which involved the hands, began at 24 weeks and then showed a rapid decline; leg stereotypies increased to a peak at 14–32 weeks and then showed a rapid decline. These stereotypies were also associated with the infant's general level of motor development, as indicated by the standard Bayley scales.

Thelen (1979) noted that infant stereotypies showed one feature of the original FAPs, that once they had started they appeared to be largely internally driven. They appeared to be 'released' activities under strong central control, that is, they possessed the characteristics which led the classical ethologists to postulate the 'innate releasing mechanism' or IRM. However, they do differ from the ethologists' FAPs in that they are not obvious precursors of mature behaviour, and have an apparent lack of goal-direction. Thelen suggested that they represent a transitional phase in the development of behaviour, occurring prior to more complex behaviour which is ordered into goal-directed sequences.

Thelen (1981) went on to investigate the circumstances under which these stereotypies are shown. She found that they occurred in a range of contexts, those involving states of low arousal being the most potent for eliciting stereotypies, at ages other than 12 to 18 weeks when kinaesthetic or positional changes and social interactions were also very effective. Sometimes stereotypies occurred in response to no definable circumstances. Thelen (1981) suggested that stereotyped behaviour may occur when the infant is highly aroused, and that some stereotypies have a communicative function, for example, calling attention to distress. However, this does not mean that they are goal-directed. In other contexts, Thelen suggested, the stereotyped movements themselves may serve to increase arousal by the stimulation they produce.

The behaviour studied by Thelen was not the same as the FAPs described by the classical ethologists. Nevertheless, by following ethological descriptions of FAPs, and of related stereotyped movements such as displacement activities (Tinbergen, 1952a), Thelen first called attention to the existence of these frequent and extensive forms of behaviour during infancy; and second, identified common aspects in the causation of stereotypies and FAPs. The most important of these was their apparent lack of responsiveness to external stimulation once they had been triggered. In this respect they are similar to what Bowlby (1969) identified as non-goal-directed systems which underlie crying and smiling during the first sixth months of life, and also to behaviour such as the egg-rolling of the grey lag goose described above.

The behavioural system: attachment

As indicated in the Introduction, the Dutch classical ethologists Baerends and Tinbergen considered an animal's behavioural repertoire in terms of motivational systems or 'instincts', whose control was hierarchically arranged (Tinbergen, 1942, 1951). The early model by Baerends (1941) of the nest-provisioning behaviour of the digger wasp involved a complex chain of behavioural acts, occurring in three phases. The first involved egg-laying and some initial provisioning (of a caterpillar) for the future larvae, the second further provisioning, and the third the final provisioning and closing of the nest. In order to depict these activities in a theoretical model, it was necessary to consider how they occurred together in an organized and integrated sequence (Figure 5.7). A later version of this scheme (Baerends, 1976), shown in Figure 5.8, emphasized their hierarchical organization and their ultimate control by a 'reproductive system', which competes with other major systems, for example, those underlying feeding or sunbathing, for the control of behaviour.

Essentially, the concept of the behavioural system, elaborated in Baerends' later work (e.g. Baerends, 1976), involved a series of control systems, each organizing a set of causally related forms of behaviour, and subserving a particular biological function, such as aggression or parental behaviour. The behavioural system provides a description of the relations between the various activities, and usually involves a scheme depicting their control by a hierarchically arranged series of closed-loop systems, such as the one shown for nest provisioning (Figures 5.7 and 5.8). Figure 5.9 shows Baerends' scheme for the interruption of incubation behaviour in the herring gull (Baerends, 1970, 1976). To the right are the lower-level activities, and the systems which control these are arranged hierarchically to the left. The highest-order systems are those labelled P (preening), E (escape) and N (nesting and incubation). The diagram itself was derived from detailed observations of the behaviour of the herring gull, but it is to be regarded as a

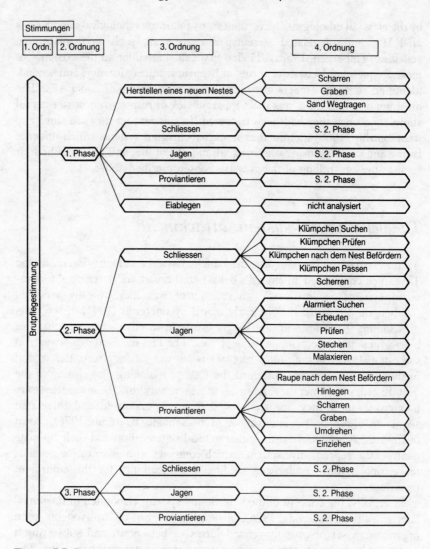

Figure 5.7 Diagram to show the hierarchical organization of nest-provisioning behaviour in the digger wasp: original diagram taken from Baerends (1941). For a detailed description see Figure 5.8.

schematic representation (or 'software model') of how these three types of behaviour are controlled, and the causal connections between them.

Bowlby (1969) used this approach as a central component of his theory of human attachment. Attachment was viewed as equivalent to other major functional systems, such as mating or parental behaviour (Bowlby, 1969). The control of behaviour involved a set of closed-loop systems, each involving 'set-goals' and flexibility according to specific circumstances, and operating within an over-arching structure (Bowlby, 1969). The set-goal of proximity-keeping was seen as being mediated by systems which become increasingly sophistic-ated during ontogeny and incorporate representational models of people, places and the self in them (Bowlby, 1980a, p. 651).

Bowlby's view of attachment as a behavioural system involved a number of radical departures from that of attachment as a drive or a trait. This view had persisted in developmental psychology as a result of the influence of social learning theory, which linked attachment to the concept of dependency. As

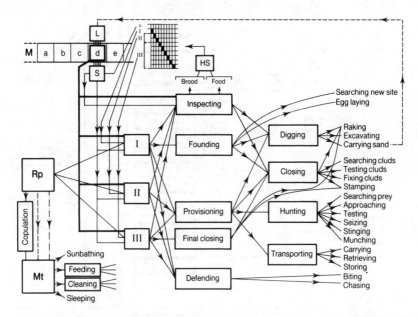

Figure 5.8 A later version of the hierarchical organization of provisioning, based on that shown in Figure 5.7. The 'fixed action patterns' shown in the right-hand column are controlled by four sub-systems ('digging', etc.), each controlled by higher-order sub-systems ('inspecting', etc.). Systems for each of the three phases of nest-provisioning control these sub-systems: founding is exclusive to phase I and final closing to phase III, but the other systems are controlled by each of the phase-systems. The phases are controlled by higher-order systems for reproduction (Rp) and maintenance (Mt). M represents a memory containing information on the nests already completed, a to e. Each phase begins with inspecting, and if a larva is found, its size and the food remaining determine (via summation unit HS) which phase will occur, i.e. how many caterpillars are to be fetched. The black blocks in the grid from HS represent the caterpillars stored in the three phases. If no larvae are found, the memory is scanned (via S), attention being directed to the oldest uncompleted nest, which is inspected. If no such nest is located, phase I (founding) takes place. The location of a new nest is learned (unit L) during digging. During a phase, only one nest receives attention (represented by the heavy bars) (Baerends, 1976, Figure 2).

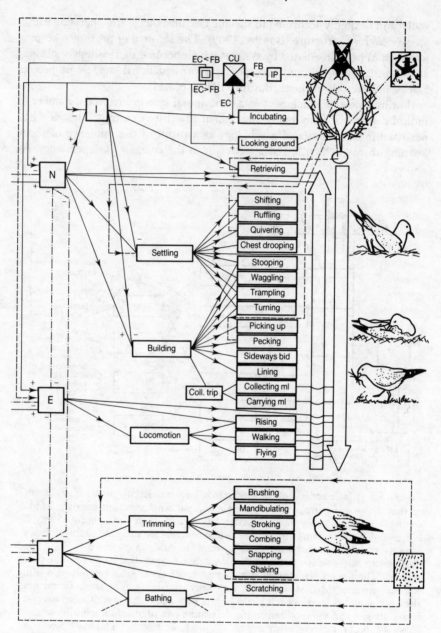

Figure 5.9

Sroufe and Waters (1977) pointed out, this way of looking at attachment viewed it not as a behavioural system but as an intervening variable. In this case, attachment was used as a hypothetical variable, the existence of which simplified the relationship between several inputs and several outputs. Figure 5.10, taken from Hinde (1974) shows how an intervening variable can be used in this way to postulate the central state of aggression. However, as Hinde pointed out, the concept is only useful to simplify data in specific cases, and he cautions against the assumption that it corresponds to particular processes within the brain.

According to the intervening variable view of attachment, the various forms of attachment behaviour provide measures or indices of its strength. Critics of the concept of attachment pointed out that the various behavioural measures showed only low intercorrelations with one another, regarding this as evidence against a single concept of attachment. However, as Sroufe and Waters (1977) pointed out, this argument involves a misunderstanding of the construct of attachment in Bowlby's work, where it referred to a behavioural system and not an intervening variable. The crucial difference is that there is not a single entity representing the strength of attachment. Instead, there is a hierarchically arranged system controlling a repertoire of behavioural acts, which can be used in different combinations and to different degrees according to circumstances. Specific types of attachment behaviour may occur as alternatives, and different ones used to different extents at different ages, so they will not necessarily show associations with one another. A similar misunderstanding about the nature of the behavioural system, and the appropriateness of using intercorrelations between different types of behaviour within the same system, had earlier arisen in ethology (Hinde, 1958; see Baerends, 1976). The behavioural system, is, however, fundamentally different from the intervening variable, and it entails a more flexible and complex model of behavioural control.

In the case of attachment, the top-level goal ('set-goal') is that of maintaining proximity with the attachment-figure, or a feeling of security that she or he is nearby. Specific types of behaviour are controlled and integrated to serve this goal, via more situationally-flexible sub-goals, in the way

---

Figure 5.9 Model depicting the control of interruption of incubation in the herring gull. Behaviour is shown on the right, hierarchically controlled by sub-systems (e.g. settling) and higher-order systems (N = incubation; E = escape; P = preening). The large vertical arrows on the right represent orientation towards or away from the nest. Feedback from the clutch is processed in unit IP, goes to a comparator (CU) where it is compared with a stored expectancy (EC) based on the input for incubation fed through a unit (I), necessary to explain the inhibition of settling and building when there is no discrepancy: if feedback from the clutch is greater than expected, N is activated; if it is less, E is activated. The main systems mutually inhibit one another. P occurs as interruptive behaviour through disinhibition of N and E. P can be activated by other stimuli for preening such as dust or rain. E can be stimulated by disturbances other than deficient feedback from the clutch (see top right) (from Baerends, 1976, Figure 5; after Baerends, 1970).

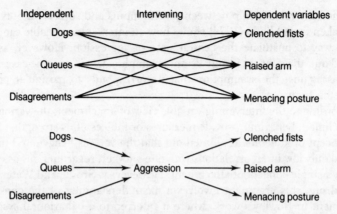

Figure 5.10 Diagram (from Hinde, 1974, Figure 3.1) showing, at the top, the relations between three independent and three dependent variables, and below the use of a single intervening variable to explain these relations.

Baerends depicted for the control of animal behaviour. During the course of development, increasingly varied means of achieving the overall goal are adopted. At first, the systems underlying the control of behaviour are not 'goal-corrected', i.e. the behaviour acts like the fixed action pattern in the classic example of egg-rolling by the grey lag goose (Tinbergen, 1951; see p. 91 above). Behaviour such as crying begins when the mother is not nearby, but it does not vary according to her proximity, or whether she has just left or is returning (Bowlby, 1969). Gradually, in the second half of the first year, more sophisticated behavioural control becomes apparent. For example, the child may monitor the mother's whereabouts and follow her so as to maintain proximity. During the second year of life the child begins using calling as an alternative way of seeking reassurance that the mother is nearby. In both these cases, the behaviour is modified according to feedback concerning the mother's position in relation to the child.

Although Bowlby (1969) did not follow the ethologists in depicting attachment behaviour in a schematic form, it is possible to draw the essential outlines of his view of the control of attachment (Figure 5.11). As a form of motivation, it is essentially discrepancy activated – it is a reaction to the absence of something in the environment which corresponds to a representation in the child's brain. This representation is proximity to the mother and, as indicated above, is the top-level set-goal. Attachment behaviour is activated when comparison of the input with the set-goal, the desired state, reveals a discrepancy signal. This can be seen as activating one or more of several possible subsystems which provide alternative, or complementary, ways of retaining proximity. Which ones are activated depends on the situation, age and individual characteristics of the child. The consequences of behaviour – if the mother responds – are likely to be the reduction of the

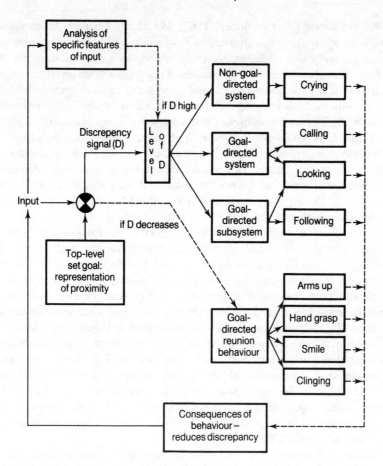

Figure 5.11 A simplified view of attachment behaviour viewed as a behavioural system. See text for explanation.

discrepancy signal by changing the input, and subsidiary behaviour such as arms up and hand grasp which are shown on reunion. As Bowlby (1969) indicated, the exact forms of attachment behaviour vary at different ages, and in different circumstances, so that the representation in Figure 5.11 provides only the broadest outline of the organization of attachment as a behavioural system.

Motivational analysis of childhood aggression and rough-and-tumble play

One problem encountered in the study of childhood aggression is the difficulty in distinguishing between aggressive behaviour and related forms of playful behaviour (Blurton Jones, 1967, 1972c). In Chapter 2, ethological studies demonstrating the distinction between rough-and-tumble play and aggression in young children were described, in order to illustrate the methods underlying this type of analysis. This approach involved the search for groups of behavioural activities tending to occur more in some individuals than in others, and in temporal proximity within a particular individual (Chapter 2). The assumption was that such associations reflect motivational groupings. This would not, however, apply where behavioural acts from the same motivational system occurred as alternatives to one another: for example, in the case of fear, active escape and immobility may provide alternative responses, and hence would not be associated with one another (Archer, 1973, 1979). The type of behavioural system Bowlby suggested as underlying attachment was also of this type (see previous section).

Nevertheless, an approach based on looking for associations between activities has proved useful in distinguishing aggression and rough-and-tumble play. The factor analyses carried out by Blurton Jones (1972c; see Chapter 2) showed that the two types of activity were not temporally associated. This was confirmed in later studies (e.g. Boulton and Smith, 1989). In terms of a behavioural system, the associations between the various acts found by Blurton Jones (1972c) are illustrated in Figure 5.12. Some acts are common to both types of behaviour, but most are not, so that control can be depicted as two separate systems. In one case, the behaviour ceases when the specific goal, for example, obtaining a toy possessed by the other child, has been achieved. In the other case, feedback from the partner enhances the activity. Later sequential analysis of rough-and-tumble play suggests that it has an episodic organization within the child's whole behavioural repertoire (Boulton and Smith, 1989).

Further studies have identified other features which distinguished the two types of behaviour. Smith and Lewis (1985), Humphreys and Smith (1987) and Boulton (1991a) found that rough-and-tumble episodes included more participants, and that regular partners were more likely to be liked and nominated as best friends than in the case of aggressive exchanges. Children as young as 4 years of age could distinguish fighting from rough-and-tumble. Fry (1987) and Boulton (1991a) confirmed that there were distinctive expressions associated with the two types of behaviour (see Chapter 8), and many detailed aspects of behaviour, concerning physical actions and affect, could be used by children to distinguish between them (see also Costabile *et al.*, 1991).

Motivational conflict: childhood autism

The classical ethologists' interest in motivational conflict was applied to a topic in child development, childhood autism, by Tinbergen and Tinbergen

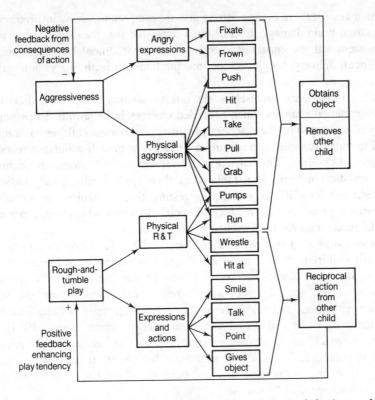

Figure 5.12 Schematic diagram of actions comprising aggressive behaviour and rough-and-tumble play in pre-school children, based on the associations found in the factor analysis carried out by Blurton Jones (1972c, Figure 4.3). Hierarchical control of behaviour is derived from classical ethological models.

(1983). They also used methods derived from ethology, carrying out detailed, but qualitative, observations of behaviour, stressing the need to carry these out as unobtrusively as possible in view of the extreme test-shyness of autistic children.

Tinbergen and Tinbergen (1983) remarked that childhood autism had puzzled child psychiatrists for years. Rutter (1978) summarized its essential features as follows: it begins before 30 months of age; it involves impaired social development out of keeping with the child's intellectual level; it involves delayed language; and the child is resistant to change. The Tinbergens amplified this list to include some further features, based on their observations. These included failure or near-failure to form normal social relationships, reluctance to enter into an unfamiliar world and frequent performance of a limited repertoire of mannerisms or stereotypies.

Tinbergen and Tinbergen discussed the existing possible explanations, and argued against there being a strong genetic component, or the involvement of structural brain damage. Instead, they suggested that the evidence was more consistent with the impact of a series of early environmental stressors, such as a difficult delivery, hospitalization, moving house or birth of a sibling early in life.

The Tinbergens themselves set out to identify immediate short-term environmental changes which preceded changes in behaviour. In particular, they concentrated on the reactions of autistic and normal children to strangers and strange situations, and identified a range of approach-avoidance reactions in normal children. The balance was invariably shifted towards avoidance in the autistic children. The Tinbergens then applied ethological studies of motivational conflict to autism, suggesting that it involves an imbalance towards a pronounced avoidance of social situations which would normally evoke tendencies for both avoidance and approach.

It was suggested that there is no sharp dividing line between autistic and normal children, so that there are degrees of motivational imbalance that occur in social situations. As a treatment for autism, the Tinbergens advocated two very different approaches: one involved trying not to be intrusive, responding positively to any signs of approach behaviour, and withdrawing when withdrawal behaviour occurs (Kramer *et al.*, 1984); the other approach involved holding therapy, which was justified on the grounds that it eventually broke down avoidance behaviour. It is, however, more difficult to understand how holding therapy follows from the Tinbergens' motivational conflict hypothesis.

A similar view of childhood autism was developed independently by Richer. He continued earlier research involving quantitative methods of observation (e.g. Hutt and Ounsted, 1970). Richer (1976) compared autistic with non-autistic children in an outdoor playground, and found that autistic children rarely started or continued social interactions, they avoided eye contact and were situated more at the periphery. They were also less aggressive and showed a much lower threshold for defensive and flight behaviour. In an experimental study, Richer and Coss (1976) found that autistic children looked more at adults who had both eyes, or one eye, covered than at adults with both eyes exposed. The autistic children also showed more flight behaviour and stereotypic patterns than normal children.

These and other findings led Richer to suggest that autistic children show a predominance of fear or flight motivation, and when this competes with other forms of social behaviour, it leads to conflict behaviour (Richer, 1983, 1988). It again follows that therapy should be based on encouraging social approach rather than avoidance. Richer argued that whether an autistic child will approach or avoid depends on the unpredictability or ease of the particular activity, and the intrusiveness, or social demand, placed upon the child by another person's behaviour. He suggested that 'easy' activities, such as rough-

and-tumble play, can allow another person to involve the child in more intrusive behaviour than otherwise would be tolerated. He also suggested that the child's approach behaviour is bimodally distributed in relation to intrusiveness, so that behaving in a low *or* high demand way can both be effective. Thus therapy based on high intrusion, such as holding the child (Richer and Zappella, 1989), will be effective *in addition* to that based on encouraging approach behaviour.

Richer's argument that intrusive therapies such as holding follow from motivational conflict theory overcomes a common objection to the Tinbergens' approach, namely that it predicts that only low intrusive therapeutic methods would be effective (Fein *et al.*, 1986, pp. 201–2; Howlin and Rutter, 1987, p. 145). Such criticisms are in one way misplaced because Tinbergen and Tinbergen (1983) themselves did advocate the very intrusive therapy of forced holding. The efficacy of both forms of therapy advocated by the ethological theorists remains to be assessed by studies using comparable samples and double-blind objective outcome measures (cf. Richer, 1988).

Richer (1988) suggested that other childhood behaviour problems can be understood in terms of motivational conflict. Children showing timidity and obsessionality are viewed as also showing the fear-dominated motivational pattern of autistic children, but with a lesser degree of fear motivation. Again, intervention is aimed at reducing fearfulness. Temper-tantrums are viewed in terms of a motivational conflict between angry avoidance of the frustrating parent, and attachment behaviour. The conflict can again be broken either by leaving the child or holding it – in this case to break an approach-avoidance conflict. These examples raise the possibility of applying motivational conflict theory to other forms of disturbed behaviour. They are, however, best regarded as preliminary speculations, based on a qualitative analysis and interpretation of behaviour, and the therapies following from them await objective assessment.

Although these speculations about the nature of autism are rooted in ethological motivational theory and rely to some extent on observations carried out under naturalistic conditions, they do not involve application of the quantitative ethological methods described in Chapter 2 to the behaviour of autistic children. Van Engeland *et al.* (1985) did carry out an observation of this type, comparing the social behaviour of a group of autistic children with that of a control group of primary school children. Although they found more gaze-aversion by the autistic children in the presence of an adult, this behaviour was not part of a general tendency to avoid social interactions. Factor analysis carried out on the various behavioural acts shown by the two groups (see above and Chapter 2) indicated that gaze-avoidance did not show a high loading on factors containing elements indicative of avoidance. Furthermore, elements suggesting proximity with others actually occurred more often in the autistic group, and there appeared to be no overall tendency to avoid the experimenter by the autistic children.

This study again indicates the usefulness of quantitative ethological methods, and suggests that the motivational conflict hypothesis needs to be treated with caution until there is more evidence of this type.

The motivational conflict hypothesis of autism emphasizes the primacy of socio-emotional deficits. In doing so, it shows a marked contrast to the more widely accepted view, that autism arises from a central cognitive disorder (Fein *et al.*, 1986). However, Fein *et al.* showed that there is considerable evidence supporting the primacy of some form of social deficit, although not necessarily the one indicated by the motivational conflict hypothesis.

In developmental psychology, recent research on autism has proceeded in a totally different direction from the one indicated by the Tinbergens and Richer. There would appear to be no contact between the two approaches, and indeed they might as well be researching two totally different conditions.

One very promising line of current research has centred on the development of the ability to understand the beliefs, knowledge and intentions of others in young children (e.g. Hobson, 1981; Baron-Cohen *et al.*, 1985). This ability to impute mental states to oneself and others, and to use them in social interactions, has been discussed in relation to animals, as the 'intentional stance' (Dennett, 1983), and as a 'theory of mind' (Premack and Woodruff, 1978). Baron-Cohen *et al.* (1985) have suggested that autism involves a specific failure to develop this ability. Their hypothesis has been tested in a number of ways, each of which has provided evidence to support it.

One method involved the understanding of a false belief (Baron-Cohen *et al.*, 1985; Baron-Cohen, 1992). For example, the child is introduced to two drawings of characters, Sally and Anne. Sally puts a marble into a basket. While Sally has gone for a walk, Anne transfers the marble to a box. Sally comes back. The child is asked where Sally will look for her marble, i.e. where she believes it to be. Although 80 per cent of control children (and 80 per cent of Down's syndrome children) were capable of realizing that Sally could hold a false belief, only 20 per cent of autistic children could do so.

This study has been replicated using variations in the methodology, and there is converging evidence of other types that autistic children cannot understand beliefs as causes of emotions, nor can they use mentalistic explanations. The deficit seems to be specific to *conceptual* role-taking, involving what others are thinking.

As Baron-Cohen (1992) remarked, the theory of mind deficit is not necessarily the central developmental feature involved in autism. Research has concentrated on children of three years or over, which is the time of the onset of autism. Other studies have searched for possible precursors at earlier ages, and the indications are that a comparable deficit in understanding others as intentional agents is involved. For example, using the pointing gesture to direct attention of another child to an object is deficient in autistic children (Baron-Cohen, 1992).

In the ethological observational study of autistic children by van Engeland *et al.* (1985), factor analysis revealed a factor that the control children showed and the autistic children lacked. This concerned inferential communication, and included high loadings on behaviour such as pointing, looking at the partner, gesturing and looking at objects. Another quantitative observational study, which involved Ainsworth's strange situation test (see Chapter 3), found no substantial differences in attachment behaviour between autistic and control children (Dissanayake and Crossley, 1989); but they did find that autistic children rarely engaged in sharing behaviour, for example, they did not show objects to their mothers or take objects to them. These findings clearly support the theory of mind deficit hypothesis, although neither set of researchers was apparently aware of it.

Where does this leave the ethological motivational conflict hypothesis? The results of two quantitative observational studies support the theory of mind hypothesis rather than the conflict hypothesis. The studies involved in establishing the theory of mind are also much more rigorous and experimental than those involved in establishing the conflict hypothesis, which had not proceeded beyond qualitative observations. Having said this, the theory of mind deficit is not necessarily the primary one, and several specific theories have been advanced, either involving cognitive or emotional deficits, as the source of the theory of mind deficit (Baron-Cohen, 1992).

Although essentially agreeing that autism involves an impairment in understanding that other people have minds, Hobson (1990a, b) has argued that the term 'theory of mind' is misleading, since it implies that a reflective sense of self develops first, and only then does the child infer that others also possess this attribute. Instead, Hobson suggested that the understanding that others are conscious agents develops from early social interactions, and occurs prior to a reflective sense of self. The main point of departure of Hobson's view is that instead of a cognitive ability apparently emerging around 18 months of age, as Leslie (1987) suggested, there is an impairment in a biologically-based capacity for engaging in and representing personal, and especially affective, relatedness.

Identification of this deficit, whether it be essentially cognitive or concerning relatedness with people, certainly explains many of the features of autism. In particular, it addresses the abnormal social and communication development of autistic children. However, it says little about those aspects emphasized by motivational conflict theorists, such as stereotypic behaviour, and the affective components associated with social withdrawal. The two approaches would appear very difficult to integrate. Of the two, the 'understanding of mind' hypothesis appears the more promising although perhaps limited in scope. The motivational conflict hypothesis, on the other hand, may have proved premature in identifying approach-withdrawal as the central deficit involved, but it could yet prove valuable for focusing on the social interactions of autistic children.

Ethological motivational conflict and categories of aggression

It is often difficult to distinguish between the various forms of aggressive behaviour shown by children. The classification of aggression has always been problematic both in animal behaviour and in human research (Archer and Browne, 1989), and there are several ways in which categories have been distinguished. For example, one common distinction for human aggression is between the form it takes, whether verbal or physical, and another is between hostile or angry aggression and instrumental or manipulative aggression, where the aggression is used specifically to gain some other end.

Based on observational studies of the aggressive behaviour of children in nursery schools, Manning *et al.* (1978) developed the classification of aggression further, deriving their categories from inferred intent, based on the context of the aggression. Hinde (1985c) and Attili and Hinde (1986) built on this approach by speculating about the motivational basis of the different types of aggressive behaviour, using ideas about motivational conflict from ethology.

Manning *et al.* (1978) investigated a small group of nursery school children and classified aggressive incidents into three main categories. The first was specific hostility, which was used to obtain access to objects or places, and occurred widely in both more and less aggressive children. It corresponded to forms of manipulative behaviour identified in earlier classifications (Archer and Browne, 1989). The second category, harassment, enabled the child to get his or her own way and to assert an opinion. It was directed towards annoying or teasing the other child, and corresponded to hostile aggression identified in earlier classifications. It included physical harassment, teasing and threat. The more aggressive children tended to show mainly harassment rather than specific hostility (Manning *et al.*, 1978). The third type of aggression was 'game hostility', which arose during the course of a game (but was not the same as the playful rough-and-tumble described by Blurton Jones; see Chapter 2). It included intimidating or restricting activities such as gripping around the throat and bullying.

In a study comparing 'difficult' and well-adjusted children selected by teachers from four Edinburgh nurseries, Manning and Herrmann (1981) described two groups of difficult children, one of which was aggressive and the other dependent or demanding. The 'normal' children's aggression was again mainly manipulative, whereas that of the aggressive children displayed motives of power, superiority and dominance. Both types of difficult children were apparently self-centred in their play. The aggressive children would assertively pursue their own goals which interfered with co-operative play. The demanding children showed more 'game hostility' (Manning and Sluckin, 1984).

To the three forms of aggression identified by Manning and her colleagues,

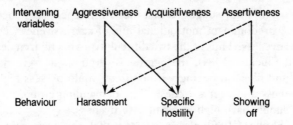

Figure 5.13 Suggested relationships between intervening variables and observed behaviour, adapted from Smith (1989), based on Hinde (1985c). The dotted line suggests a weak or subsidiary link.

Attili (1985) added a fourth, defensive or reactive aggression, which is equivalent to the defensive forms of aggression identified in studies of animal aggression (see Blanchard and Blanchard, 1989; Archer, 1988a, 1989/90).

Attili and Hinde (1986) and Hinde (1985c) used this classification, together with an ethological motivational approach, to suggest the variables underlying aggressive behaviour in children. They suggested that both specific hostility, harassment and also showing off, identified in the work of Hold (Chapter 7), could be explained in terms of three motivational variables, aggressiveness, acquisitiveness and assertiveness (Figure 5.13). Harassment was viewed as arising most directly from aggressiveness, possibly also involving assertiveness; specific hostility would depend on moderate levels of both aggressiveness and acquisitiveness; showing off would be most directly related to assertiveness.

Underlying this approach is the idea that specific types of motivation compete with one another when both are aroused simultaneously (Hinde, 1970, Chs 9 and 17). Several outcomes are possible under these circumstances. One variable may suppress the influence of the other, or it may facilitate it; or both may be suppressed, leading to the occurrence of a third type of activity; or they may combine to produce intermediate types of behaviour, as was suggested in ethological studies of animal displays (e.g. Tinbergen, 1952b; Hinde, 1953a). In the case of children's aggression, the motivational variables were viewed as combining to produce intermediate types of behaviour, whose forms reflected their mixed motivational origin.

Since, according to this scheme, the different types of aggressive behaviour would have different goals (underlying different intentions), they would also show different attributes. For example, when goal-acquisition is involved, the performance of an aggressive act is more likely to lead to an apparent decrease in aggressive motivation, i.e. to look like catharsis. Conversely, in the case of harassment, the child will be more likely to continue when the victim is distressed (Attili and Hinde, 1986).

The work of Manning and her colleagues had already shown that individual children varied considerably in the predominant type of aggression they showed. Attili and Hinde suggested that these differences arose because they differed in the predominant motivational mix of aggressiveness, acquisitiveness and assertiveness. Thus of the two difficult types of children described by Manning and Sluckin (1984), the aggressive group who were dominating, quarrelsome and likely to be angry if opposed, would possess high levels of both assertiveness and aggressiveness. The demanding group, on the other hand, would simply have high levels of assertiveness.

Attili and Hinde (1986) also suggested that the two main forms of aggression – specific hostility and harassment – show different changes during the course of development in the pre-school years, specific hostility showing a more rapid decline as the child learns alternative ways of obtaining his or her goals. However, from a variety of studies there is evidence for consistency in patterns of aggressive behaviour between individuals, but there is little evidence concerning whether the same type of aggression shows consistency.

As Smith (1989) pointed out, the distinctions drawn in these studies are ultimately based on inferences made about the children's intentions, usually taking into account cues such as emotional expressions and context. It is worth pointing out that this type of motivational analysis is based on convergence of indirect inferences about intent, and it contrasts with the analysis made by Blurton Jones (1972c), described in Chapter 2. This was based on an established ethological method of motivational analysis, involving factor analysis of detailed categories of behaviour to determine which ones occurred together as recognized groupings. Aggressive acts such as fixate, frown, hit, push and take–tug–grab were located as a distinct factor, clearly identifiable from rough-and-tumble play. In this study, the different forms of aggression identified in Manning's work were not apparent.

It should be possible to identify the hypothetical variables suggested by Attili and Hinde (1986) as underlying the different forms of aggression (Figure 5.13), through factor analysis of individual differences in children's aggressive behaviour. First, it would be necessary to define clearly the different types of behaviour, harassment, specific hostility and showing off. Second, individual differences in the extent to which these are used should relate to factors representing the intervening variables which are supposed to underlie them. Thus behaviour comprising specific hostility should be loaded on both the factors for acquisitiveness and aggressiveness.

Conclusions

As indicated earlier, the transfer of ethological motivational concepts and models to developmental psychology is limited, and in this chapter I have considered several unconnected examples. Lorenz's application of the social releaser concept to the responses of adults to infantile features has generated considerable research which has essentially confirmed the original insight and extended it to perceptions of baby features in adult faces. The concept of fixed action pattern stimulated a study of stereotyped behaviour in human infants, which produced some interesting parallels in the principles of motivational control.

Bowlby's theory of attachment involved a particular view of motivational control, the behavioural system, which was derived from the classical ethology of Baerends and Tinbergen, and which had radically different implications for the understanding of attachment from principles derived from social learning theory.

The concept of behavioural system could also be seen in the research of Blurton Jones who used ethological methods to analyse categories of behaviour in pre-school children. In particular, he clearly demonstrated the distinction between aggression and rough-and-tumble play, which was further elaborated in later research.

Ethological studies of motivational conflict inspired a different and controversial approach to childhood autism by Tinbergen and Tinbergen, and by Richer. They suggested that the central deficit involved an imbalance between tendencies to approach and to withdraw. The main problem with this view was that the observations on which it was based were mainly qualitative. Experimental studies, as well as a quantitative ethological analysis, both revealed more support for the 'theory of mind deficit hypothesis', although this did leave some aspects of autism unexplained.

Motivational conflict was used in a different way by Attili and Hinde (1986) to generate hypotheses about the motivational basis of categories of childhood aggression, although these hypotheses still require testing involving the sorts of quantitative ethological methods used by Blurton Jones and others. In fact, it was apparent at several points throughout the chapter that this type of motivational analysis could prove fruitful in several contexts.

Chapter 6

Functional explanations

Introduction

One of the four aims of ethology distinguished by Tinbergen (1963) was to study the function or survival value of behaviour. This aim also played a prominent part in the social ethology of Crook (1970a, c; Chapters 7 and 8). Later, function was singled out to form a separate approach, known as sociobiology (Wilson, 1975), which sought to identify the adaptive significance of behaviour, and to use this knowledge for integrating studies of animal and human behaviour (Chapter 1).

Originally, sociobiological theory concerned almost exclusively the adaptive significance of adult characteristics. The genetic determinism of many of the earlier discussions obscured consideration of development. A notable exception was the theoretical model of Trivers (1974), which specified the adaptive consequences of the conflicting interests of parents, offspring and siblings.

It was soon realized that it was important to consider how behaviour contributes to an animal's total reproductive success over the whole lifespan, rather than only during adulthood. Ways in which overall fitness could be maximized through the selective allocation of resources to survival mechanisms, growth and reproduction at different life-history stages led to an appreciation of why many animals – including mammals – suppress reproductive capability until they have attained a suitable size. Such a selective allocation of resources was referred to as a 'life-history strategy' (Chisholm, 1987; Horn and Rubenstein, 1984). Life-history strategies can also vary within a species, as a consequence of different rearing conditions.

In this chapter, I shall first summarize some of the basic concepts and theories of sociobiology, and then describe their applications to developmental psychology. The functional approach to human behaviour involves both potential benefits and pitfalls, and these are considered in the final two sections of the chapter.

General orientation and the problem of helping behaviour

Sociobiology is the systematic application of Darwin's (1859) theory of natural selection to the study of behaviour. Although Darwin clearly predicted that behaviour, like morphology, would be subject to selective pressures, the precise implications of his theory for the study of behaviour were not generally realized until relatively recently. The spurious argument that behaviour evolved for the good of the species or group usually went unchallenged both in zoology (e.g. Lorenz, 1966; Wynne Edwards, 1962) and in psychology (e.g. Scott and Fredericson, 1951), until the time of the earliest sociobiological writings. Maynard Smith (1964) challenged the group selection view, and Hamilton (1964, 1972) addressed the issue of how helping behaviour could evolve by selection operating at an individual rather than a group level. The precise implications of the theory of natural selection for the evolution of behaviour were then worked out in a number of other models.

Hamilton's model was based on the realization that the true unit of selection is the gene. This allowed individual animals in which genes are located to be regarded as temporary vehicles for them (R. Dawkins, 1976). A gene will be perpetuated if it leads to behaviour that is more adaptive than that resulting from an alternative gene at the same position on the chromosome, or locus. When selection is viewed in terms of alternative genes, the overall (or 'inclusive') fitness of an individual becomes a more complex matter. It includes increases and decreases in fitness resulting from interactions with other individuals sharing the same genes, i.e. relatives. When relatives help one another, their fitness will be enhanced. This provides the major reason why helping behaviour has evolved in animals.

The adaptive significance of interactions between close kin is complicated by their relative ages. Reproductive value (Fisher, 1930) is an age-dependent measure of the individual's potential contribution to future generations. It increases from the beginning of life, and decreases from when the first offspring are produced, reaching zero at the end of reproductive life (Figure 6.1). This older concept has been combined with that of inclusive fitness to analyse age-related changes in human behaviour (e.g. Daly and Wilson, 1988a; Crawford, 1989).

The implications of natural selection operating at the level of the individual (or gene) are that helping behaviour only evolves under certain circumstances, either between close relatives (see above) or when there is mutual or reciprocated benefit in unrelated individuals (Trivers, 1971; Krebs and Davies, 1986). Unless these circumstances apply, animals will act so as to enhance their own fitness, even if this is at the expense of another individual. Direct fights over resources and predation provide obvious examples. More subtle is a wide range of activities described as 'manipulative'. Animals act so

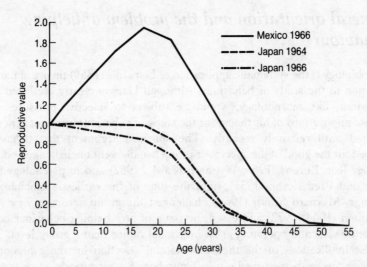

Figure 6.1 Graph showing female reproductive value (i.e. numbers of offspring expected during remainder of their lives) plotted against age for three contemporary societies (from Crawford, 1989, Figure 2; copyright APA, reproduced with permission).

as to influence the behaviour of others when this will aid their own fitness. The cuckoo relies on the host species' parental response being indiscriminate when it places its own eggs in the host's nest. Such cases do not provide stable evolutionary states. The elegant studies of Davies and de Brooke (1988) show that a host bird will evolve strategies to counter the nest parasite, for example, rejecting dissimilar eggs. Krebs and Dawkins (1984) argued that manipulation underlies the evolution of social signals, which have more in common with advertisements than the transmission of accurate information (Chapter 9).

Underlying the concept of manipulation is a recognition that the adaptive interests of individuals – even close relatives – do not coincide. Parents and offspring, siblings and mated pairs will all benefit from different consequences of their interactions with others: the precise ways in which they do so have been worked out in a series of models, beginning with those of Trivers (1972, 1974).

Sex and age differences

Darwin (1871) referred to selection which depended on differential access to the other sex as 'sexual selection'. It usually takes the form of competition between males for females, and choice of male characteristics by females. The results are the evolution of male features which aid competition and attract females. It was not until a century later that the reason why sexual selection took these forms was elaborated. Building on an experimental study of sexual behaviour in the fruit-fly by Bateman (1948), Trivers (1972) identified a crucial sex difference in the initial contribution to the reproductive process in a wide range of animals. Because eggs are larger than sperm, and cannot be moved so readily, the female initially contributes more in time and energy to the future offspring. The result is that the strategies which enhance fitness are different for males and females, the male typically maximizing the numbers of fertilizations and the female discriminating between potential mates.

This provides only an overall picture. There will, in practice, be a variety of strategies in specific cases. They can be understood in terms of the pattern of parental care. Where both sexes contribute, because male parental care is necessary for offspring survival, this will balance or even reverse the difference resulting from the nature of the gametes. Where the female is able to rear young without the male's assistance, accentuated inter-male competition will occur. This will be associated with costly and risky male strategies, and the evolution of polygyny.

Trivers (1974) considered the evolutionary implications of the conflict of interests between parents and their offspring, and between different offspring from the same parents. If we consider the case of one parent and two offspring, the parent is, on average, equally related to each offspring, and will therefore tend to allocate resources equally between them. Each offspring is only half related to its sibling; consequently, it can enhance its own fitness by gaining a greater share of the parental resources for itself.

The analysis becomes more complicated when age changes are considered. The fitness interests of both offspring and parents change with age: it becomes advantageous to the parent, at a certain point, to use its resources to produce new offspring rather than caring for the existing ones. At this point, however, it will still be in the present offspring's interests to seek to retain parental resources for itself rather than to share them with a new sibling. These and other deductions from the model will apply to all animals with prolonged parental care, including humans.

Developmental issues and life histories

The parent–offspring conflict model was the only early one which specifically concerned developmental issues. The main sociobiological theorists worked in the tradition of Wright, Huxley and Haldane, and concentrated on whether particular genes contributed to adaptation, rather than on the means through which they did so. Waddington, on the other hand, did address this issue. He identified three time-scales over which adaptive changes occurred (Waddington, 1957). Long-term changes involve relatively inflexible mechanisms, which are unlikely to change within a lifetime. The earlier sociobiologists concentrated on these types of adaptive change, leading to an overemphasis on genetic determinism (Wilson, 1975, 1977; Barash, 1977; cf. Rose *et al.*, 1984). Medium-term changes involve flexibility through developmental change: animals show different behavioural development in accordance with the adaptive requirements of their rearing environments. Short-term adaptive changes are under central nervous control. They include both physiological and behavioural adaptations.

Over the last fifteen years, many examples of short-term behavioural flexibility have been demonstrated in animals. Food foraging has been extensively studied in relation to models predicting that it will optimize a value closely related to long-term fitness (M. S. Dawkins, 1986, Ch. 1). Fighting strategies vary according to assessments of the opponent's fighting ability and the value of the disputed resource (Archer, 1988a; Archer and Huntingford, in press). In many insects, fish and amphibians, the decision whether or not to show parental care is affected by conditions such as the presence of predators, the availability of other mates and the numbers in the brood (e.g. Keenleyside, 1983; Townshend and Wootton, 1985).

In many cases, members of the same species and sex use different life-history strategies, involving different patterns of behaviour, to maximize their fitness. These may only involve the short-term adoption of a behavioural option because a more preferred one is unavailable, or the animal is poorly equipped to use it (Dominey, 1984). Such examples are best referred to as 'alternative tactics'. A widespread example is the 'sneaky copulator', a male that achieves fertilization by unobtrusive matings, thereby avoiding inter-male competition. This occurs in highly competitive species such as the elephant seal (Le Boeuf, 1972).

Of more interest in the present context are alternative life-history strategies, where the specializations begin early in life. They may either be controlled by an inherited difference or represent the same genotype responding to different environments (Huntingford, 1984a). An example of the first type is provided by Gross (1985). In some salmon species, one type of male matures at a much younger age than another, and attains only a fraction of its size. The two forms later gain access to females in different ways, by sneaking or by fighting. In this case (but not others: Dominey, 1984) the lifetime reproductive success of the two forms is approximately the same, intermediates having reduced fitness, a stable equilibrium being achieved in the population.

The alternative strategy which is conditional on environmental conditions during development provides an example of Waddington's medium-term adaptative change. A possible example is provided by a study of a small sample of mountain gorillas in the wild by Harcourt and Stewart (1981). Young males either leave their family group to seek mates elsewhere, or stay to take over leadership of their natal group. Harcourt and Stewart found that a close relationship with the leading male in infancy was associated with later staying in the group of origin, whereas a more distant relationship in infancy was associated with leaving it. This form of strategy is of particular interest because it has been applied to a number of human examples.

Finally, a concept frequently used to distinguish between reproductive strategies in different animal groups is that of r and K selection; r-selected species have a high reproductive rate, short generation time, small size and fluctuating birth- and death-rates; K-selected species have a low reproductive rate, long lifespan, larger size and more stable populations. Typical r-selected species are small invertebrates, and typical K-selected species are birds and mammals. It should be noted that this distinction is by no means as clear-cut as was originally supposed (see Horn and Rubenstein, 1984), and that it provides principally a descriptive term to compare the *relative* strategies of different species. Nevertheless, it has also been applied to different strategies *within* species – including the human species. In such cases, we are concerned with the conditional reproductive strategies outlined above. To label these as r and K changes the meanings of the terms and can be potentially confusing, for example, implying that such alternative strategies are necessarily controlled by an inherited difference (Mealey, 1990).

Applications to developmental psychology

The sociobiological models and concepts discussed in the previous section have been applied to a range of issues in developmental psychology, for example, child abuse, socialization, sex differences and attachment styles. In each case, they provide a different vantage-point from the causal explanations familiar to psychologists (Archer, 1991).

Daly and Wilson (1981, 1985, 1987, 1988a) used a sociobiological framework to generate predictions about the conditions under which child abuse, infanticide and neglect would be likely to occur. In particular, they applied the concepts of inclusive fitness and reproductive value to cross-cultural and historical data. They found support for the prediction that child abuse, neglect and infanticide would be more common in conditions indicating low reproductive value, such as uncertain paternity, rearing by a step-parent, lack of resources, or defects in the child. Infanticide was found to decrease as both the mother and the child became older, findings predicted by the decreasing reproductive value of the parent with age and the increasing value of the child for the parent between birth and maturity.

Based on the sexual selection theories of Darwin, Bateman and Trivers (see above), Low (1989) derived hypotheses about differences in child-rearing patterns for boys and girls. She suggested that boys would be taught to be more aggressive, competitive and self-reliant, whereas girls would be trained to be more industrious, responsible, obedient and sexually restrained. Low examined child-rearing patterns in 93 societies represented in the ethnographic record, and found overall that these patterns were widespread. She speculated that they provided preparations for different ways of maximizing reproductive success in males and females.

Using the concept of alternative reproductive strategies, Low also suggested that these patterns will vary with the social conditions so as to produce adult behaviour adaptive for each sex in the particular society. Various ethnographic surveys (e.g. Ford and Beach, 1951) have shown that most human societies for which there is information allow polygyny (Chapter 8). Low predicted, on the basis of there being conditional reproductive strategies, that the more polygynous the society, the more boys would be taught to strive and compete. This was generally found to be the case in her ethnographic survey. However, it was complicated by whether the society was one that was stratified in terms of status, or whether it allowed more open competition and social mobility. Stratification mitigated the competitive pattern found in males. In societies where women had control over resources, the typical socialization pattern of obedience for girls was also less pronounced.

Trivers' parent–offspring conflict model has been widely used to provide fresh insights into parent–child relationships (Bateson, 1985; Barash, 1977, 1982; Hinde, 1986). It explains, albeit in a *post hoc* fashion, many features of the interactions between parents and their children. In general terms, the model predicts that children will demand more resources from their parents than the parents are prepared to give; that a child will value his or her own interests more highly than those of a brother or sister; that parents will value children of the same age to the same extent. More specific predictions from the model are that weaning should be achieved through the mother's rather than the offspring's initiative; that parents should suppress and stop sibling conflict, and encourage co-operation; and that young should exaggerate their degree of dependency by mimicking features of earlier developmental stages.

The same model also provides a different way of looking at the process of socialization. It is regarded as a conflict of interests between two types of individual, rather than as the transfer of culture, as is the usual viewpoint in the social sciences. The evolutionary perspective implies that parents use their position of power to exaggerate the importance of moral strictures, and these serve their own interests by reducing the time and effort required in parenting or by reducing sibling conflicts.

Daly and Wilson (1988a, b) used Trivers' model to provide a novel perspective on homicide in the family: they derived predictions about when offspring will be most likely to kill their own parents. These were based on the contrasting interests of parent and child concerning the allocation of parental resources, which also undergo considerable change with age according to their reproductive values. From the viewpoint of enhancing the parents' fitness, the offspring become more valuable with increasing parental age; from the viewpoint of enhancing the offspring's fitness, parents become less valuable with age. It follows that homicide by a natural parent should decrease with age, and parricide should increase with parental age (and with parental age at the time the child was born). All three hypotheses were supported in Daly and Wilson's presentation of Canadian homicide statistics from 1974–83.

Alternative strategies and human development

I have already referred to Low's suggestion that the pattern of sex differences found in polygynous and monogamous societies can be attributed to different socialization practices representing conditional strategies. This is one of several comparatively recent applications of the concept of alternative strategies to human development. It provides another novel way of looking at the process of socialization. Instead of involving the arbitrary consequences of the environment in which the child is reared, the rearing environment is seen as triggering a particular developmental response because in the past this led to adult behaviour which was adaptive for the prevailing social conditions. In other words, selection will have produced conditional developmental strategies, which use parental or rearing styles as cues to the environmental conditions present in adulthood (Hinde, 1986).

Draper and Harpending (1982, 1987) suggested that cues in early development associated with father-absence indicate the sort of society in which the child is growing up, and stimulate an appropriate pattern of social development. This involves intense male rivalry and a lack of parental care. If the father is present during the early years, a different developmental pathway is followed, the end-point being more adaptive for a society where men are less competitive, form more stable relationships and show a high level of parental involvement.

Cross-cultural data indicate that in societies where father-absence is the custom, there is early intense nurturance followed by peer-rearing. In males, this is associated with competition, aggressive displays and antagonism to females, producing a pattern of male dominance and female subordination which fits the boy for life in a society where 'machismo' is at a premium. The effect of father-absence on girls is less clear-cut, owing to rigid controls on their sexual behaviour in many societies. When controls are absent, a pattern of early sexual interest, negative attitudes to males and unstable sexual relationships is indicated, a pattern which again may be adaptive for life in that society.

A second application of conditional strategies concerns attachment. In Chapter 3, I described Ainsworth's classification of mother–infant attachment styles which was based on the laboratory procedure known as the strange situation. Bowlby (1969) regarded the secure type of attachment as the adaptive form, and the other two (avoidant and ambivalent: Table 3.1) as maladaptive because the mother was not used as a secure base. Lamb *et al.* (1985) suggested that there is adaptive flexibility in both the reactions of the infant and the mother, rather than there being a single form of attachment which is well adapted for all circumstances. All three attachment patterns can be viewed as adjustments by infants to varying styles of parental care, and they may represent alternative developmental pathways to maturity, given the particular circumstances the child experiences. Lamb *et al.* viewed cross-cultural variations in the frequency of each attachment style in this light. For example, in a sample from north Germany the avoidant form of attachment was more common, and this was explained as an adaptation to independence training initiated by the parents.

A similar analysis of attachment was offered by Main (1990). She viewed the behavioural system (Chapter 5) for attachment as context-sensitive. Environmental conditions are assessed, and if appropriate, secondary strategies which either maximize or minimize the output in relation to the caregiver are activated. These correspond to attachment styles which exaggerate infant dependence or independence respectively.

In a more wide-ranging theory, which combines the hypotheses about father-absence and attachment, Belsky *et al.* (1991) argued that there are two possible developmental pathways. One is characterized by a stressful rearing environment, the development of insecure attachments and subsequent behaviour problems. Puberty occurs early, and sexuality is precocious, leading in adulthood to unstable relationships and limited investment in child-rearing. In other words, this is a combination of the pattern suggested for father-absence and that suggested for avoidant attachments. The other pathway is the opposite of this pattern. As the authors indicate, many aspects of the theory are not new. In fact, only the suggestion that pre-pubertal rearing influences the timing of puberty has not been suggested before. However, the integration of a large body of evidence within a single functional framework provides a theory of much wider scope than the earlier more specific hypotheses.

Hinde (1991) pointed out that the two contrasting developmental pathways roughly correspond to r and K reproductive strategies. These concepts have been applied to differences between human racial groups by Rushton (1985, 1988) in a highly controversial theory with strongly racist implications. Essentially, people of Afro-Caribbean origin were characterized as likely to be small-brained, of low intelligence, to have unstable marriages, to be impulsive, mentally ill, aggressive, active, criminal, highly sexed, promiscuous and fecund. These diverse features were viewed as a consequence of their racial group being specialized for a r-selected reproductive strategy (i.e. a high reproductive rate). Not surprisingly, the theory aroused much criticism and hostility, and I shall not cover the arguments here. However, one very interesting point was raised by Mealey (1990). While not necessarily disputing Rushton's data, as others have, she suggested that the pattern of racial differences which Rushton interpreted in terms of race-specific r and K strategies could be more plausibly viewed in terms of environmentally-dependent reproductive strategies. Her argument converges with that of Belsky *et al.* It involves strategies corresponding broadly to the r and K distinction being available to all human groups. Since racial groups are distributed in different environments, these conditional strategies will be differently utilized by them.

The main reason why the r and K concepts have proved so objectionable when applied to human racial groups lies in their connotations of biological improvement. Originally, r and K were used to refer to broad evolutionary trends (Chapter 8). For example, there is a trend towards K selection within the primate group. Therefore labelling a human racial group as r-selected strongly implies that it is biologically primitive. In view of these connotations, it is misleading to state (as Rushton also has) that the term is simply descriptive when used within a species. It clearly carries with it implications from its earlier use in connection with biological improvement, and as Grammer and Stockl (1989, p. 4) commented, 'History has shown with painful consequences to humankind how ideas about rank orders of races can be used for political justification of injustice.' It would seem in any case that the r and K concept is misapplied *within* a species, and any broad differences of the sort Rushton claimed to identify can parsimoniously be considered in terms of 'alternative strategies' (Mealey, 1990).

Short-term adaptive flexibility

Short-term adaptive flexibility in the mechanisms controlling behaviour has been demonstrated in many animal studies (see previous section). There are relatively few comparable studies of humans, but two examples are available.

Behavioural ecologists interested in whether derivations from selectionist thinking can be used to predict the way in which animals forage for food developed a set of predictions collectively known as 'optimal foraging theory', or OFT (Pyke *et al.*, 1977). OFT predicts that animals should behave in the short term so as to optimize some value, such as minimization of energy costs or maximization of energy intake, which is assumed to be related to long-term fitness (M. S. Dawkins, 1986). Specific models are tested by calculating the time and energy costs of particular types of foraging behaviour in relation to the value of the food obtained. Some tests have involved collecting field data, whereas others involve artificially constructed patches of food.

OFT has been used by some anthropologists to study the foraging behaviour of traditional societies, and there are studies of fruit-picking by adults in industrial societies (e.g. Hart, 1986). Hay and Lockwood (1989) used OFT in relation to the strategies employed by 6- and 10-year-old children to carry out a simulated hunting task in a computer game. The children were presented with cartoon drawings of various animals (worth different points) as the prey items. Different random arrays of the animals were generated on each occasion, varying the numbers of high and low values on each occasion. Predictions from OFT were that pursuing low-value prey would depend on the relative density of the different types, that the foraging path would tend to be forward-directed, and that the child would begin searching in the area where higher-value prey items were located. The results generally supported these predictions in that the responses were affected by density and value of the prey items, there was a forward tendency in the searching paths, and the 10-year-olds tended to begin foraging in the area containing higher-valued prey. Although these findings were in accordance with OFT, there were some aspects of the results which did not entirely fit, for example, the children took prey items with zero value. There were also complex age and sex differences.

I referred earlier to animal studies showing that the occurrence and intensity of parental care often varied with cues associated with the fitness-related outcomes of such care. Daly and Wilson (1981, 1987) viewed human child abuse and neglect within the adaptive framework generated by these studies. They argued that the motivational strength of parental care varies with features which predict its consequences for fitness. For example, if parenthood is doubtful, or the quality of the young poor, or the resources for rearing them unfavourable, parental feelings will be weakened, and the likelihood of abandonment, neglect or abuse of the young is increased.

Daly and Wilson initially applied this theory to evidence on human child abuse and neglect from the United States, United Kingdom and New Zealand, arguing that the pattern of a higher incidence of child abuse in households with step-parents, and with mentally retarded or emotionally disturbed children, supported the theory, as did the higher incidence of neglect in conditions of poverty (Daly and Wilson, 1981).

Their approach provides a novel conceptual framework for viewing child abuse, which could form a basis for more predictive research in the future (Daly and Wilson, 1985, 1987). It is important to recognize, however, that such functional hypotheses are not alternatives to causal ones, but instead provide an additional tier of explanation. They indicate why parental feelings vary under such conditions, but they do not demonstrate how this is achieved, i.e. the causal mechanisms involved (Archer, 1988b, 1991; MacDonald, 1987).

The value of the functional approach

The main value of a functional approach is that it enables behaviour to be viewed from the wider vantage-point of the theory of natural selection. This can, and has, led to the recognition of general principles which were not apparent from other viewpoints. In turn this has enabled unrelated findings to be integrated, and further novel hypotheses to be generated. This point is illustrated by an example from animal behaviour – imprinting – before considering further examples from developmental psychology.

In his pioneering studies of imprinting, Lorenz (1937) viewed the learning involved in the following response as forming the basis for choosing a sexual partner during adulthood. Later experimental studies showed that there were two distinct forms of imprinting, filial imprinting – following the parent – and sexual imprinting – learning features associated with a future sexual partner (Chapter 4). Bateson (1985) used a functional approach to provide a more complete understanding of this distinction. Filial and sexual imprinting have different functions, the first, to enable parents to be recognized, and the second, to enable appropriate sexual partners to be chosen in adulthood. These different functions indicate why they occur at different times during development. Filial imprinting occurs soon after hatching, as it forms a necessary basis for offspring to parent attachment. Sexual imprinting takes place later in development, since it involves the learning of adult features.

Sexual imprinting is governed by functional principles which apply widely, including to humans (Bateson, 1978b, 1979): first, fitness is enhanced by an optimal balance between the negative and positive aspects of assortative mating; second, any early learning process must occur when adult rather than juvenile features would be learned. As indicated in Chapter 4, Bateson (1978a, b, 1979, 1980a, 1982) suggested the following mechanism to fulfil these requirements in the case of mate choice in the Japanese quail. First, the sibling characteristics are learned during a phase after juvenile features have been replaced by adult ones. Second, during adulthood, mate-choice is influenced by a preference for individuals whose features are slightly discrepant from those of siblings (see Figure 4.5).

This example shows how selectionist thinking can produce a broader understanding of the two forms of imprinting. Similarly, in relation to human behaviour, the theory of natural selection can be used to integrate diverse and apparently fragmentary findings. For example, Daly and Wilson (1988a) argued that their analysis of data on various types of homicide more closely fitted the selectionist framework than it did a series of more fragmentary alternatives from the social sciences, such as the Freudian theory of parent–offspring conflict, and a gender role theory involving a pattern of arbitrary cultural diversity. Their work, outlined above, illustrates how selectionist thinking can be used to generate fresh ways of looking at homicide and child abuse.

In an earlier section I also summarized Low's (1989) evolutionary analysis of rearing patterns in boys and girls. In psychological accounts, the overall context of childrearing is usually viewed from a historical perspective – if it is considered at all: different patterns for boys and girls, and in different societies, are viewed as arising from historical forces whose influences are transmitted to the next generation through parents, teachers, other adults, television, and so on. An alternative perspective is the structural one, in which the behaviour of individuals or groups is seen as reflecting in a fairly direct way the power relations in society. This has been applied to sex differences in social behaviour, such as aggression and influenceability (Eagly, 1987), and to some aspects of childhood gender roles (Archer, 1989, 1992).

Both these explanations are proximal ones, in that they do not address the ultimate source of the sex differences. They are essentially concerned with how events at a macro-level influence individuals and their social interactions. Low's sociobiological analysis provides an additional tier of explanation. It provides an overall view of the origin of consistencies and variations in socialization patterns. It can also enable the source of male power to be traced at least in part to the reproductive conflict of interest between males and females, and to the cultural consequences of this (Hrdy, 1981).

A functional approach can often be used to focus attention on the nature of the underlying mechanisms. This was apparent in Bateson's research on sexual imprinting, and also in studies of other forms of learning (Bateson, 1984; Crawford, 1989; Maynard Smith, 1982).

The ethological tradition has acknowledged the importance of functional considerations for analysing motivational mechanisms since the early work of Baerends and Tinbergen. In Chapter 5, I considered the 'behavioural system' in relation to attachment. A functional viewpoint was crucial to Bowlby's view of attachment: it was seen as a product of a specific type of motivational system which specified goals related to fitness (through flexible means). This enabled it to be viewed as a biological system akin to other biologically important motivations, rather than being based on the arbitrary operation of generalized learning principles.

In this example, the function of the behaviour is clear, but the earlier psychological theories prevented its being seen in functional terms at all. In other cases, such as sleep, the principal biological function is far from clear, and this obscures the nature of the causal mechanisms controlling it. McFarland (1989) assessed the competing views that sleep either involves restorative processes or it has evolved to keep animals out of danger at times of vulnerability (Meddis, 1975, 1977). Both theories are supported by only some of the available evidence. McFarland proposed an approach which addresses the functional significance of sleep in terms of a balance between costs and benefits. In doing so, he is using the framework which underlies modern functional models in animal behaviour (M. S. Dawkins, 1986).

A second form of behaviour whose biological function is unclear is play (Chapter 8). Most researchers view it in terms of the benefits it confers for a later developmental phase. Martin and Caro (1985) have questioned this assumption (see Chapter 8). If their view is correct, the orthodox assumption would turn out – in functional terms – to be the equivalent of the restorative theory of sleep. It would be something assumed to be the case because it fits with common sense, but for which there is really only limited evidence.

Fagen (1977) used the cost-benefit approach to construct a functional model of play. He considered its age-related costs and benefits for the animal's lifetime reproductive success, to generate a model which predicted a number of its general features. In certain environments, it will be an optimal behavioural strategy, it will occur predominantly in K-selected species (producing smaller numbers of offspring with prolonged parental care) and will tend to occur at younger ages, although it can sometimes occur in adults. Behaviour required in adulthood should appear in play as soon as, or soon after, it appears in the animal's general repertoire.

Two important principles are apparent from these examples. The first is that knowledge of evolutionary function can often guide investigations of causal mechanisms. The second is that the cost-benefit approach, which underlies all modern functional thinking, can help to illuminate the functional significance of behaviour such as sleep and play, where the advantages for fitness are not immediately obvious and may even be counter-intuitive.

Criticisms and limitations of the functional approach

The sociobiological approach has aroused much critical comment. Perhaps the most serious and comprehensive criticism was that of Gould and Lewontin (1979), who referred to functional thinking as the 'adaptationist program'. They attacked its underlying assumption that all behaviour is adaptive, arguing that evolutionary history and the overall design of the animal so constrain the path of evolutionary change that it is misleading to view adaptation without considering such constraints. Gould and Lewontin regarded the whole enterprise of sociobiology as a misleading way of approaching the evolution of behaviour. While their specific criticisms, notably the neglect of constraints, have been acknowledged by many of the more thoughtful researchers in this area, their overall dismissal of the functional approach is generally viewed as a failure to recognize the many achievements of the sociobiological revolution, particularly concerning animal behaviour.

The point that an animal can only develop new adaptations from existing features is acknowledged in functional models – for example, foraging strategies – in terms of 'constraints', and the importance of these has been increasingly recognized in recent years. Only certain types of adaptations are possible, given the starting point. In other types of model, which involve a branch of applied mathematics called game theory (e.g. Maynard Smith, 1977), the starting point is acknowledged to be crucial for which forms of behaviour turn out to be adaptive in particular circumstances.

It is now widely recognized that behavioural features also need to be viewed as constrained by the requirements of other activities, rather than each one being ideally adapted to its environment. There will be a trade-off between the advantages and disadvantages of particular activities, so that some may turn out to appear sub-optimal. Motivational priorities are particularly important for ensuring that an animal's behavioural repertoire is organized so as to maximize fitness overall (McFarland, 1989).

Some behavioural and physiological responses are maladaptive under many circumstances. Many of these can be viewed as by-products of features which *are* adaptive in other contexts. This has often been overlooked by enthusiastic human sociobiologists whose efforts to endow every aspect of human behaviour with functional significance has been taken to extremes. Preferences for oral and anal sex among middle-class Americans, suicide, begging in the street and grieving are among the diverse assortment of human activities which researchers have sought to fit into the adaptive framework.

In the case of grieving, Feirman and Feirman (1989) suggested that it aids energy conservation, and Crawford (1989) that it enables help to be solicited from close associates. However, examination of the behavioural and physiological features of grief shows that it involves a variety of conditions which are clearly maladaptive, such as poor appetite, loss of sexual interest and ill health (Archer, 1988b). Viewed in a wider context, grief can be seen as the by-product of the process of forming attachments or close personal relationships. Its maladaptive features occur either because it is not possible to evolve attachments without also showing strong emotions when these are severed (Parkes, 1986), or alternatively because the emotional reaction aids reunification in cases of temporary separation (Bowlby, 1973).

It is, however, worth noting that selectionist thinking can nevertheless contribute to the understanding of such maladaptive by-products of adaptive features. Crawford (1989) viewed anorexia nervosa in the context of a functional framework related to alternative tactics and reproductive competition. In many animals, there are mechanisms for socially induced suppression of reproduction both in males and females. This can be understood in functional terms: it is advantageous for lifetime reproductive success to delay reproductive activity when social and other environmental conditions are unsuitable. Such circumstances include insufficient body mass (hence delayed sexual maturation until puberty), poor food resources (hence breeding seasons) as well as the effects of social competition. Recent research has shown the sensitivity of reproductive neuroendocrine mechanisms to social companions in several mammal species (e.g. Abbott and Barrett, 1990; Faulkes *et al.*, 1990; Sachser and Lick, 1991). In some, these effects are stress-mediated, whereas in others they are not. The extreme example from mammals is the naked-mole rat where one large reproductive female is supported by around 40 to 90 other individuals, all of whom except one or two males are reproductively inactive (Faulkes *et al.*, 1990).

Crawford (1989) speculated that anorexia nervosa in young women may represent a maladaptive by-product of such mechanisms for matching reproductive activity to social conditions. He suggested that young women will always have been under social pressure from other females, and also from the attentions of peripheral males. Mechanisms which temporarily delayed the beginning of reproduction when the chances of success were low would enhance overall lifetime reproductive success. Crawford speculated that in some modern urban settings social pressures have become accentuated and may evoke an exaggerated response in some individuals.

Most sociobiological hypotheses are concerned with behaviour adaptive in current circumstances. It is important to distinguish between this and adaptations to previous environments in which the animal or human has evolved (Tinbergen, 1963; Gould and Vrba, 1982). The distinction is particularly important for humans, whose evolutionary environment is very different from the current ones. It is for this reason that human sociobiologists such as Blurton Jones (1986, 1989) and Caro and Borgerhoff Mulder (1987) have studied traditional societies, and others such as Low (1989), Daly and Wilson (1988a) and Voland and Engel (1990) have used cross-cultural and historical evidence.

Another confusion found in some sociobiological writings is between functional and causal explanations. For example, Littlefield and Rushton (1986), in a study of grief intensity following death of a child, contrasted attachment (a causal mechanism) with a functional theory derived from genetic relatedness.

Function, development and immediate causation are distinct forms of explanation. They represent three of the four ethological explanations described by Tinbergen (1963). Explaining behaviour in functional terms involves the identification of characteristics associated with genes producing greater fitness for their bearers than alternatives at the same locus. The precise route from genes to behaviour is a separate question, which is the concern of developmental explanations. As indicated by the existence of reproductive strategies, because behaviour is subject to the influence of natural selection, this does not mean that it is 'genetically determined' – in the sense of being unaffected by the developmental environment (Bateson, 1985). This point was frequently misunderstood by both supporters and critics (e.g. Rose *et al.*, 1984) of the earlier human sociobiology.

The same general point applies to immediate causation. Functional explanations are concerned with the consequences of behaviour – its end-result – but the mechanism through which this is achieved is independent of its functional significance.

Some mechanisms which control behaviour are rigid in the sense that they lead to the same type of response irrespective of changes in environmental circumstances. For example, the parenting responses of many birds is directed to whichever chicks are in their nests, a rigidity of responding which has been exploited by the cuckoo (Davies and de Brooke, 1988). The initial parental response of adult humans may be directed at certain facial and bodily configurations known as 'baby features' (Chapter 5), a rigidity of responding which has been exploited by Walt Disney cartoons (Eibl-Eibesfeldt, 1989), the breeders of lapdogs (Lorenz, 1950a) and the makers of teddy bears (Hinde and Barden, 1985).

Other behavioural control mechanisms are more flexible in that they involve a general disposition to act in certain ways which, when taken overall, will lead to enhanced fitness. Emotions such as anger fall into this category, and the mechanism underlying their control often involves a discrepancy-activated negative feedback system (Archer, 1976, 1988a).

A third type of mechanism enables behaviour to be varied in an adaptive way according to environmental cues. Examples were described in connection with optimal foraging theory and conditional tactics. As indicated above, Daly and Wilson argued that the motivational strength of human parental care varies with features predicting the consequences for fitness. Where parent-hood is doubtful or the quality of the young poor or rearing resources are unfavourable, parental feelings are lessened.

The discussion in this section shows that there are many potential pitfalls in applying functional principles to human behaviour. Nevertheless, these do not affect the central principle of natural selection. Sociobiology is not a single theory, but a diverse set of models and hypotheses all derived from the principle of natural selection and applied to particular sets of circumstances. It is the particular assumptions and limitations incorporated into the specific models which may be falsified. The principle of natural selection itself forms the foundation of modern biology. While it may not be quite as essential for human psychology, its relative neglect by psychologists leaves a gap in their understanding of many forms of human behaviour.

Predictive hypotheses

Whether functional principles are truly predictive, rather than being confined to providing additional explanations for features which are already known, is a matter of dispute. Hinde (1986) claimed that they are seldom predictive, the sort of cross-cultural evidence used to assess most of them being restricted to showing associations (Hinde, 1987; Umbertson, 1986). However, empirical researchers, such as Daly and Wilson (1988a) and Low (1989), do regard themselves as applying functional hypotheses in a predictive manner.

In the previous section, it was noted that the relationship between evolutionary adaptations and behaviour may be indirect or direct. This implies that the clearest tests of functional predictions can be drawn from behaviour which varies adaptively with environmental cues. Daly and Wilson's hypo-thesis about parental motivation (see above) is one example. In this case, however, the data were not derived from the same individuals under different circumstances. They are therefore subject to the reservation that only associations, rather than causal connections, are being demonstrated. Even so, the demonstration that data derived independently from anthropological, historical or criminological records conforms to predictions derived from biological principles is impressive.

Research on optimal foraging theory described in an earlier section (Hay and Lockwood, 1989) used this theory in a predictive manner in a laboratory experiment. Although the conditions under which the 'foraging' took place were artificial, it did enable the strategies involved to be tested against those predicted by foraging theory.

The relatively few examples of direct tests of sociobiological hypotheses from within developmental psychology would support Hinde's view that functional hypotheses are at present seldom predictive. But this situation is changing. As indicated above, whenever we are dealing with a flexible disposition which has been shaped by natural selection in an uncertain environment so as to maximize an attribute related to fitness, it should be possible to test whether variability in responding does accord with selective principles. Depending on the behaviour in question, this could be achieved in a laboratory simulation, under contrived real-life or field conditions, or it could use existing social science data, as Daly and Wilson have.

Chapter 7

Dominance and other group processes

Introduction

In an important and influential paper, Crook (1970a) characterized the development of the classical ethology of Tinbergen and Lorenz, and the synthesis of Hinde (1966, 1970), as concerned primarily with behaviour at the individual or dyadic level, and concentrating mainly on issues of mechanism and development. Crook outlined a separate ethological research tradition ('social ethology') based on the pioneering work of Espinas, Kropotkin and Allee, who studied the social behaviour of animals from a more sociological vantage-point: they were concerned with social structure and its ecological context. Social ethology maintained this group approach, notably in the primate field research which flourished from the 1960s onwards.

Crook identified three perspectives in social ethological research. The first two were concerned with the relationship of social structure to ecology and to population dynamics. The first of these is considered further in Chapter 8. Both were to play an important part in the later development of the sociobiological approach of the 1970s, discussed in Chapter 6. The third perspective was social systems research, the study of behavioural processes which maintain the structure of the group. Perhaps the most widely used concept to describe such processes has been that of social dominance, although as Crook pointed out, it is one whose limitations had been realized by a number of primate field researchers.

The concept of social dominance is much older than Crook's social ethology. It was introduced into non-human primate research and into observational studies of children in the 1930s (e.g. Hanfmann, 1935). More recently, some developmental psychologists have assessed dominance by peer-rating methods (e.g. Edelman and Omark, 1973; Weisfeld et al., 1980), but most recent research on dominance in children has involved ethological observational methods. In this chapter I shall restrict the discussion to observational studies.

The term 'social dominance' requires careful definition, since it can be used in a number of different ways. When applied to a single animal or child, it can be used in a descriptive sense to indicate an aspect of their behaviour, as in the phrase 'a dominant animal'. When describing a relationship between two individuals, it means that the behaviour of one of them (the subordinate) is limited by that of the other (the dominant), i.e. there is a power or status imbalance between them. One likely consequence of this is that the dominant will consistently have priority of access to a resource both of them would otherwise seek to obtain (although this becomes less straightforward in primate social groups: de Waal, 1986). Dyadic dominance arises through previous social learning, for example, through aggressive encounters between the pair (Rowell, 1966), or through the recognition of cues indicating status, such as size or behaviour (Barnard and Burk, 1979). Applying the concept of dominance to pairs of individuals in this way is relatively straightforward, although in some cases the outcome of their interactions may be complicated by situational conditions, for example, where one of them is on its home ground, or has potential allies or a kinship group present.

The concept of dominance is usually not restricted to a dyadic relationship, but is used as an organizing principle for the pattern of relationships in a social group. The two uses need to be carefully distinguished (Hinde, 1978). The terms 'dominance order', 'dominance hierarchy' and 'peck order' have been used to describe the overall pattern of relationships within a group. A new set of questions is raised in the group context, principally concerning the measurement of dominance hierarchies and the extent to which dominance can account for the social organization of the group. These and other issues have been extensively considered in the animal studies: it is recognized that there are many limitations to the concept of dominance, both in a dyadic and group context. These limitations have seldom been acknowledged in studies applying dominance to children. In this account of dominance, the relevant theoretical background to the issues from animal research will be introduced before considering its implications for studies of dominance in children.

After considering the historical background to research on dominance, the following issues will be discussed: first, the evolutionary function of dominance; second, the extent to which the overall pattern of dominance relationships in groups of animals forms a linear hierarchy; third, whether the overall pattern of dominance in the group can be predicted from the outcome of dyadic encounters; fourth, the usefulness of dominance as an explanatory concept, whether different measures of dominance produce the same ordering of individuals, and whether it is related to other forms of social behaviour. Social dominance has often been regarded as a group organizing force, but it is clear that relations based solely on competition cannot explain why individuals in a group stay with one another. Alternative explanations of group cohesion are considered, in terms of affiliative processes.

The historical background to research on dominance

The origin of the term 'dominance' is generally attributed to Schjelderup-Ebbe (1922), who derived a linear dominance hierarchy from a study of the direction and frequency of pecks among a group of chickens. Later research on animals assessed dominance not only by the numbers and direction of attacks, but also by the outcome of aggressive encounters and by the priority of access to resources which social dominance was supposed to confer.

In the 1930s and 1940s, the concept of dominance was taken up by biologists interested in the social organization of animals, such as Allee (1938, 1942) and Zuckerman (1932), and comparative psychologists studying group processes in captive rodents or primates, such as Maslow (1936) and Scott (1944, 1946). It soon became apparent that dominance orders were frequently more variable and flexible than the linear hierarchy suggested by Schjelderup-Ebbe, and that different assessment methods could produce different results (e.g. Uhrich, 1938).

In his book *Social Behaviour in Animals*, Tinbergen included a brief section on dominance ('peck-order'), in which he outlined several important points which were to foreshadow later critical assessments of the concept. The first was its dependence on individual learning: 'Each individual learns, by pleasant or bitter experience, which of its companions are stronger and must be avoided, and which are weaker and can be intimidated. In this way the "peck-order" originates, in which each individual in the group knows its own place' (Tinbergen, 1953, p. 71). The second – written at a time when many biologists and most psychologists accepted group-selectionist thinking (Chapter 6) – entailed the realization that any beneficial consequences, even for subordinates, would occur at an individual level: 'Individuals that do not learn quickly to avoid their "superiors" are at a disadvantage both because they receive more beatings and because they are an easier prey to predators during fights' (*ibid.*, p. 71). Tinbergen's third point concerned the limitations of dominance as a principle of social organization:

> The American literature contains many valuable contributions to the problems of peck order. [*Here Tinbergen was referring to the work of Allee cited above.*] In many of these papers, however, peck-order is claimed to be the only principle of social organization. This leads to distorted views; peck-order relationships form only one category among the numerous types of social relationships in existence. (*ibid.*)

These three statements, embedded within a short section on dominance, turned out to be very much ahead of their time and to contrast with most other writings about dominance published up to that point. One exception to this was the work of David Lack who had already realized the adaptive value of subordination some years before the publication of his influential book on the regulation of animal numbers (Hinde, personal communication). 'The peck-

(a) A linear, or transitive, relationship

(b) A triangular, or non-transitive, relationship

Figure 7.1 The possible relationships between three animals (A, B and C). Arrows indicate the direction of defeat in aggressive encounters (based on Bernstein, 1981, p. 423).

order probably has survival-value even to the lower members of the hierarchy which are displaced, since they will not waste their energies disputing with stronger individuals which would win anyway' (Lack, 1954, p. 151).

The primate fieldwork which began in the 1960s reiterated and extended the limitations of the concept of dominance outlined in Tinbergen's book (for reviews, see Hinde, 1974; Wilson, 1975). One prominent critic, Gartlan (1968), argued that dominance had often been assessed in conditions where it was a function of food deprivation or confinement or territoriality. Studies of wild populations indicated the existence of the following complications. In some cases, triangular relationships occurred: here animal A is dominant over B who is dominant over C, but C dominates A – instead of being subordinate to it, as would be expected if dominance were linear, or 'transitive' (Figure 7.1). In other cases, reversals in dominance relations occurred through time. A third complication was the existence of 'central hierarchies', involving a nucleus of stable dominance relations surrounded by a series of temporary alliances for particular purposes. Later field studies, such as those of Datta (1988) and Johnson (1987), have emphasized the importance of alliances, usually based on kinship.

The first human ethological study of dominance relations was carried out by Grant (1965a) on a group of psychiatric patients. At around the same time, Blurton Jones (1967) suggested that the concept of dominance would not be useful for describing the social organization of pre-school children. Although also accepting reservations about its usefulness, McGrew (1969, 1972a) nevertheless did calculate a dominance order from the outcome of paired disputes over objects or space in groups of pre-school children.

In the United States, studies of group processes in children, inspired by the social ethology of Crook, began in the mid-1970s. Although these researchers used Crook's writings as a starting point, they generally did not heed his acceptance of the criticisms of the concept of dominance made by primate researchers such as Gartlan (1968) and Rowell (1966).

In the remaining sections of this chapter these critical points are considered in detail, in relation to their relevance for studies of social dominance in children.

The functions of dominance

As far as a dominant animal is concerned, the beneficial consequences of dominance would appear to be straightforward – it confers priority of access to resources, including preferred mates. The extent to which empirical studies support this association is variable (see next section). Nevertheless, more recent studies indicate that maintaining dominance has its costs in terms of higher levels of fighting (Rohwer and Ewald, 1981), higher energy expenditure (Hogstad, 1987) and stress-related effects on the immune system (Masataka *et al.*, 1990).

As indicated above, Tinbergen (1953) correctly identified the functions of subordinate behaviour in terms of individual advantage: it avoided the costs of injury which fighting a dominant animal would entail. This view contrasted with that of the earlier North American researchers (Allee, 1942; Scott and Fredericson, 1951), and with that of many of Tinbergen's ethological contemporaries. Lorenz regarded dominance as functioning at the group level as a regulating force that minimizes the amount of overt aggression: 'A society may derive a beneficial firmness of structure from the state of tension arising inside the community from the aggression drive and its result, ranking order' (Lorenz, 1966, p. 41, Bantam edn, 1971).

Primate field workers such as Gartlan (1968) and Rowell (1974) questioned the evidence for this 'policing' function, which was later seen as incompatible with the more precise thinking about evolutionary function which developed from the work of Maynard Smith (1964), Hamilton (1964) and others (Chapter 6). As Tinbergen (1953) had realized, acceptance of dominance relations will increase the fitness of individual subordinates because entering into fights which the individual is ill-equipped to win will entail high costs in terms of injuries.

Barnard and Burk (1979) have followed up this line of reasoning, setting out some simple models for the evolution of dominance relations, based on the game theory approach (Maynard Smith, 1982), in which the outcomes of interactions between various strategies are calculated in a pay-off matrix. The importance of such models lies in their suitability for considering cases where the fitness of any strategy depends on the nature and frequencies of the alternative strategies in the population. Barnard and Burk followed earlier models of fighting strategies which emphasized the importance of assessing the opponent's fighting ability in advance of a contest (Parker, 1974). Although they recognized that such assessment may be based on learning from the outcomes of previous fights (see above), they also argued that selection would favour individuals which were able to assess the fighting ability of others by status-related cues, and to behave accordingly. These cues would be such that they could not be mimicked without high costs, so as to avoid the evolution of bluff and counter-bluff.

Although existing treatments of the benefits of subordinate behaviour are correct to emphasize the high costs of losing fights, and hence the benefits of acting on cues indicating dominance, they are limited to considering only the immediate costs and benefits of fighting. They do not consider the context of an aggressive encounter within the larger social group. de Waal (1986) has argued that, in primate societies, aggressive interactions occur in the context of close relationships, and it is important to balance their potentially disruptive effects with mechanisms for affiliation. In this case, aggression will entail added costs for the dominant as well as the subordinate, in terms of its potential damage to the relationship. As de Waal (1989a, p. 244) put it: 'one sometimes cannot win a fight without losing a friend'. This is an important point which most functional models of animal fighting have not included when considering its costs for fitness (Archer and Huntingford, in press). de Waal's research on the affiliative mechanisms which accompany dominance relations in primates is considered in a later section.

In contrast to these developments in animal ethology, most researchers on dominance in children who have speculated about its function appear to accept the group-selectionist view, that it provides a regulating force for the group. Examples can be found in the work of most of the major US researchers in this area (LaFreniere and Charlesworth, 1983; Savin-Williams, 1976, 1980a; Strayer and Strayer, 1976; Strayer, 1980a; Strayer and Noel, 1986; Weisfeld, 1980). There appears, therefore, to be a wide gulf between theoretical advances in animal ethology and the concerns of researchers studying group processes in children from an ethological perspective. One can only assume that adherence to the group selectionist view has arisen through lack of interest in functional issues. Acceptance of the view that dominance provides a regulating function is, however, particularly puzzling when one considers that competition is a potentially *disruptive* force in a social group: as de Waal realized, additional affiliative mechanisms are required to counter-balance these effects, if group cohesion is to be achieved. In future, consideration of the functions of dominance in groups of children should focus on its advantage for individuals, notably the avoidance of costly aggressive encounters, and the social costs of competition.

It may seem that the evolutionary function of dominance has little relevance for the concerns of most researchers interested in group processes in children. This is not so. As Appleby (1985) pointed out, it can have a profound effect on how dominance is conceptualized. The group selection view that dominance is an organizing force for the group assumes that there is usually a linear hierarchy, and that the animal's precise position in this is of importance. In other words, dominance is seen from the viewpoint of overall group organization. The implications of the individual selection viewpoint are entirely different. The animal need only know its own position relative to those with which it interacts. Its position in the overall hierarchy is now relegated to a convenient summary of group processes from the observer's rather than the animal's perspective. The implications of group selectionist thinking for studies of social processes in children will become more apparent in the following section, where the methodological limitations of assuming a linear hierarchy are discussed.

Limitations to the linear hierarchy

Primate field researchers such as Gartlan (1968) and Rowell (1966, 1974) agreed with Tinbergen's statement that dominance relations were the outcome of dyadic learning. But they also emphasized that this process could change over time and be modified by situational cues. It would therefore be expected that the dominance order would show non-linearity and reversals at a group level. Gartlan in particular questioned the common assumption – which can be traced to Schjelderup-Ebbe's work – that dominance hier-archies would be linear.

More recently, Appleby (1983) has argued that many animal researchers have simply assumed that a linear hierarchy is the most appropriate way to describe group processes and arranged their data to conform to this assumption without testing for linearity. In this way, apparent linearity is reported when it may not be present. A common method has been to present a matrix showing the outcome of every possible dyadic encounter, and to regard a low proportion of reversals as indicating a linear dominance hierarchy (see Figure 7.2 for an example of a matrix applied to a group of pre-school children).

Appleby (and Chase, 1974) demonstrated that the probability of apparently linear or near-linear hierarchies arising by chance is greater than would be expected intuitively, especially in small groups. Figure 7.3 (Appleby, 1983, Figure 4) shows diagrammatically the possible combinations of dominance relations for the simplest example of three individuals. Here the probability of a completely linear hierarchy arising by chance is 75 per cent. For larger group sizes, the probability can be calculated from a few simple formulae (Appleby, 1983, Table 5). For example, in a group of four ($N = 4$) there will be six possible dyadic relationships ($R = 6$), producing 2^R (64) possible combinations of relationships for the whole group. Of these, $N!$ (24) will be completely linear. The probability of finding a linear relationship by chance is

Targets

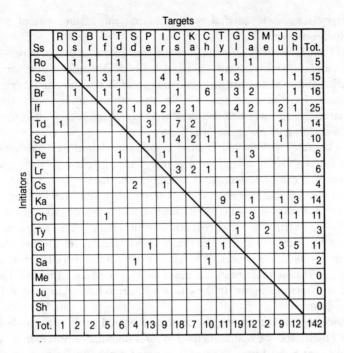

Ss	Ro	Ss	Br	Lf	Td	Sd	Pe	Ir	Cs	Ka	Ch	Ty	Gl	Sa	Me	Ju	Sh	Tot.
Ro		1	1	1									1	1				5
Ss			1	3	1			4	1		1		3			1		15
Br		1		1	1			1		6			3	2		1		16
If					2	1	8	2	2	1			4	2		2	1	25
Td	1						3		7	2				1				14
Sd							1	1	4	2	1			1				10
Pe				1				1					1	3				6
Lr									3	2	1							6
Cs					2			1					1					4
Ka											9		1		1	3		14
Ch				1									5	3		1	1	11
Ty													1		2			3
Gl						1				1	1					3	5	11
Sa					1				1									2
Me																		0
Ju																		0
Sh																		0
Tot.	1	2	2	5	6	4	13	9	18	7	10	11	19	12	2	9	12	142

(Left axis label: Initiators)

Figure 7.2 A matrix showing the outcomes of every possible dyadic encounter among a group of pre-school children studied by Strayer and Strayer (1976) (from Smith, 1989).

therefore 37.5 per cent. The probability of obtaining a linear hierarchy by chance is also above 5 per cent for a group size of five.

Appleby also showed that where there is incomplete information about all the dyadic relationships, or there are reversals in dyadic dominance, the probability of obtaining a linear hierarchy by chance is further increased. This is shown diagrammatically in Figure 7.4 (Appleby, 1983, Figure 3). Of course, the likelihood that there will be incomplete information about all possible dyads increases as the group size increases. It is therefore necessary, as Appleby emphasized, to test statistically for linearity, using the method of Landau (1951) or Kendall's coefficient of consistency.

In Grant's (1965a) ethological study of dominance relations in a group of psychiatric patients, the hierarchy was calculated from a matrix of aggression–submission behaviour between each dyad. Although the result was referred to as a 'relatively straight line rank' (Grant, 1965a, p. 102), no test of linearity was undertaken. McGrew (1969, 1972a) also used the matrix method (illustrated in Figure 7.2) to calculate a dominance order from the outcome of paired disputes over objects or space in groups of pre-school children. In both studies there were many omissions and several reversals in the dyadic matrix;

no linearity tests were carried out, rendering the assumption of a linear hierarchy problematic.

Strayer and Strayer (1976) sampled the free-play of a group of pre-school children, and derived relatively rigid and stable dominance relations from the systematic comparison of the outcome of aggressive encounters between each pair (Figure 7.2). No statistical test for linearity was undertaken, and data were unavailable for over half the pairs, thus greatly increasing the probability of obtaining linearity by chance (Appleby, 1983).

Savin-Williams (1976, 1977) used a mixture of both observational and sociometric methods in a study of a group of six 13-year-old boys on a five-week summer camp. Dominance was inferred from a range of activities including physical assertiveness, verbal commands and refusal to comply with the other. A matrix was calculated from dyadic comparisons, and a linear hierarchy presented. For a group of six, there is a 2.2 per cent probability that linearity will occur by chance when there are no dyadic reversals (i.e. where all the dyads fit the linear order). Where there are three reversals (as in Savin-Williams, 1976) the probability increases to 94.4 per cent (Appleby, 1983, p. 605). It is therefore highly unlikely that a linear relationship existed in this group of boys.

Methodological reservations also apply to a related study by Savin-Williams (1980b) which used the matrix method to infer dominance orders in groups of five adolescent girls. There is an 11.7 per cent probability of finding a linear

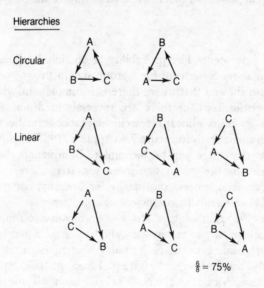

Hierarchies

$\frac{6}{8} = 75\%$

Figure 7.3 The probability of linearity in a group of three individuals, A, B and C. All possible combinations are shown, six being linear and two non-linear (from Appleby, 1983, Figure 4).

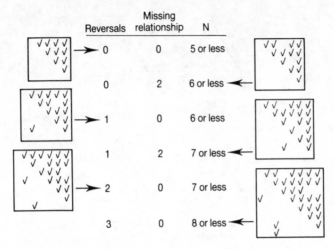

Figure 7.4 Some examples of hierarchies with levels of linearity that have a more than 5 per cent probability of arising by chance (from Appleby 1983, Figure 3, original caption).

relationship by chance, even without reversals (which there were), in a group of this size (Appleby, 1983, p. 605). Since it was also found that these groups did not operate as cohesive wholes but tended to split into pairs or threesomes, the assumption (as in the matrix method) that a single dominance order could adequately describe such data would appear unfounded in this case.

The same problems are apparent in the calculations of dominance for a number of other studies of children's group processes (e.g. Jones, 1984; LaFreniere and Charlesworth, 1983; Melson and Dyer, 1987; Sluckin and Smith, 1977; Strayer, 1980b; Strayer and Noel, 1986; Strayer and Trudel, 1984; Vaughn and Waters, 1980). Orders based on dominance were constructed, but linearity was not established. The dyadic matrix method used in these studies is based on the assumption that a dominance order describing group processes can be inferred from paired interactions. As indicated above, this is an unrealistic assumption for larger group sizes, since there will be an increasing likelihood that some children will not interact with one another.

The studies of children reviewed so far indicate that there are a number of methodological difficulties in applying the dyadic matrix method to infer a linear hierarchy. The method is unreliable for small group sizes; in larger groups, not all members of the group interact with one another, thus increasing the probability of obtaining apparent linearity by chance, and questioning whether a hierarchy based on dyadic relationships is appropriate in these cases; thirdly, some dyadic dominance relations involve reversals, which again increase the possibility of spurious linearity.

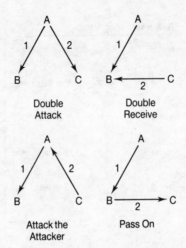

Figure 7.5 The four possible triadic attack sequences. Attacks are numbered in order of occurrence (from Chase, 1985, Figure 1, original caption).

These reservations apply to the concept of a linear dominance hierarchy. They do not affect the issue of whether specific dyads show dominance–subordination relationships, which can occur irrespective of the overall dominance structure, or lack of it (Hinde, 1978; Bernstein, 1981). They do, however, reveal severe limitations to the way that dominance has been used as a group-organizing concept in studies of children.

The triadic model of dominance

Several researchers on social dominance in animals have questioned the link between the outcome of dyadic encounters and overall group structure, which is implicit in the matrix method (Chase, 1980, 1985; Francis, 1988; Landau, 1951; Nelissen, 1985). It easy to see that concentration on dyadic encounters would not take alliances into account. It might also omit other influences of the social context in which the dyadic encounter took place.

One attempt to provide an alternative to the dyadic method in animal research was that of Chase (1980, 1985, 1986). He viewed dominance as an emergent property of *triadic* rather than *dyadic* interactions, describing these triadic interactions in terms of four possibilities (Figure 7.5). They depend on whether the initiator or recipient of the initial aggressive act attacks the third party, or whether the third party attacks the initiator or recipient of the original aggressive act. In a study of small groups of hens, Chase (1985) found a predominance of transitive triadic relationships (i.e. double attack or double receive in Figure 7.5) and he argued that this basic arrangement would, when repeated in a larger group, lead to the emergence of a linear hierarchy (a view he termed the 'jig-saw model').

Slater (1986) questioned whether Chase's model provides an explanation of dominance at the group level, arguing that it is unremarkable that there should be a bias towards transitive relations in groups of three animals, since individual differences, or any feature that correlates with winning or losing an encounter, should ensure this. Appleby (1985) made a similar point, arguing that a few individual differences and chance (see previous section) would explain Chase's results. Slater argued that Chase's model provides at best only a description of dominance relations in the small groups of hens from which he obtained his data. Indeed, in the absence of further information about the nature of these interactions, and the individuals involved in them, this must be the case.

A further criticism of Chase's model questions how triadic interactions would be ordered in larger groups of animals. Appleby (1985) pointed out that it is not clear how the ordering of triadic interactions could be controlled to produce a pattern of linearity in a large group: even in a group of 10, there would be 120 possible triads, and any individual would belong to 36 of these; in a group of 20, each individual would belong to 171 triads. How a linear hierarchy could emerge from such a large number of interactions is not explained by Chase.

Strayer and Noel (1986) applied Chase's model to a study of 2–3-year-old pre-school children by investigating the frequency of each type of triadic interaction in three groups. However, the results did not support the applicability of Chase's model even at a descriptive level: first, triadic interactions were in the minority (approximately one in five interactions); second, when they did occur, they were equally distributed across Chase's four categories, indicating a random pattern rather than the predominance of interactions where the original winner attacks the third party or the third party attacks the original loser (Chase, 1985; see Slater, 1986). Strayer and Noel appeared unaware of these limitations, and presented correlations of triadic interactions with dominance rank and measures of affiliation (some aspects of triadic behaviour were related to dominance relations but none was related to affiliation). On the basis of this study, Chase's model does not appear to be applicable to dominance relations in children.

In a further study of very young children (aged around one year), Strayer (1989) did find a predominance of transitive interactions (85 per cent) compared to circular ones (15 per cent), and he suggested that there may be a developmental shift to the more equal distribution at 2–3 years of age. Nevertheless, the reservations about Chase's model described above must cast doubt on the ability of these findings to explain the overall pattern of dominance in the group.

The finding of Strayer and Noel that most dominance-related interactions were dyadic rather than triadic provides limited – but qualified – evidence to suggest that a dominance order derived from the outcome of paired encounters may provide a realistic description of the overall pattern of interactions in the group. The qualifications are that any individual is unlikely to interact with all the others, that linearity cannot be assumed (i.e. the likelihood of reversals should be allowed for), and that the influence of other individuals and changes over time on the dyadic relationships should be taken into account.

These reservations apply to existing attempts to construct a linear dominance order from dyadic interactions. Whatever the limitations in this respect, the concept of dominance may still be useful for other purposes, for example, if it is able to summarize the nature of dyadic relationships (as an intervening variable: Hinde and Datta, 1981), or if dominance rank can, despite its measurement limitations, predict other aspects of the individual's behaviour.

Dominance as an explanatory concept

The two issues raised at the end of the previous section are related in that they are both assessed by examining the associations between measures, either between alternative measures of dominance or between measures of dominance and other types of behaviour. As indicated in an earlier section, the issue of the relationship of dominance to other aspects of behaviour has important implications for the evolutionary function of dominance. One would expect dominant animals to have priority of access to resources, including those necessary for reproduction.

Commenting on studies relating to the supposed link between dominance rank and measures of reproductive success, Bernstein concluded that this has 'been contradictory in some cases and merely assumed in others' (Bernstein, 1981, p. 426). In practice, there are many complicating factors which might obscure such a relationship, such as sperm competition (Parker, 1970), alternative reproductive tactics (Chapter 6) and respect for ownership – which may be explained in functional cost-benefit terms (Archer, 1986b) or by mechanisms promoting tolerance in social relationships (de Waal, 1989a; Senar et al., 1989).

The interrelations among a wider range of dominance measures are variable (Bernstein, 1981). The difficulty with making sense of the research evidence is that the types of animals used, the contexts of the studies, and the measures used to indicate dominance, have been so diverse: for example, aggressive behaviour, grooming, avoiding shock, supplanting another individual, food and water priority, and sexual responses, have all been used as measures of dominance (Bernstein, 1981).

Reviewing studies of primates, Hinde (1974) concluded that the associations among different measures of dominance, and between dominance and features supposedly related to it, such as grooming and mounting were typically low. The usefulness of the concept as an intervening variable in this context is therefore limited, although, as indicated in a later section, differences in the styles of dominance relations between different species may account for some of the variability in these findings (de Waal, 1986).

Ethological studies of children have often shown fairly high associations between dominance and the rank-order of the children on other forms of social behaviour. In most cases, these results are not relevant to the status of dominance as an intervening variable (see above), since the measures generally cannot be construed as alternative measures of dominance. Instead, they provide evidence of external validity for the concept: whatever the behaviour representing dominance measures, it bears a consistent relationship to other aspects of social behaviour.

McGrew (1969, 1972a) calculated a dominance order from the outcome of paired disputes over objects or space in groups of pre-school children, and examined their associations with other measures. He found that they were closely related to adults' ratings of aggressiveness in mixed-sex groups (McGrew, 1969), thereby providing some evidence for dominance as an intervening variable in this case. He also found that dominance was related to measures of activity and sociability for boys (McGrew, 1972a), showing some degree of external validity.

Other ethological studies of pre-school children have also found that dominance measures are related to other types of social behaviour. Strayer (1980a) found that dominance position was highly correlated with receipt of 'altruistic' or prosocial behaviour from other children. LaFreniere and Charlesworth (1983) found that dominance correlated with social activity and with the attention directed to that child by others, but not with sociometric measures of popularity (see section on dominance and affiliation). Jones (1984) also found that dominance rank was positively related to greater social play activity, more play partners and more requests for play.

These findings indicate that dominance position can be used to predict other social attributes in children. The finding that dominance position was often found to be related to more affiliative aspects of social behaviour is of particular interest. It would not be predicted from a purely competitive conception of dominance. However, it does suggest a link between success in competitive episodes and more affiliative social interactions. Two different approaches have sought to modify the concept of dominance so as to take account of such a link with affiliative processes. One is the concept of attention structure, discussed in the next section; the other, discussed in the section after, is de Waal's hypothesis that dominance relations involve a balance of competitive and affiliative aspects, the latter being necessary for group cohesion.

Attention structure

Chance (1967) originally applied attention structure to non-human primate groups as an extension of the concept of dominance. He argued that persistent attention by subordinates towards dominant animals was a feature of all rank-orders in monkeys and apes. He regarded the structure of directed attention in the group as a fundamental feature of the rank-order in primates, replacing the phylogenetically more primitive form based on aggressive behaviour and priority of access. This additional tendency of the subordinate to attend to and 'look up' to the dominant animal introduces a feature which provides an affiliative or group-cohesive aspect to relationships based on dominance. In this way, it provides a balance to competitive tendencies, which is necessary if group structure is going to be explained in terms of dominance relations.

From the start, Chance (1967) applied the concept of attention structure to both non-human and human societies, and it has perhaps proved more influential for studies of group processes in children than it has in non-human primate research. Before reviewing studies of children, it is necessary to examine what attention structure involves. Hinde (1974) was critical of the concept, commenting that it merely redefines dominance in terms of attention-attraction rather than priority of access or fighting ability. He argued that aggressive displays by dominant animals *are* attention-attracting to subordinates, but this does not mean that attention-getting is their primary aspect. Hinde also questioned the implication that attention necessarily has an affiliative or cohesive effect: in the case of a subordinate watching a dominant, it could just as easily signify wariness which is likely to be followed by moving away. Hinde concluded that attention structure is merely a re-description of dominance and commented that 'this does not seem a very profound procedure' (Hinde, 1974, p. 354). I would agree with Hinde's criticisms, and add that a much better attempt to solve the paradox of how dominance, based on social conflict, can be linked to group cohesion, is provided by de Waal's concept of the style of dominance (see next section).

Crook (1980) also viewed attention structure as being derived from dominance, but he suggested that it might assume additional importance in the human case in view of the ability of certain high status individuals to influence others in ways unrelated to overt aggressiveness. Researchers investigating attention structure in children have also tended to look at a wider variety of characteristics than those associated with competitive dominance (e.g. 'showing-off': Hold, 1976). Possibly in these cases, the concept becomes more than a redefinition of dominance.

In a German study of pre-school children, Hold (1976) defined social attention as being looked at by three or more children simultaneously, and found that it could be used to rank the children in each of four groups. Their position in the rank-order was closely related to their position in the order of initiating and organizing activities and also related to rankings of aggressiveness. Abramovitch (1976) assessed dominance in pre-school children by the outcome of dyadic property disputes and found that high-ranking children also tended to be looked at more than low-ranking ones, but that dominance and attention structure were not identical.

Later studies of pre-school children found that attention structure was closely related to a wide variety of other measures. On the one hand, it was related to competitive and potentially anti-social actions, such as threat and physical aggression (Hold-Cavell, 1985; Hold-Cavell and Borsutzky, 1986) and also to dominance order (LaFreniere and Charlesworth, 1983; Melson and Dyer, 1987; but not in the study of Vaughn and Waters, 1980). On the other hand, it was also related to prosocial activities, such as sociometric measures of popularity (LaFreniere and Charlesworth, 1983; Vaughn and Waters, 1980), initiating and organizing activities (Hold, 1980), affiliation and physical attractiveness (LaFreniere and Charlesworth, 1983). It would seem, therefore, that 'attention structure' describes more than dominance relations. It appears to represent the child's prominence in the group, which reflects *both* the receipt of a high level of prosocial behaviour from peers *and* the ability to dominate them in disputes. In the sense used in these studies, it does seem to represent more than a re-description of dominance (Hinde, 1974), but the concept still appears too general to illuminate the underlying processes. It may be important to one's position in a group to be noticed a lot, but there are many different reasons for being noticed.

Dominance and affiliation

de Waal (1986) has provided a rather different solution to the same problem of how to extend the concept of dominance to account for group cohesion. He widened consideration of the interactions between dominant and subordinate to take into account both their competitive and affiliative aspects. Although de Waal was ultimately concerned with the social group, his unit of analysis was the dyadic social relationship whose overall pattern was viewed as forming the group's structure.

Analyses of aggressive interactions and their consequences in captive groups of rhesus monkeys (e.g. de Waal and Yoshihara, 1983) and chimpanzees (de Waal and van Roosmalen, 1979), together with comparisons with the behaviour of other primate species, led de Waal (1989a) to refer to the 'style' with which dominant–subordinate relations are undertaken. These were viewed as varying along a continuum from the despotic to the egalitarian, depending upon the extent to which the relationship is needed by the dominant partner. If it is important, and the subordinate can leave the group with minimal risk, the relationship will tend to be egalitarian. In these cases, where group life is particularly beneficial for the animals concerned, as in chimpanzees, there will be mechanisms for ensuring social bonding in conditions of potential conflict. There will be both formalization of dominance relations, with clear signals of subordination, together with conditional reassurance by the dominant animal. Categories of behaviour which faciliate reconciliation and social bonding after a conflict, or when it is likely to occur, include behaviour involving bodily contact, such as embracing, kissing and grooming, and also offering gifts. In the Bonobo (Pygmy chimpanzee) sexual invitations are also offered under such circumstances: a vast increase in sexual invitations was found in conditions of potential competition for food, and after aggression had occurred (de Waal, 1989b, 1990).

de Waal (1986) argued that when dominance relations lack such affiliative mechanisms, they prevent rather than aid group cohesion. By realizing that behaviour which results in social cohesion must counterbalance competitive tendencies, rather than arising from them, de Waal has turned on its head the older attempts to explain group structure in terms of dominant–subordinate relationships (see, for example, the quotation from Lorenz in the section on the functions of dominance). de Waal's approach also explains some findings which are difficult to reconcile with more straightforward conceptions of dominance relations: it explains, for example, why the the dominant animal is often sought after or followed by others in the group, and why there is often a higher degree of flexibility in priority of access than would be expected (see section on dominance as an explanatory concept).

In seeking to apply de Waal's approach to the social behaviour of children, a change of emphasis is necessary: instead of setting out to construct an overall hierarchy, the focus of attention would be on the interactions which followed conflict, to determine whether reconciliation behaviour occurred. de Waal (1986) referred to a study by Montagner, in which he reported that children often spontaneously gave an object to their former antagonist. Montagner suggested that this was a prelude to physical contact between the children (as has been observed after conflict in non-human primates).

Sackin and Thelen (1984) identified, in pre-school children, a group of non-subordinate, friendly, forms of behaviour which were prevalent at the termination of conflicts. These conciliatory activities included invitations to co-operate in play, apologies, symbolically offering a toy, sharing an object, or physical contact such as holding or stroking. A separate class of behaviour occurring after conflict was referred to as appeasement acts (from Strayer and Strayer, 1976). These included flinching, cringing, withdrawing, flight, asking the antagonist to stop, and crying or screaming. From an analysis of the behaviour of twenty 5-year-old children, Sackin and Thelen found that although subordinate behaviour was consistently associated with separation after a conflict, conciliatory behaviour was nearly always followed by peaceful interactions between the former antagonists.

Other findings from studies of group processes in pre-school children can interpreted in the light of de Waal's approach. LaFreniere and Charlesworth (1983) found that some dominant individuals were viewed unfavourably by the other children, whereas others were popular (as assessed by methods). They speculated that there are two types of social power expressed explicitly and forcefully, and the other that is implicit, more on recognition of authority by the subordinates. This distin interesting parallels with the distinction between despotic and ᴗᵢᵉrant dominance styles in primates (de Waal, 1989a).

Strayer (1980b) found that the dominance order of pre-school children was significantly correlated with the order with which individuals received affiliative acts from other children. He explained this either in terms of subordinates 'appeasing' the dominants, or seeking to elicit from them behaviour incompatible with aggression. Again, these suggestions would readily fit de Waal's emphasis on the importance of the balance between competitive and affiliative behaviour in the negotiation of dominance–subordination relationships.

Principles of social organization

The approaches described in the previous two sections are both responses to the recognition that a concept based only on competitive interactions is insufficient to explain social structure, the pattern of relationships within the group. As indicated earlier, Tinbergen (1953) was one of the first to recognize this limitation, which some social ethologists later addressed by suggesting alternative ways in which group structure could be described and explained.

One of these was the introduction of the sociological concept of 'role' by Bernstein and Sharpe (1966) and Gartlan (1968). The term was used to describe specializations of individuals for certain types of activities important for the group. Gartlan (1968) examined the time different age and sex categories of vervet monkey spent in various types of behaviour. From this he identified their specializations in the troop. For example, certain categories of individual performed look-out functions, others led the troop more often and others engaged in more territorial displays. As Hinde (1974) recognized, there are a number of difficulties in seeking to transfer the role concept from humans to animals. In humans, a role is associated with a certain position or status in the society, with rights and duties (its effects on others), and it describes the normative, or generalized, behaviour of different individuals performing the role (Hinde, 1978). It represents much more than the necessarily behavioural analysis upon which primatologists have based their concept of role. These reservations would apply equally to the use of the role concept in observational studies of young children.

Recognizing that dominance is too limited a concept even to provide a description of social structure, Hinde (1974) reviewed a range of methods which had been used by primate field researchers such as Kummer, Deag and Bygott to describe social structure. The simplest is the sociogram, which is a diagrammatic representation of the frequency of interactions between individuals, or of their spatial distribution. It can provide a useful picture of the overall patterns of behaviour shown by a group of animals, but becomes very complex if the researcher seeks to represent several different types of interaction by this means. Sociograms can provide a useful initial representation of interactions in terms of broad categories such as 'spatial proximity', 'affiliation' and 'negative interactions', but cannot be applied much beyond these broad categories.

Sociograms have been used in the analysis of affiliative networks among groups of children. Affiliative behaviour is found to be much more frequent than that associated with conflict (Strayer and Trudel, 1984), again justifying approaches such as de Waal's which give it prominence. Strayer (1980b) presented two types of sociogram of children from several groups of pre-school children. One was based on proximity and the other on various categories of prosocial or affiliative behaviour, such as approaching, glancing and gently touching the other (Figure 7.6). Most affiliative behaviour was reciprocated and directed towards a limited number of other children, who

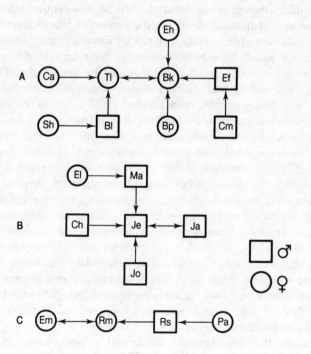

Figure 7.6 An example of a sociometric representation of directed affiliative activity, such as approaching and glancing towards the other. The arrows summarize first preferences of each child (from Strayer, 1980b, Figure 9.7).

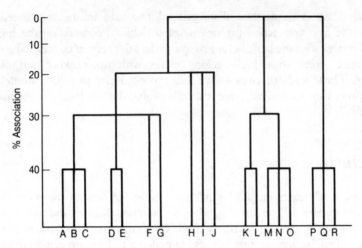

Figure 7.7 Dendogram showing the percentage of times birds (jackdaws) A to R were seen feeding together on a study area. Thirty per cent or higher association corresponds to the resident birds nesting closely together (derived from Röell, 1978, Figure 4).

tended to be those with whom the child was most often located (Figure 7.6). As indicated previously, it also tended to be directed towards children who were more dominant.

Sociograms are a very simple form of description of group relationships. Hinde (1974) and Morgan *et al.* (1976) have reviewed others, principally the use of various cluster analysis methods to simplify data generated by a matrix of interactions between members of a group. The resulting arrangement can be expressed as a dendrogram, a diagram depicting the different degrees of relatedness of each individual to the others in its social group or community. It can be used to represent particular categories of behavioural interaction, or more general measures such as the frequency of association (Hinde, 1974, p. 375). So far, this method has not been used for studies of children, but it would certainly be suitable for doing so. Figure 7.7 shows its application to the description of associations between individual jackdaws on a feeding area (Röell, 1978).

There have been a number of other suggestions concerning alternative descriptive and analytical methods for representing social networks at a group level. Pearl and Schulman (1983) described the application of block models, derived from mathematical sociology, to the analysis of rhesus monkey societies. The result of this analysis is represented in the form of a complex sociogram, for example, depicting which part of the group is the focus of various activities by other group members. Lunardini (1989) analysed the social behaviour of individuals from a confined group of Japanese monkeys by correspondence analysis, a method similar to factor analysis (but applicable to nominal data). This method distinguished two axes in the non-breeding season: the first concerned the degree of sociability, contrasting the highly social females with the peripheral juvenile males; the second concerned social importance, contrasting high-ranking males with low-ranking and older females. These sorts of analysis are likely to be useful in future studies of group processes in children, once researchers abandon the legacy of the linear hierarchy.

Conclusions

There are weaknesses in social ethological studies of dominance in children, arising from the failure to recognize the methodological and conceptual limitations of the dyadic matrix method. Concentration on dominance as a principle of social organization has also impeded a fuller appreciation of more affiliative group processes. Nevertheless, even in research carried out within the dominance framework, the importance of affiliative behaviour for group cohesion has been apparent. What is required in the future is a more explicit focus on this topic. One approach would be to use the methods outlined in the previous section, seeking to represent group relationships free from the straitjacket of the linear hierarchy. Another would be to study affiliative behaviour within the context of dominant–subordinate dyads, using de Waal's concept of dominance style.

Chapter 8

The comparative method

Introduction

In psychology, the term 'comparative' has been used in a broad sense to refer to any comparison of human behaviour with that of other species. This meaning encompasses some of the topics already covered in earlier chapters. In the case of animal models (Chapter 3), a single convenient example is chosen from the animal kingdom, and is used to represent a simpler version of the complex human case, rather like a 'preparation' in physiological zoology. General principles of development, such as the sensitive period (Chapter 4), also involve some degree of comparison, since they occur in a wide range of species. Likewise more specific processes, such as sexual imprinting, may be found in many species of birds and mammals. Here, the emphasis is on the principles themselves rather than on a systematic comparison between different species.

In both psychology and ethology, the term 'comparative' has been used in a more specific sense, to indicate systematic comparisons between different species, including humans. This was the principal aim of the branch of psychology referred to as 'comparative'. The comparative method, which was one of the foundations of modern biology, became an integral part of classical ethology. Lorenz (1941, 1950b) used it to make inferences about the evolution of behaviour. Behaviour patterns, such as ritualized displays, were compared between related species in the same way that anatomical features had been, to infer their likely divergence from an ancestral form. In the absence of evidence about behaviour from the fossil record, this was the main way in which evolutionary history, one of Tinbergen's four aims of ethology (see Chapter 1), could be inferred (Tinbergen, 1951). The comparative method has also been used to study evolutionary function (Gittleman, 1989), which was considered in Chapter 6.

Comparative psychology

Comparative psychology arose early in the history of psychology, in Britain and later in the United States, following the influence of *The Descent of Man* (Darwin, 1871) and *The Expression of the Emotions* (Darwin, 1872), together with the writings of the early British psychologists Spencer and Bain (Boakes, 1984). The aim of comparative psychology was to study psychological processes across a range of animal species (Dewsbury, 1984), thus providing a broad comparative background of animal studies for human psychology. The progression towards this goal was, however, stunted in the 1920s (Beach, 1950), or even earlier (Burkhardt, 1987), by the advent of behaviourism, under whose influence the range of species and topics studied became very restricted. With a few notable exceptions, such as Beach, Dewsbury, Lehrman and Schneirla, the old aim of generating a broad comparative background independent of the need to apply animal findings to the human case was abandoned.

The study of development, in particular the influence of early experience, formed an important part of comparative psychology (e.g. Denenberg, 1973; Harlow *et al.*, 1965; Kuo, 1967; Schneirla, 1959). Some classical ethological research was integrated into developmental comparative psychology, for example, by Ambrose (1968), and in Fantz's (1967) research on visual perception in early infancy (see also Rheingold, 1967). However, the relevance of the ethological research was largely restricted to its implications for the nature–nurture issue (Chapter 4) and concepts such as the fixed action pattern (Chapter 5).

Hodos and Campbell (1969) and Lockard (1971) have argued that the essentially non-evolutionary framework within which many comparative psychologists operated seriously restricted the theoretical basis of their comparisons. Others, such as Dewsbury (1984) have disagreed, arguing that evolutionary comparisons can be found throughout the history of the subject. Although there were undoubtedly those who maintained this perspective, the dominant impression from the mainstream 'comparative' journals was of a preoccupation with studying a narrow range of processes in a few species without an evolutionary perspective (Tinbergen, 1942; Beach, 1950; Hodos and Campbell, 1971), and of the use of the comparative method to study mechanisms underlying different levels of abilities in different species. Since these criticisms were written, the comparative approach, together with an interest in evolutionary questions, has been reintroduced into comparative psychology (Galef, 1987), following the influence of ethology.

In some ways the restriction of subject-matter and the pre-Darwinian framework of behaviourist comparative psychology can be seen as arising from a human-centred emphasis in the discipline of psychology. For students of human psychology, animal findings are generally only interesting when they generate principles or comparative data directly applicable to humans. Although researchers such as Beach (1950) and Dewsbury (1984) sought to counter this trend and to emphasize that the aim of comparative psychology is to study a broad spectrum of non-human animals, this has not, until recently, had much impact on research. It has had little, if any, impact on the perception of comparative psychology by other psychologists. The dominant impression is still of comparisons with animals made exclusively from a human-centred viewpoint, with the sole purpose of throwing some light on the human case.

Biology and the comparative method

From the previous discussion, I would argue that the full development of a comparative perspective on animal behaviour required a discipline that could flourish independently of the need to be applied to the human case. Ethology was such a discipline, arising within the biological tradition and encompassing the comparative method as used in biology to make inferences about evolution. It has been argued that the recent re-emergence of the comparative method in comparative psychology has depended on the influence of ethology, and of sociobiology on the subject (Galef, 1987).

In ethology, the comparative method has been used to trace the evolutionary history of specific forms of behaviour. It has also been used to provide evidence which can help to assess functional hypotheses (Chapter 6). It should be noted that these aims are rather different from those of traditional comparative psychology, which was primarily concerned with causation, for example, by comparing learning mechanisms in different species.

As Tinbergen (1963) pointed out, it had been realized since the turn of the century (e.g. Huxley, 1914) that many aspects of behaviour which were characteristic of a species show differences between closely related species. The study of these differences, along the lines established for morphological structures, enabled inferences to be made about the evolution of behaviour. Tinbergen remarked that evolutionary history and function had both been addressed in these early studies. However, it was not until the work of Konrad Lorenz in the 1930s that the comparative method was used extensively to tackle these questions.

Inferences about the evolutionary history of behavioural characteristics rely almost entirely upon comparisons between closely related living species, in view of the limitations of the fossil record for studying behaviour. Conclusions are drawn about characteristics which are similar on the basis of phylogenetic relatedness, by examining shared features in related species. These are known as homologous features. In a monophyletic group (i.e. one descended from a single ancestor), homologies can be contrasted with dissimilar features, which may reflect the extent of adaptive radiation into different environments.

As is the case with morphology, similarities in behaviour can arise not only from phylogenetic relatedness, but also from convergent evolution. In this case they are referred to as analogous. Limbs specialized for moving through the water, or for flying, or for digging, show a common appearance and morphology despite originating from entirely different structures in diverse taxonomic groups. Atz (1970) argued that convergent evolution is more prevalent in behaviour than in morphology, because of intense selection pressures and constraints on the possible behavioural options.

Eibl-Eibesfeldt (1971) provided a number of examples of analogous behavioural characteristics: these include a similar pump-like way of drinking which has evolved in different groups of birds living in dry regions, and the use of behaviour patterns from care of the young as appeasement gestures during courtship. In both cases, similarity results from the similarity of function, and from design constraints which limit the range of ways in which animals can accomplish a particular function (Gould, 1976). Analogous characteristics are found in phylogenetically unrelated species, living in similar habitats, and are used to study evolutionary function rather than historical change.

Behavioural homology is most useful for considering detailed evolutionary changes within a closely related group. There has also been interest in tracing broader evolutionary trends both within biology and comparative psychology. The concept of biological improvement was proposed by Darwin (1859) in *On the Origin of Species*, and developed in later work by Simpson, Rensch and Huxley. The argument here is that certain forms can be studied as examples of progressive evolutionary change, even though they do not themselves represent a historical sequence. They must, however, represent parallel trends in evolutionary history (Yarczower and Hazlett, 1977; cf. Hodos and Campbell, 1969).

Evolutionary improvement, according to Huxley (1958), refers to a trend towards greater specialization, increased efficiency in particular structures and functions, greater differentiation of functions, and higher general organization. Gould (1976) linked improvement to design criteria and optimization in an engineering sense. Huxley (1958) used the term 'anagenesis' to refer to the evolutionary trend towards improvement. Anagenesis is associated with the classification of animals into 'grades' (Huxley, 1958), on the basis of their complexity, rather than their ancestral lineage. Grades refer to specific features, such as thermo-regulation, learning, brain size and parental care, so that the grade into which an animal is placed will vary with the specific characteristic (Gould, 1976).

Comparative psychologists such as Harlow and Bitterman compared the learning of species from widely differing vertebrate groups. This aroused criticism from Hodos and Campbell (1969) for not taking account of evolutionary relationships (see above). Application of the principle of anagenesis comes nearest to justifying the comparative approach in this case

(Yarczower and Hazlett, 1977), although it must be stressed that the concept
of grade cannot be applied to cases of convergent evolution. It remains a
useful way of conceptualizing macro- as opposed to micro-evolutionary
changes (Gould, 1976). In a later section, its application to the evolution of
parental care is considered.

The comparative method in ethology

Lorenz (1941, 1950b) used the comparative method to study the behaviour of
closely related species, for example, the courtship patterns of the Anatinae
(ducks and geese). The specific movements show both common features
across different species and also slight differences between species which can
be used to infer phylogenetic relatedness. Figure 8.1 shows a later study by
Tinbergen (1959), which illustrates the different sequences of 'oblique long
call' in two related species of gull. Although the same sequence can be seen in
the two species, the herring gull emphasizes (b) and the common gull (c).

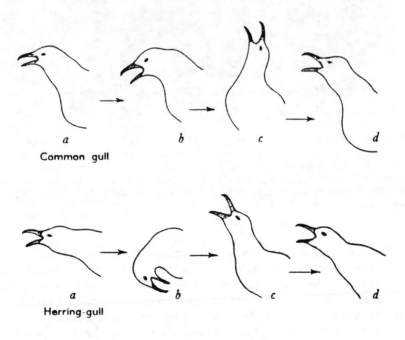

Figure 8.1 Variations in sequences of the 'oblique long call' in two related species
of gull. The head is held in the oblique position at the start (a), it is then jerked
down as the bird starts to call (b), is then thrown back (c) and is gradually lowered
as the call dies away (d) (from Tinbergen, 1959, Figure 4).

Figure 8.2 Comparison of the behaviour of the peacock and domestic cock to show affinities between courtship display in the former and food-enticing in the latter. Top left shows food-enticing in both species; top right shows courting impeyan pheasant (left) and peacock pheasant (right). Below is a courting peacock, with the hen in front searching for food (from Eibl-Eibesfeldt, 1971, Figure 16, based on several drawings in Schenkel, 1956).

Based on a detailed comparison of displays within the Anatinae, Lorenz (1941) constructed a diagrammatic representation of the phylogenetic relatedness of the various species. Later studies have used the comparative method in a similar way, although the emphasis has been more on tracing the origins of specific forms of behaviour rather than using behavioural features as aids to taxonomy. A study by Schenkel (1956) showed that the male peacock's courtship display can be traced from a food-enticing display of the sort seen in the domestic fowl: both are regarded as arising from a common ancestor (Figure 8.2). van Hooff (1967, 1972) has used the same broad comparative approach to devise a hypothesis of the phylogenetic origin of laughing and smiling, based on homologous expressions shown in living apes and Old World monkeys. (This is shown below in Figure 9.5 and is discussed in Chapter 9).

Inferences about analogous behavioural features are drawn not from systematic comparisons of related species but from a broader body of descriptive information. For example, where feeding of the young has evolved in a particular group, adult friendly gestures very often incorporate some aspect of this (see above). There have been many suggestions that specific human behavioural features are analogous with those of other species. Here we enter dangerous territory. The pop ethology of Ardrey (1967), Morris (1967) and Lorenz (1966) was based on selective use of examples apparently demonstrating such analogies. As Gould (1977a) pointed out, to infer a common causal basis from analogies is unwarranted, since only homologies provide a sound basis for doing so. Many of the supposed analogies described by the pop ethologists only resemble one another at a very general level: the 'monogamy' of geese and humans falls into this category (Lorenz, 1966). More specific analogies, based on superficial resemblance, often strain credibility: the supposed similarity between the sexual swellings on the chests of female gelada baboons and women's breasts (Morris, 1967) is an example of this sort.

Another problem is that cultural diversity has produced so many different forms of human behaviour to choose from that it becomes all too easy to select one which is apparently like the behaviour of another species. For example, the use of the erect penis as a threat display, found in monkeys such as the hamadryas baboon, has been compared with the use of the phallic sheath by Papuans, and the occurrence of the erect penis on figures supposedly guarding religious places in various cultures (Wickler, 1967; Eibl-Eibesfeldt, 1971).

Having sounded this warning, a careful comparison based on analogous features can illuminate the way similar problems have been solved in different groups of animals. Analogous features in two communication systems, bird song and human language, are considered later in this chapter. In social ethology (Chapters 1 and 7), it became apparent that social organization is closely related to ecological conditions, so that analogous features may be found in the social behaviour of species which are not closely related phylogenetically. Such analogies have played an important part in making inferences about human evolution (e.g. Crook, 1980) and are considered in the next section.

The concept of evolutionary grade has seldom been applied to issues in ethology. One exception is the discussion by Noakes (1981) of evolutionary trends in the context of development among fish, from which he drew inferences about other vertebrate groups including humans. This analysis is considered in the next section.

In the remainder of this chapter, I consider some examples where a comparative perspective can illuminate issues in developmental psychology. The first concerns the context of development, including variations in parental care and associated features such as the numbers of young produced and the relative pace of development. This topic shows how macro-evolutionary concepts such as improvement can be applied to comparative evidence. Associated with the context of development is the mating system used by the species. This is considered in relation to the social ecology of evolving humans. It illustrates the use of analogies in relation to the evolution of human social organization.

The third topic is play. Although this has been studied extensively in animals and humans, the comparative evidence has been considered to be inadequate from a zoological perspective (Gittleman, 1989). Ideally, the database should be evenly distributed across taxonomic groups and be relatively consistent in the form it was collected. Despite these reservations, of the specific topics relevant to developmental psychology play provides the best available comparative base. It enables some inferences to be made about functional and historical evolutionary questions, although, as indicated, there are gaps in the evidence.

The final topic is a comparative assessment of bird song and language development to illustrate analogous features in two different vocal communication systems.

The context of development

The context of development is affected by the overall method of reproduction used by the species. This includes the type of fertilization, the context of embryonic development, the occurrence and form of parental care, the numbers of young produced and the relative pace of development.

The reproductive habits of fish are more diverse than those of other vertebrate groups. Noakes (1981) classified them into 'reproductive guilds', according to ecological criteria, such as where and when they spawn, embryological features such as the amount and quality of yolk, and their mating and parental behaviour. This classification was based on the notion of evolutionary improvement (see above), rather than reflecting phylogenetic relatedness. Certain broad trends are apparent, enabling primitive forms to be distinguished from advanced ones.

Noakes distinguished three major reproductive guilds, non-guarders, guarders and bearers. In the first case, the fish spawn in the open and leave the brood to develop unguarded, or else they hide them. In either case, there is no parental care and no parent–offspring attachment. The young hatch soon and are altricial (immature when hatching). Many are produced and mortality is typically high. This represents an r-selected reproductive strategy (see Chapter 6).

Guarders provide parental care in the form of protection, for at least the embryonic and larval stages, the first being characterized by endogenous nutrition and the second by external feeding. The young hatch after a few days, and are either located on a substrate or in a nest. Proximity with the parents enables the young to interact with them, and there have been suggestions of imprinting-like phenomena in some types of fish which guard their young, for example cichlids (Noakes, 1981).

In the case of bearers, the earlier stages of development are completed inside the parent's body. In mouthbrooders, this occurs within the buccal cavity. In other species, the embryos are nurtured within the main part of the body: the young are born at a fairly advanced stage of development, and there is little contact with the parents, internal development serving the function of guarding in other species. The young are either born singly, or in broods of up to fifty, so that contact with siblings will vary accordingly.

Noakes commented that in very general terms these guilds correspond to the distinction between r- and K-selected strategies, the bearers being more K-selected (i.e. a greater investment in fewer offspring). However, this generalization may not hold in detailed comparisons at a species level.

Since the classification into guilds represents a progressive evolutionary trend, i.e. anagenesis (Huxley, 1958), we might expect some correspondence between guild membership and whether the fish comes from an ancient or a modern evolutionary line. However, this is not the case: some ancient forms are internal bearers, and some more modern forms belong to a primitive guild. This occurs because r-selected primitive features have been adapted for unpredictable evolutionary environments and K-selected advanced features for stable evolutionary environments. This emphasizes the point that both phylogenetic history and the evolutionary environment are important influences on evolutionary change.

Consideration of the context of development in fish enables mammalian reproduction to be placed into a wider framework. The main trend in mammals is towards K-selection accompanied by prolonged internal protection of the embryos. This is combined with extensive provision of nutrition directly from the mother, both before and after parturition. A second trend, which usually accompanies this (R. Martin, 1975), is towards precocial young: birth occurs at a fairly advanced stage of development, as in the case of internally brooding fish. These progressive evolutionary trends are again complicated by the association between reproductive strategy and environmental stability (R. Martin, 1975): K-selected species tend to live in stable environmental conditions and r-selected ones in fluctuating conditions.

Nevertheless, a typical 'primitive' mammal can be characterized as having a brief gestation period and producing large litters of immature ('altricial') young: they are small, blind, helpless and hairless – in other words like embryos (Gould, 1977a). In these animals mortality is high, the lifespan is short and the brain size small. Examples include insectivores, rodents and small-bodied carnivores. In a typical 'advanced' mammal, gestation is long, fewer young are produced and they are relatively well-developed at birth. Mortality is low, lifespan is longer and brain size is larger (R. Martin, 1975). Examples include cetaceans, ungulates and primates.

Martin noted that all living non-human primates showed a 'precocial complex' of features. Humans provide a marked exception to this since they are developmentally immature at birth. There has apparently been the secondary development of an altricial form, but within a K-selected line that in other respects shows 'advanced' features. In presenting this argument, Gould (1977a) drew upon the work of the Swiss zoologist Portman, published in the 1940s, but little known in the English-speaking world. Portman specifically referred to humans as 'secondarily altricial', and argued that there is an extension of the embryonic period beyond parturition. In other words, human babies are the equivalent of the embryonic state in an ape. Gould (1977a) listed a number of ways in which they show features characteristic of the foetal stage in other primates, and he argued that human babies only reach the developmental equivalent of an ape at parturition by 8 months to 1 year.

One puzzling finding which would be explained by this hypothesis is the marked increase in testosterone levels found in boys from 1 to 3 months following birth (Forest *et al.*, 1974; Winter *et al.*, 1976). It is usually assumed that hypothalamic sexual differentiation is completed before birth in humans (Money and Ehrhardt, 1972; Hines, 1982). This appears to be the case in other primates (e.g. Goy *et al.*, 1988), but not in altricial mammals such as rats (Goy and McEwan, 1980), mice, rabbits and gerbils (Probst, 1987). These findings suggest that sexual differentiation of the hypothalamus may continue beyond the pre-natal period in the secondarily altricial human infant, thus explaining the significance of the post-natal testosterone increase.

There are two other hypotheses associated with the view that humans are secondarily altricial. The first is that human evolution has entailed a marked slowing of development (Gould, 1977a, b), with human adults retaining the juvenile features of other primates. The human-like appearance of the infant chimpanzee is dramatically illustrated in Figure 8.3 (Gould, 1977b; from Naef, 1926). The use of ancestral juvenile forms as the basis for adult features is an interesting mechanism of evolutionary change, known as neotony: it enables apparently radical phenotypic changes to result from alterations in the timing and control of development which may rely on relatively small changes in the genotype (Gould, 1977b). It also emphasizes the importance of alterations in the developmental process for evolutionary change (e.g. Gottlieb, 1987; Lickliter and Berry, 1990).

The second hypothesis explains why the extended embryonic development does not all take place in the uterus: the size of the infant's head is too large in relation to the human pelvis. As Gould put it: 'There are not, I am confident, many human females who could give birth successfully to a year-old baby' (Gould, 1977a, p. 75).

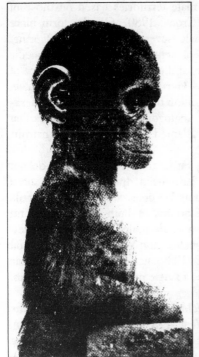

Figure 8.3 Infant and adult chimpanzee, illustrating human-like features of the former (Naef, 1926, Figures 4 and 1; from Gould, 1977b, Figure 61).

Social ecology and mating systems

Associated with the developmental immaturity of human infants is a pro-longed phase of dependence on the parents. Bruner (1972) identified this as a trend within primate evolution which allows greater flexibility and learning of behaviour. In the apes and especially in the hominid line it is even more marked. In apes, there is maternal buffering and protection of the young throughout a long period dominated by play, which includes participation in play by adults, and a lesser emphasis on threats and punishment as ways of controlling the behaviour of the young. In the human case there is extended association between parents and a measure of bi-parental care not found in our nearest living animal relatives.

Although the trend towards prolonged immaturity is apparent in the great apes, and indeed in primates generally, the specifically human features of bi-parental care and some degree of monogamy are absent in our nearest living animal relatives. In both orang-utans and chimpanzees, mating consortships last only a few days. The former is relatively solitary whereas the chimpanzee lives in loose mobile social groups with male territories based on those of females which depend on food sources (Crook, 1980). Gorillas form more stable family groups, with a single large male, several females, and offspring. These rather different social structures represent adaptations to the specific ecological niches in which the species live, and emphasize the importance of the socio-ecological approach (Crook and Gartlan, 1966; Crook, 1970a, b, 1980) for understanding the social organization of a species. This consideration has led social ethologists to look for analogous features in species that are not closely related to humans but are adapted for life in similar environments.

Evolving hominids lived in open country rather than the forest or woodland conditions of the great apes. Analogies have been drawn from the social organization of baboons which are also adapted to open country living (Crook, 1980). The essential features are: large groups of both sexes, long-term relationships between the sexes, but with a single male and several females; overt male competition for access to females; and extensive collaboration between males in group defence. Crook (1980) has argued that the basic reproductive unit in hominid evolution was a single male and several females, together with the children.

The degree of polygyny shown by a species is generally associated with the degree of anatomical sexual dimorphism (e.g. Trivers, 1972: see Chapter 6). In the human case, it is nowhere near as marked as in baboons, suggesting that the basic human pattern was mild polygyny (Short, 1980; Hrdy, 1981). Although also agreeing that 'men incline to polygyny', Symons (1979) argued that there are marked differences between the sexual dispositions of men and women which become masked by the compromises made in heterosexual relationships, and by moral restraints. The human species may show moderate sex differences in structure, but profound differences in sexual preferences, which are then subject to compromise and restraint.

In contrast to this emphasis on polygynous tendencies, others have suggested that human evolution has resulted in pressures for monogamy. In *The Naked Ape*, Morris (1967) argued that adaptations for 'making sex sexier' in humans, such as prolonged sexual receptivity in the female, were adaptations for promoting the long-term pair bonds, which are absent in living relatives of the human species. Similar views have been expressed by Eibl-Eibesfeldt (1975), Barash (1977) and others. The fossil evidence for hominids can also be interpreted as supporting the hypothesis of a gradual evolutionary change towards pair-bonding (e.g. Lovejoy, 1981; Johanson and Edey, 1981).

Arguing against true monogamy in the human species, Hrdy (1981) pointed out that, among primates, monogamous species do not generally show sexual activity across the female cycle, whereas some polygynous species do. She argued that this feature of human female sexuality has evolved so as to disguise paternity and guard against male infanticide which is widespread in primates when paternity is certain. Essentially the same argument was advanced by Symons (1979) as one of two possibilities for the loss of oestrus, the other being to obtain sought-after meat from males.

Comparative evidence from further afield in the mammalian world may throw some light on this puzzling proliferation of hypotheses. Dewsbury (1988) concluded that there are three dimensions of monogamy in mammals: first, mating is exclusive (although extra-pair copulations occur in apparently monogamous species: Mock and Fujioka, 1990); second, there is bi-parental care; and third, the male and female associate together. On these criteria, Dewsbury argued, human marriage is similar to the monogamous relationships found in other mammals. He argued that although surveys of human societies, such as that of Ford and Beach (1951), have found that in most cases men are permitted more than one wife at a time, only a few males actually achieve polygamy. Most are in practice monogamous.

To some extent, the variability in human mating systems can be understood in terms of ecological pressures (Crook, 1980; Dewsbury, 1988). Again, comparative evidence is useful for illustrating this, since there is similar variability in animal species. For example, the dunnock shows a gradation from polyandry (when food is scarce and females have large ranges) through monogamy to polygyny (Davies and Lundberg, 1984). In humans, polyandry is also found where economic conditions would render monogamy (or polygyny) disadvantageous (Crook, 1980; Crook and Crook, 1988). Perhaps the view of Symons most accurately describes human mating systems. He regarded the precise reproductive unit as variable, but resulting from compromises between radically different inclinations in men and women, which were filtered through different ecological and cultural constraints. He argued that human marriage reflects economic and political considerations rather than stemming directly from the sexual inclinations of men and women.

The dispute about whether humans are truly monogamous would seem to obscure an important feature of human evolution, that there was increased selection pressure towards long-term association between parents. The exact form this would take probably varied with the ecological conditions, and later became subject to cultural rules which reflected the conditions under which the culture developed. The important feature is the contrast between the short consort pairs found in chimpanzees and the prolonged relationships between the sexes associated with human parenthood. As Alcock commented: 'The evolution of human reproductive and sexual behavior owes a great deal more to the unique ecological pressures operating on humans and rather little to our primate ancestry' (Alcock, 1975, p. 484).

Although close mother–offspring relationships are seen in chimpanzees (van Lawick-Goodall, 1967; van de Rijt-Plooij and Plooij, 1987), and indeed in primates generally (e.g. J. Altmann, 1980; Hinde, 1974; Jolly, 1972), it is the contribution of the father that distinguishes the social context of humans from that of chimpanzees. Functional considerations (Chapter 6) indicate that bi-parental care occurs when there are circumstances which prevent successful rearing by only one parent (Trivers, 1972; Maynard Smith, 1977). Passingham (1982) argued that it is the immature state of the human infant, combined with its inability to cling to the mother, owing to the absence of body hair and the use of the big toe for walking rather than grasping, which makes it particularly vulnerable. The mother has to hold and carry the infant in her arms, thereby restricting her activity, particularly when she has to transport it over long distances (Rheingold and Keene, 1965). In a comparative assessment of the infant care systems used by mammals, Blurton Jones (1972b) concluded that the evidence supports the view that humans are adapted for carrying infants (as opposed to leaving them in caches). The main evidence supporting this is the milk composition and suckling frequency, which are both characteristic of demand feeding. In this case, comparative evidence was derived from a broad survey of mammals to indicate how their infant care systems are adapted to particular ecological niches, i.e. from analogous features.

The human mother is therefore more restricted than is the case for other primates, including the chimpanzee. Passingham (1982) argued that the basic division of labour found in most traditional societies, of women gathering plant food and men hunting (Martin and Voorhies, 1975; Rosaldo, 1974; Slocum, 1975), probably follows from this restriction. In conjunction with this would be the development of an economic unit between the father and mother.

In the previous section, I considered comparative evidence relating to the social context of human development. In doing so I considered the application of the macro-evolutionary concept of improvement, enabling human development to be seen in a broad context. I also considered the specific characteristics of human development which make them different from those of our nearest living relatives. In this section, I considered the human family from the viewpoint of comparisons made of analogous species, and also from the functional viewpoint of selection pressures producing bi-parental care.

Play

There is a considerable amount of research on animal play, both descriptive and experimental, and it has been summarized in several integrative reviews (Aldis, 1975; Fagen, 1981; Smith, 1982; Bekoff, 1984). It is often said (following Groos, 1898) that play seems functionless, in that there are apparently no immediate benefits (Bekoff, 1984; but see Barber, 1991). In studies of human play, emphasis has been placed on its supposed benefits for *future* development, a question that is bound up with the practical issue of whether play is beneficial (Smith, 1982; Smith and Cowie, 1988). Ethologists have also been concerned with the possible benefits in adulthood which might be associated with earlier play, in order to make inferences about the selective forces operating during the evolution of play. It is therefore not surprising that both those whose prime concern is with animal play and those mainly interested in human play should have adopted a comparative approach for assessing the possible functions of play (e.g. Aldis, 1975; Fagen, 1981; Smith, 1982).

Several hypotheses about the benefits of play for later development have been advanced on the basis of comparative evidence. They identify either motor training (Fagen, 1976), socialization or cognitive training (Aldis, 1975; Bekoff, 1984; Smith, 1982) as important.

Smith (1982) undertook a survey of the comparative evidence to assess the plausibility of the various hypotheses, and their applicability to human play. Other reviews of animal play (Ficken, 1977; Fagen, 1977, 1981) reveal that it is generally found in K-selected species, i.e. those producing few well-cared-for offspring (see above), and it is usually restricted to the early parts of the lifespan. Smith compared play in species with different adult patterns of social behaviour, and examined sex differences in species with different mating systems, to assess specific functional hypotheses. He concluded that the characteristics and distribution of play in animals were in general terms consistent with the motor training or exercise hypothesis of Fagen (1976), that the young of many species would not receive sufficient exercise for optimal development if they did not play.

Locomotor or exercise play, which involves running around, leaping and repetitive manipulation of objects or the body, is the type of play which most closely fits Fagen's hypothesis. Although it occurs widely in the young of mammals and birds, its frequency varies between taxonomic groups: it is particularly common in rodents (Pellis and Pellis, 1983) and in birds (Ficken, 1977). Locomotor play is more difficult to identify than other forms of play, and in rodents it is often associated with social play (e.g. Poole and Fish, 1976; Pellis and Pellis, 1983), where it is found in several contexts including the termination of a play bout. This suggests that it also serves specific functions when incorporated into social play.

Locomotor play is common in non-human primates, and is found in the young of great apes, including orang-utans (Fagen, 1981). In humans, it is found in different cultures, and shows a peak at 3–4 years of age (Smith, 1982). Later it merges into another category of play, object play, which involves manipulation of objects following exploration (Hutt, 1966).

Fagen (1976) was aware of the limitations of his exercise hypothesis for explaining the function of all types of play. In particular, he identified social and manipulative play as requiring further explanation to account for the specific forms they take.

Most play takes place in a social context, and rough-and-tumble play is perhaps the most common form of social play. In Chapter 5, I discussed the motivational separation of rough-and-tumble play and aggression in humans. This separation is also apparent in non-human mammals, with different

(a)

(b)

Figure 8.4 Play faces: (a) chimpanzee's open mouth face; (b) similar expression in human child (from Smith and Cowie, 1988, Figure 5.1; (a) after van Hooff, 1972; (b) after Smith, 1974).

targets of attack being found in the rat (Pellis and Pellis, 1987) and the hamster (Pellis and Pellis, 1988) for the two types of behaviour. Specific play signals have also been described in the rat, for example, play soliciting, tail- and hair-pulling, crawling over or under, and darting (Poole and Fish, 1976; Thor and Holloway, 1983). These are analogous to play signals in other mammals including primates, where a play face is found (Figure 8.4).

In agreement with other researchers (e.g. Aldis, 1975), Smith (1982) concluded that there was most support for the functional hypothesis that rough-and-tumble play exercised socially competitive skills, for fighting and predation, which could only be practised indirectly by young animals. The sex and species differences in rough-and-tumble play followed differences in adult fighting patterns, with males from polygynous species showing the greater amounts of both rough-and-tumble and inter-male aggression.

Einon (1980, 1983) argued that the distribution of rough-and-tumble play in mammalian groups was inconsistent with the view that it provided enhanced aggressive skills, but instead supported a connection with flexibility and social responsiveness. She also argued that it was related neither to dominance relations nor to individual differences in aggression. This argument partly rested on the claim that there are two types of play-fighting, 'juvenile fighting' (Taylor, 1980), which is a less harmful form of adult fighting, and true rough- and-tumble, which involves rapid role-reversal, play signals and an absence of damaging acts. Hole and Einon (1984) argued that the two forms of play- fighting have been treated as one, and that separating them is necessary in order to distinguish their functions, rough-and-tumble play for practising social skills, and juvenile fighting for practising adult fighting. Juvenile fights are found both in species that do show rough-and-tumble play, such as the rat, and those that do not, such as the housemouse. In the former, it is argued that juvenile fighting increasingly replaces rough-and-tumble play as the animal nears sexual maturity (as may be the case for humans: Neill, 1976).

Isolating animals that show rough-and-tumble play, such as rats and ferrets, during the time they do so affects later activity levels, habituation, extinction and discrimination learning (Hole and Einon, 1984). These effects are specifically reversed by one hour a day of rough-and-tumble play (Einon *et al.*, 1978), and are not shown in species where this form of play is absent (Einon *et al.*, 1981). Einon and Potegal (1991) have also found that rats deprived of social play show greater immobility in response to attack as adults. These experimental findings provide a clear indication that future benefits can be conferred by rough-and-tumble play: whether it provides the only effective experience is doubtful, especially since the changes in adulthood are very similar to those produced by other forms of early restriction (Archer, 1988a).

Hole and Einon's view that there are two sorts of play-fighting coexisting in the young of social muroid rodents has been criticized by Pellis (1988). Again examining comparative data, he concluded that in diverse species of mammals, including the carnivores, the same bodily target sites are attacked and defended during both play and serious fighting. Yet his own detailed observations on several species of muroid rodent, including the rat and golden hamster, showed that playful target sites were different from those used in serious fights. They consisted of areas such as the nape of the neck, which are involved in amicable behaviour, greeting and grooming. Pellis argued that in these species rough-and-tumble play has evolved from amicable behaviour, whereas in the other cases it is probably derived from aggressive behaviour.

Pellis noted that although more elements of serious fighting become apparent in the rat as it nears sexual maturity, it is the nape of the neck – rather than the targets of serious attack – that continues to be attacked and defended. He therefore argued against Hole and Einon's suggestion that there is a developmental transition from one form of play-fighting to another in this species. Pellis's findings suggest that rough-and-tumble play may be analogous rather than homologous in different species, and its apparent similarity, in say the rat, wolf and rhesus monkey, is the result of convergent evolution. Its function may also be different in different species: in some cases it forms a genuine preparation for adult fighting (Boulton and Smith, in press), and in others it serves another more affiliative function. However, Pellis cautioned against supposing that this distinction represents adaptations for solitary and social living respectively, since both forms of play are found in group-living and in solitary species.

Rough-and-tumble play is also a consistent feature of human play in most cultures that have been studied (e.g. Boulton and Smith, in press), with males showing higher levels than females in modern western and hunter-gatherer societies (DiPietro, 1981; Blurton Jones and Konner, 1973). It tends to occur in an amicable, non-aggressive context, between children who are friends (e.g. Smith and Lewis, 1985; Boulton, 1991b; see also Chapters 3 and 5). In a study of children aged 7–11 years in a British playground, Humphreys and Smith (1987) found that 11-year-olds tended to choose partners who were generally viewed as slightly weaker than themselves, but strength did not influence partner choice at younger ages. They suggested that rough-and-tumble serves an affiliative function at younger ages, and that it becomes more important for fighting skills and dominance at older ages, although the immediate motivation is still non-aggressive. This is reminiscent of the developmental change found in rats (see above), and is supported by the finding of Neill (1976) that some 12–13-year-old boys showed rough-and-tumble which was more like serious fighting. However, a later study by Boulton (1991b) of 8 and 11-year-olds did not find that initiators were consistently stronger or weaker than recipients, as Humphreys and Smith did.

The present evidence enables two apparently opposing views of the functions of human rough-and-tumble play to be formulated. The first is that it represents affiliative behaviour, similar to that found for rats (Boulton, 1991b). The second is that it enables fighting skills to be practised and non-threatening dominance contests to occur. It is possible that both functions may coexist, either in terms of the developmental progression suggested by Humphreys and Smith, or in terms of individual differences. Smith and Boulton (1990) suggested that specific children may use rough-and-tumble in different ways from the majority, for example, to enhance dominance or inflict injury. They take advantage of properties such as non-injury, self-handicapping and role-reversal. Sutton-Smith and Kelly-Byrne (1984) also emphasized the potential for playful activities to be used as part of bullying or terrorizing other children.

As in the cases of locomotor play (see above) and object play (see below), human rough-and-tumble play becomes incorporated into fantasy play or specific games with rules, such as tag and other team chasing games, at older ages (Boulton and Smith, in press).

Object or manipulative play has been found in carnivores, including the domestic cat (e.g. Barrett and Bateson, 1978; Caro, 1981), cetaceans, corvids and parrots (Fagen, 1976), and in some primates (Fagen, 1981). Although we might expect object play to be closely associated with predatory skill-learning in animals such as the cat, Caro (1981) found that the relationship between the two was complex. Some measures of play showed increased associations with predatory behaviour in 8–12-week-old kittens, whereas others became less closely associated with age. During this time, there appeared to be a reorganization in the control of behaviour patterns associated with play, predation and aggression.

Smith (1982) suggested that the origins of human aimed throwing games can be found in predatory skill learning, and noted the increased importance of skills involving manipulating objects in humans, a trend which is also apparent in the great apes, particularly chimpanzees (van Lawick-Goodall, 1970). Smith also suggested that a moderate amount of 'trial and error' play, involving the manipulation of objects, had been selected in the higher primates, provided that it could occur safely. Bruner (1972) linked the emergence of object play in the chimpanzee and human lines with the importance of observational learning as ways of mastering skills required during adulthood. In human children, objects are used to represent other objects: manipulative play becomes a matter of finding new ways of using an object once it has become familiar (Hutt, 1966; Fagen, 1981).

Fantasy play is usually viewed as a characteristically human form of play. It keeps the young child active when it is reasonably safe to be so, fantasy serving to direct the play by providing internal goals which structure it and bring it to a more complex level than would otherwise be possible (Singer, 1973; Smith, 1982). Fantasy enables play to transcend the simple practice or sensorimotor level. In non-urban societies the content of such play is based more directly on adult subsistence activities together with an oral tradition of children's games; however, in urban western societies, these have become increasingly subject to the influence of historical, national or fictional characters and activities transmitted by the media (Sutton-Smith and Kelly-Byrne, 1984): this applies more to boys' play than to that of girls (Archer, 1992).

Although Smith regarded fantasy play as a human form of play, there are some reports of instances of fantasy play in chimpanzees. These were reviewed by Jolly (1991). Hayaki had described an adolescent male who made a day nest near some adult males, and used tree and shrub branches apparently as substitutes for another chimpanzee, directing play faces, and acts of aggressive and sexual behaviour to them. Vicki, the chimpanzee raised by Cathy Hayes in an unsuccessful attempt to teach her human speech, at one stage showed evidence of an imaginary pull-toy. Like human children, young chimpanzees go through a stage of dragging objects behind them. At this time, Cathy Hayes noticed that Vicki was trailing one arm behind her as though dragging an imaginary toy on a string, and would stop as if it had become caught on objects, and she made movements as if to untangle it. On one occasion, Cathy went through the motions of untangling the rope for her, after which Vicki went off as if the string was now free. Examples from the sign-language-trained apes include Washoe bathing, soaping and drying her dolls, and signing to them (Gardner and Gardner, 1975). It is clear from these and other descriptions (Jolly, 1991) that fantasy play does occur in chimpanzees.

If, as Smith (1982) suggested, the function of fantasy play is to transcend sensorimotor or practice play, we would expect the potential for such play to exist in chimpanzees, and perhaps in other species whose cognitive functioning is beyond the sensorimotor stage (Chapter 10).

Smith's comparative assessment led him to draw various inferences about the possible functions of play from variations between species. A more critical comparative assessment of the functions of play was made by Martin and Caro

(1985). They noted that there are wide variations in play even between related species, that in some cases adults play, and in those animals that do play, it can vary with the prevailing conditions. This suggests that it may be a precarious activity, beneficial in some circumstances, but not in others.

Martin and Caro argued that there was insufficient evidence to support the basic assumption underlying all the theories discussed so far, namely that play early in development enables the animal to perform better some other activity in adulthood. Similarly, they argued that there was no consistent evidence that play enables children to solve problems or perform skills better than other forms of experience do. They suggested that too little attention has been directed to assessing the possibility that play may have immediate, rather than delayed, benefits, and they also raised the possibility that the benefits of play could be minor.

If this were the case, Martin and Caro argued, we should not expect play to be a costly activity, as has often been assumed. There is, however, little evidence concerning the costs of play. Martin (1984) measured the energetic cost of play in 10–12-week-old kittens, using a calorimeter chamber. He found that it accounted for between 4 and 9 per cent of the total energy expenditure, excluding growth, and that play occupied 9 per cent of the total time. Martin suggested that these findings cast doubt on the common assumption that play is very costly. However, these amounts are not necessarily insignificant: Miller and Byers (1991) found that running play accounted for only 2 per cent of total daily energy expenditure in pronghorn fawns, yet calculated that a fawn that did not play could expect to weigh 7 per cent more than one that played by week 12 of its life. They pointed out that because mortality in hard winters disproportionately affects fawns, this potential difference is not a trivial one. In other species, the time spent in playing is between 1 and 10 per cent (Fagen, 1981) – again, not necessarily insignificant proportions.

Martin and Caro used comparative evidence to reveal how little is known about the role of play in development, and to show how certain unquestioned assumptions have limited research on both animal and human play. The prevalent view among developmental psychologists is that play is important for the mastery of skills and for the opportunity to carry out new sequences of behaviour in safety (e.g. Bruner, 1972; Singer, 1973). Reviewing the empirical evidence on the consequences of human play, Smith (1988) concluded that most studies have concentrated on the supposed cognitive benefits of play in an educational context, but that the evidence from both correlational or experimental studies is unconvincing on this point. For example, the studies of Simon and Smith (1983, 1985) sought to control for possible experimenter effects and lack of adequate control groups which were characteristic of earlier studies. They found little or no beneficial effects on problem-solving as a result of play rather than comparable forms of experience. Smith (1988) concluded that the evidence on the supposed benefits of play for social competence is stronger than that for cognitive abilities, although it has been less thoroughly studied.

These findings support Martin and Caro's scepticism about the assumed benefits of play. Other doubts about common assumptions made in studying play have been voiced by Sutton-Smith and Kelly-Byrne (1984), who referred to 'the idealization of play' by adults. They argued that in this century, western society has moved away from regarding play as trivial or irrelevant to viewing it as positive and useful for later development. Smith and Cowie (1988) suggested that play is one way of acquiring social competence, but that there are alternatives. Similarly, Martin and Caro (1985) suggested that play may have important benefits under some circumstances, but that they may be obtained in other ways (the principle of equifinality: Chapter 4). Essentially, this is a view of play which does not presuppose that it necessarily serves a generalized function or functions, but that its occurrence is sensitive to current cost-benefit requirements. In Chapter 6, this view was compared to a similar empirical cost-benefit approach to the function of sleep, again derived from comparative animal studies.

Barber (1991) advanced a novel theory of the function of play, which, like Martin and Caro's assessment, challenged the widespread assumption of future benefits for play. However, instead of merely questioning current assumptions, he went further and argued that the energy expended during play was beneficial for young animals. This argument rests on the assumption that the energy obtained from food by many young animals is surplus to their requirements. High energy activities (i.e. play) promote a defence against cold stress, enhance resistance to pathogens, prevent obesity, and facilitate protein concentration of the diet in favour of growth. Barber argued that the costs of fat storage would be very high in juvenile mammals, and that play provides a mechanism to counter this. Barber's theory relies on play activating the sympathetic nervous system, to produce these physiological effects. He outlined a number of specific predictions from the theory, which awaits further investigation.

Most attention has been directed to the function of play, but there is some comparative evidence concerning its phylogenetic origins, and how aspects of human play are related to those of other species. Fagen (1981) concluded that play occurred in some birds and in most mammals but was absent from other taxonomic groups. This suggests parallel evolution in the two groups, in view of their diverse origins among extinct reptiles. It suggests parallel responses to similar selection pressures, probably for producing flexible behaviour and perfecting complex motor patterns before they are needed (Ficken, 1977).

Ficken (1977) concluded that avian play is more difficult to separate from other behaviour than is the case for mammals, and that few data are available for this group. Nevertheless, there is evidence for object manipulation (Fagen, 1976), some types of locomotor play and for playfighting (Pellis, 1981). Sub-song (discussed in the next section) may also be seen as playful in that it allows safe exploration of the limits of vocal responsiveness prior to the establishment of adult song. The most complex forms of bird play are found in the corvids, such as the magpie and raven, which show acrobatic, object and social play (Fagen, 1981; Pellis, 1981).

In mammals, play is more widespread. It is found in most groups that have been studied, including marsupials (Fagen, 1981), although there are pronounced differences between related species. As indicated above, the forms of rough-and-tumble play shown in muroid rodents and in other mammalian groups are different, suggesting that it has evolved in parallel, rather than from a common ancestor. Rough-and-tumble is common in the young of non-human primates, including those of both the gorilla and chimpanzee (Fagen, 1981). In human children it begins early in life and continues through to adolescence (and even beyond), occurs in most cultures, and shows the sex difference found in other species (Aldis, 1975; Blurton Jones and Konner, 1973; DiPietro, 1981). We would therefore expect the human form to be homologous with that found in other primates.

Play involving manipulation of objects is uncommon in non-human primates, but does occur in chimpanzees, where it may be related to later tool use (van Lawick-Goodall, 1970; Fagen, 1981). This suggests that its occurrence in primates, cetaceans, mammalian carnivores and corvids has resulted from parallel evolution, rather than from common ancestry.

Smith (1982) viewed the fantasy play of human children as being crucially important for making play more complex and flexible, and therefore more useful for practising complex adult skills. Although fantasy play occurs in the chimpanzee, the development of symbolic play becomes much more advanced in the human child, and is greatly facilitated by language, suggesting that it was particularly selected during hominid evolution (Smith, 1982).

There are, therefore, indications from a comparative assessment of play that certain forms of play, such as rough-and-tumble and object manipulation, are to be found in widely different taxonomic groups, probably as a result of parallel evolution. In the human line, the evolution of object manipulation, and of fantasy play, would appear to be of recent origin. Although found to a limited extent in chimpanzees, they show much greater development in humans. Bruner (1972) suggested that object play became particularly important in human evolution for the mastery of skills associated with tool use.

The development of bird song and human speech

Since the studies of Thorpe (1951, 1954) and Marler (1952), ethologists have been interested in several aspects of bird song. One is the way that it can illuminate broad principles of development, such as the sensitive period (Chapter 4). Another concerns its importance as a communication system. In this respect, researchers have found a number of parallels between the development and properties of bird song and human speech. These similarities are not due to a phylogenetic relationship, but are analogous features resulting from convergent evolution (Marler, 1990; Studdert-Kennedy, 1981). As indicated earlier, this is often found when different animals confront similar environmental problems.

Marler (1990) suggested that song-learning preferences provide a simpler version ('model': Chapter 2) of the human case, and that by comparing related species of birds, the mechanisms underlying the 'innate preferences' which form the basis for later learning can be understood:

> Apart from the special cases provided by genetic abnormalities and identical twin studies, studies of human behavior usually lack the powerful leverage provided by a strong comparative dimension. If by some quirk of history Neanderthals had survived, I suspect that our perspectives on the biological substrates of human behavioral development would be radically different. Lacking this comparative dimension, students of human behavior must turn to other disciplines to appreciate the full impact of the innateness argument. (Marler, 1990, p. 566)

Marler argued that in the absence of homologies on which to understand the evolution of human language, bird song could be used as an analogous system. Of course, these parallels do not reside in the syntactical structure of language, which ensure that it is a unique form of communication in the animal world. Rather, they concern the design and development of the phonological system through which language manifests itself. Pepperberg (1991) summarized the analogous features of bird song and speech as follows: the occurrence of a practice phase, the importance of imitation, and control by specialized neural structures which are lateralized. To this some would add the existence of a neural template as a basis for learning.

In both cases, a practice period precedes the adult form, the young seeming to experiment with the sounds they can produce, with little regard for meaning. In birds this is called sub-song, which is low-intensity, generalized singing preceding true song in many songbirds. In humans, it is babbling, which occurs around 6 to 9 months, and is characterized by well-formed syllables occurring repetitively and having acoustic characteristics of adult speech (Locke, 1990).

Babbling continues beyond the beginning of speech, and it is often difficult to distinguish the two (Locke, 1990). Many initial vocalizations contain broad messages, the exact meaning of which needs to be acquired by learning. Children often use words in an over-generalized sense, and only later narrow this down to the adult meaning: for example, they may use 'dada' for all adult men, or 'doggy' for all similarly sized animals. Similarly, birds may use variations of the adult song, which are not in the normal adult repertoire.

For both human speech and song-learning, practising sounds can be self-rewarding in the early stages of acquisition. Marler (1976) suggested that the advent of control over vocal development by auditory feedback was a crucial step in the evolution of human speech learning: it enabled vocal behaviour to be modified so as to match sounds from conspecifics early in development. Both babbling and song-learning are dependent on auditory feedback, and are delayed by hearing impairment.

Imitation learning plays an important part in the development of both language and bird song. Many songbirds show local dialects, which are copied by the young imitating them (Marler, 1952; Marler and Tamura, 1964). Imitation is not a passive process: social interactions are important in learning both speech and bird song. For example, several studies (e.g. Petrinovich and Baptista, 1987) have demonstrated the superiority of a live song 'tutor' over a tape recording of adult song. ten Cate (1989) found that a bird such as the zebra finch, when exposed to a sub-standard song tutor (in this case a Bengalese finch), showed attentive listening so as actively to increase exposure to the stimulation provided by the song.

Imitation is selective, so that song-learning in species such as the chaffinch and white-crowned sparrow is usually restricted to their own species. These findings led to the concept of a neural template which guides subsequent learning (Thorpe, 1961; Marler, 1976; Chapter 4). Marler (1990) compared song-learning in two related species which show very similar songs, the song and swamp sparrow. He found a clear preference in each for learning its own song. By using computer-synthesized songs in which different aspects had been selectively modified, Marler demonstrated differences in the stimulus cues on which the preferences were based. He concluded that even for a behaviour pattern so obviously learned as song, innate mechanisms play a fundamental part. He suggested that such mechanisms are fundamental to the development of all communication systems, including language. In an earlier article (Marler, 1976), he had argued that human infants possess an innate template which enables them to detect speech sounds so that attention is drawn to these. As a result, the template becomes progressively modified by experience.

Studdert-Kennedy (1981), and other researchers of human speech development, have doubted the evidence for specialized sensory mechanisms analogous to the templates suggested for songbirds. He argued that apparent biases towards categorical perception in speech recognition are not specific to speech, and apparent evidence for phoneme recognition turns out to vary across different languages, indicating that the categories are linguistically rather than perceptually based. Instead, Studdert-Kennedy (1981) emphasized more general pattern-seeking by the human infant. He suggested that the bird mimics, which show an extension of the ability to learn song into adult life and the capacity to imitate a wide range of sounds, might provide a better analogy for the human case than do songbirds.

The mimics lie at one extreme of a continuum in terms of their lacking constraints on what they can learn. At the other extreme are birds that show the adult song in the absence of appropriate experience. Some species are precluded by their rearing conditions from learning adult song during an early sensitive period. For example, the young from brood-parasitic species, such as the cuckoo and the cowbird, have no contact with their parents. We would expect a pronounced emphasis on innate generation of song in these birds. As expected, cowbird males raised from the egg with no contact with other males produce a song which is highly effective in eliciting sexual responses from females (West *et al.*, 1990). Nevertheless, West *et al.* argued that too great an emphasis on innate generation of song obscures some important social influences on song development in this species. For example, imitation is important for learning dialects: the song of an acoustically naive bird incorporates aspects of the song from different geographical regions (West *et al.*, 1990).

Other types of social interactions are also important. Naive cowbirds may be able to produce a song, but they cannot judge the appropriate circumstances in which to use it. Interactions with females – who do not sing – cause males to alter their vocal repertoire as a result of visual feedback from the female. West *et al.* (1990) compared the subtle social influences on song-learning in this species to those affecting the babbling of human infants. They commented that although babbling has been viewed as simply emerging through matura-tion (Chapter 4), more careful examination shows that it is influenced in a subtle way by the social environment.

The final point of similarity between the development of bird song and human language lies in the existence of specialized neural structures subsuming both methods of communication. There is evidence that the brain areas and peripheral nerves associated with song are lateralized in a manner similar to those controlling human speech. In the canary, Nottebohm (1977) found that left hemispheric areas controlled song to a much greater extent than did right areas.

In the chaffinch, the right and left hypoglossal nerves provide the innervation to the syrinx, the song-producing organ. Nottebohm (1971) found that sectioning the left hypoglossus of adult birds resulted in loss of most of the song components, whereas sectioning the right hypoglossus resulted in loss of few, if any, song components. The results of these procedures carried out in adulthood were irreversible, but if either side was cut before the bird had started song-learning, it would develop normally under the control of the intact side. There is, therefore, developmental plasticity in the control of song-learning. This parallels the development of human speech, but with the following reservation: studies involving hemispherectomized patients indicate that either of a young child's hemispheres may achieve a relatively normal level of linguistic performance, but that language learning involving the right hemisphere is built upon a different method of processing than that associated with the usual left hemisphere. Therefore plasticity, but not equipotentiality, is involved (Goodman and Whitaker, 1985).

Lateralization of behaviour, and its control, is widespread in those species of birds and mammals that have been studied (Bradshaw, 1991). It involves not only vocal communication, but also emotional and cognitive processing. Although it might be assumed that lateralization of control of bird song and human language are analogous features resulting from convergent evolution (e.g. Studdert-Kennedy, 1981), Bradshaw suggested that they represent features evolved from a common ancestor. In other words, they are homologies. The most primitive fossil chordates show evidence of structural asymmetries, and fossils of extinct trilobites show signs of behavioural asymmetry, either in themselves or their predators (Bradshaw, 1991). Bradshaw argued that a common ancestor of birds and mammals showed right hemisphere involvement in emotional and spatial behaviour, and left hemisphere involvement in learned sequential behaviour. On this view, both bird song and human language were incorporated into an already existing pattern of lateralization.

In conclusion, it is apparent that the development of bird song shows a number of analogous features with human language, such as initial innate vocal preferences, learned modification by auditory feedback early in life, and the importance of imitation learning. They may also show a homologous feature in the lateralization of the neural control, which is apparently of ancient phylogenetic origin.

Conclusions

In this chapter I have illustrated the ways in which comparative studies can be used in conjunction with evolutionary principles. Although classical ethology was most closely associated with the pursuit of homologies between related species, the search for analogies between the behaviour of different evolutionary lines also became apparent, notably in the work of Eibl-Eibesfeldt and Wickler, and in Lorenz's popular writings. Analogies are concerned with parallel evolution in response to similar selection pressures. They are therefore of interest in relation to evolutionary function rather than phylogenetic history. Function can also be studied by looking for differences associated with adaptations to different environments. Another use of comparative evidence, which is apparent in comparative psychology but is little evident in ethology, concerns anagenesis, or evolutionary improvement.

Three detailed examples were considered from a comparative perspective. The first was the context of development. By taking a broad look at reproductive trends in vertebrates, and specifically in mammals, the reproductive strategy which led to the long, dependent, developmental stage of humans was seen as a feature of the primate line. It could then be separated from trends specific to human evolution, such as the secondary development of an altricial immature infant, and the prolonged association between the parents that culminated in human marriage. It was suggested that these two were linked in that the dependent infant required active carrying and protecting in a way that was not the case with ape babies, hence favouring the evolution of bi-parental care.

The second topic was play, the human forms of which have arisen from several different types of play common in animals. Upon each of these are built specifically human features. Therefore locomotor play, which occurs widely in birds and mammals, is found in 3–4-year-old children, and later merges into object play. Rough-and-tumble play also occurs widely in mammals, but there is evidence that it may have evolved in parallel in different taxonomic groups. In humans, this form of play again occurs widely in different cultures, and becomes incorporated into play with rules and fantasy play later in development. Object play is particularly well developed in the great apes, but not in primates generally, suggesting that its occurrence in other taxonomic groups, such as the cat family (F. Felidae), is again the result of parallel evolution. Object play is particularly pronounced in human development, and becomes incorporated into imaginative fantasy play as development progresses. Fantasy play, although apparent in rudimentary form in chimpanzees, is the form of play that particularly characterizes humans.

Much has been written about the functions of play, both for animals and for humans. In a broad sense, it is regarded as being beneficial for future development, but these benefits have proved difficult to specify. Comparative evidence suggests that the occurrence of play – although widespread – is subject to the influence of specific circumstances. This has led several authors to question whether it has very obvious benefits for later development, and to suggest that it be better considered in relation to more specific costs and benefits operating in particular cases.

The third topic considered in this chapter was vocal communication, specifically features common to human speech and bird song. Two of these features – the occurrence of a practice phase and the importance of imitation – are likely to have arisen from parallel evolution. They illustrate the point made by Gould (1976), that the avenues open to evolutionary change are limited by the design constraints of the ancestral organism and by the laws of physics. Given that a vocal communication system has evolved in two distantly related groups of vertebrates, there are limits to the ways in which it can be efficiently designed. One other feature, which may represent common ancestry rather than parallel evolution, is the lateralization of control of vocalization found in both bird song and human speech. In this case, the two communication systems both incorporated lateralization of function – which is of ancient origin – into their design.

Chapter 9

Non-verbal communication and the expression of emotions

Introduction

Human emotional states, such as anger, fear and joy, are associated with outward facial expressions and gestures, the counterparts of which can be observed in animals. Psychologists have studied the origins and elaboration of emotional expressions in childhood, mainly in connection with the nature of human emotions. Human non-verbal communication extends beyond the expressions and gestures associated with the emotions, to include symbolic gestures whose meaning is established by convention. Emotional expressions, although elaborated by cultural influences, can be viewed as part of our biological heritage, and their study can be greatly enhanced by adopting a comparative ethological approach of the sort described in the previous chapter.

In his book *The Expression of the Emotions in Man and Animals*, Darwin (1872) described human emotional expressions from this perspective. He regarded the expressions of animals as 'windows of the emotions', reflections of their inner feelings. He emphasized the innate basis of the common forms of human facial expression, and the similarities between these and the expressions of animals. Over the last 30 years, human non-verbal communication has been researched in a variety of disciplines, such as structural anthropology, experimental social psychology, developmental psychology and child ethology (von Cranach and Vine, 1973; Ekman, 1973; Freedman, 1964; Trevarthen, 1977; Blurton Jones, 1967; Eibl-Eibesfeldt, 1968; McGrew, 1972a). In most of these cases, Darwin's work is acknowledged as a starting point.

The early ethologists departed from Darwin in that they were not primarily concerned with the expression of emotions. Instead, they concentrated on the communication function of expressive behaviour (Charlesworth, 1982; Hinde,

1985a). The difference in emphasis came about because classical ethologists' interest in the subject arose from studies of the displays shown by animals rather than from the emotional states themselves. Displays were viewed as fixed action patterns which had changed during the course of evolution. Some examples were introduced in Chapter 8 in connection with inferring homology: displays were the main subject of inferences about the likely course of the evolutionary history of behaviour patterns. Several processes were identified as underlying the evolutionary change from a non-social response to a social display.

It was inferred that the motivational basis of behaviour often changed during the evolution of a display. In addition, it was often found that animals showed a range of displays in similar circumstances. This variability could be characterized in terms of different combinations of the activation of motivational systems, such as aggression and fear. Alternative ways of characterizing the causation of displays, and their changes during evolutionary history, were also offered in terms of a series of more autonomous and specific responses.

Another, related question concerned the information communicated to the recipient of the signal. Originally, the concept of releaser was applied to this issue: displays were seen as releasers for fixed action patterns in the recipients. The limitations of this approach became apparent in studies which revealed the conditional nature of many signals, and the complexity of the communication sequences. Later studies adopting an explicitly functional approach (Chapter 6) reopened the question of what information is transmitted by a display, by questioning the apparent implication in ethological studies that communication had evolved to transfer accurate information to the recipient. Instead, communication was regarded as involving manipulation and deception.

The ethological studies of children which began in the 1960s involved observations of social behaviour at various levels of detail (Chapter 2). The most fine-grained observations produced detailed descriptions of facial expressions and gestures (Grant, 1969; Blurton Jones, 1971; Brannigan and Humphries, 1972). To a limited extent, these studies enabled links to be made with a larger body of ethological research on animal communication. The descriptive categories were also used as a basis for some later studies of children which tested hypotheses derived from ethological research on communication. Generally, however, this is an area where the potential for linking ethological and human studies has not been realized. Consequently, most of the chapter is concerned with describing the ethological research on animals, although where possible this will be linked with studies of children. However, we begin with a topic where the link between animal and human studies has been made.

The search for an innate basis of emotional expressions in children

Darwin (1872) regarded the 'true expressions' (as opposed to those based on convention for their meaning) as being innate or universal. Later, classical ethologists viewed the displays of animals as fixed action patterns (Chapter 5), characteristic of the species, and showing a pattern of evolutionary change comparable to that of a morphological feature (Chapter 8). Associated with this view was the assumption that displays had an innate basis during development. In Chapter 4, I discussed the difficulties in using the term innate, which have been apparent from the earliest critiques of classical ethology by neo-ethologists and comparative psychologists in the 1950s. This issue is still with us today (e.g. Johnston, 1988; Barlow, 1989; Bateson, 1991; Eibl-Eibesfeldt, 1989).

As indicated in other chapters, it is Eibl-Eibesfeldt who has placed most emphasis on the importance of the innate–learnt distinction in human studies using ethological methods. The deprivation experiment – rearing an animal in the absence of its usual social influences – was used by Lorenz as an important way of supposedly isolating the innate from the learnt (see Chapter 4). In human children this is, of course, not possible for ethical reasons. The approach taken by child ethologists who shared Lorenz's viewpoint was to use children who were isolated from the major avenues of social communication as a result of being deaf and blind. This method was used by Darwin (1872), who argued that since smiling and laughing were shown by a congenitally blind-deaf child, these expressions must be innate.

In the 1930s, Goodenough, a child psychologist who used observational methods, also studied blind-deaf children for the same reason: 'the behavior of such children can be regarded as the nearest approach to "native" reaction-patterns, freed from the influence of any social milieu, which can be observed in a civilized state of society' (Goodenough, 1932, p. 328). This conclusion foreshadowed the later view that human emotional expressions were fixed action patterns (e.g. Ambrose, 1966; Bowlby, 1969).

Eibl-Eibesfeldt (1973) followed the earlier studies in observing the development of deaf-blind children and emphasizing the phylogenetically determined nature of the expressions associated with fear, rage and other emotional states. Commentaries on the same view advanced in a later article (Eibl-Eibesfeldt, 1979) reflected the widespread acceptance of the points made by the earlier critics of the innate–learnt dichotomy (e.g. Block, 1979; Bolles, 1979; Hailman, 1979).

Working in Chicago at around the same time that Eibl-Eibesfeldt was beginning his human ethology programme, Freedman (1964, 1965) also examined sensorily deprived children to seek evidence for the innate basis of human facial expressions. He commented that previous studies, such as those of Darwin and Goodenough, did indicate an innate basis for smiling. His own observations showed that although blind infants do not usually show pro-longed smiling until 5–6 months of age, they do show fleeting reflex-like smiling. Freedman carefully discussed both nativist and social learning approaches to the development of smiling, and concluded that 'the fight between nativist and learning positions has helped very little in clarifying the mechanisms behind smiling in human babies'. He recognized both the impact of critiques of classical ethology (notably Lehrman, 1953) and the difference between innate used in the sense of susceptibility to selection, and in the sense of being unaffected by external influences. While the first definition applied to smiling, the second did not. Having said this, Freedman nevertheless concluded that much of the evidence supported the innate view of smiling.

Freedman (1964) noted in passing that the universal presence of smiling in different cultures also supported its innate basis. Over several decades Eibl-Eibesfeldt has carried out cross-cultural comparisons of facial expressions to identify universal motor patterns, such as the smile and the eyebrow-flash (Eibl-Eibesfeldt, 1968, 1972, 1975; cf. Ekman, 1973; Ekman and Friesen, 1978), to which he applied classical ethological concepts such as fixed action pattern and releaser. More complex interactions, such as giving and sharing, were viewed as reducible to a few invariant forms which could be super-imposed upon one another or occur alternatively.

In the United Kingdom, the ethologically-based studies by Grant (1965a, b) of adult psychiatric patients led to a detailed description and categorization of human expressions and gestures (Grant, 1969). Observations of pre-school children began at about the same time (Blurton Jones, 1967; McGrew, 1969, 1972a), and included detailed descriptions of facial expressions (e.g. Blurton Jones, 1971, 1972c; Brannigan and Humphries, 1972; see Chapter 2), which could be used in comparative studies of phylogyny (van Hooff, 1972) and in later experimental studies of children. Like Eibl-Eibesfeldt, Blurton Jones (1967) built his approach on Darwin's work and on classical ethology; however, even in this first report, he had departed from classical concepts, emphasizing that the term 'action pattern' referred only to the consistency of behaviour and did not necessarily mean species-specificity.

Hinde (1983a) contrasted the classical ethological approach, which emphas-ized similarities and minimized the role of culture, with that of social psychologists and anthropologists who studied non-verbal communication, and who emphasized only culture. He remarked that 'a more balanced view now prevails' (Hinde, 1983a, p. 49). Most British and North American ethological research on children does take a more complex view of emotional expressions, in terms of their form, relations with external events, interaction with cognitive processes and role in social interaction (Hinde, 1985a, b). The search for the innate basis of expressions is now largely confined to Eibl-Eibesfeldt's continued adherence to the classical approach.

The evolution of displays and human non-verbal communication

Hinde (1970) described three evolutionary sources of displays which were identified in earlier comparative studies. Some appear to be derived from preparatory or intention movements for behaviour directly aroused by the situation (Tinbergen, 1942, 1952b, 1959; Hinde, 1953a): an obvious example is the incorporation of intention movements for biting or striking into threat displays. In cold-blooded vertebrates, such as iguanas, whose facial musculature and skin rigidity restricts the range of possible facial expressions, mouth opening and head nodding have become an important part of the threat displays (Eibl-Eibesfeldt, 1961). Protective movements, which are preparatory for withdrawal or fleeing, would also come into this category. As well as being derived from activities reflecting the primary motivation involved, such as aggression or flight, displays may be derived from apparently irrelevant ('displacement') activities, shown when there are conflicting motivational states (Tinbergen, 1942, 1952a, 1959). Thirdly, displays may be derived from autonomic responses, for example, changes in skin colour, or a vocalization associated with surprise or fear.

In all three cases, we are concerned with behaviour whose original function was not for communication, but which could have provided information about the actor's motivational or emotional state. Where such behaviour is of selective advantage for communication, it becomes changed during the course of evolution to assume a form which maximizes the fitness of the behaviour for its communication function. This process was identified by ethologists studying displays, and referred to as ritualization (Tinbergen, 1952a, 1959; Blest, 1961; Huxley, 1966). There is likely to be parallel evolutionary change in both the display itself and associated morphological features, such as coloured patches, which make it more conspicuous.

During the evolution of a display, the relationship between the behaviour and its causal basis is likely to change. If a behaviour pattern began by being associated with, say, an autonomic response and later came to possess a signalling function, we should expect a change in the control of behaviour reflecting the change in function, so as to enhance its signalling function (Tinbergen, 1959). Another type of change involves the display remaining at a constant level over a range of eliciting conditions. This process, referred to as 'typical intensity' (Morris, 1957), would enhance the stability of the display, making it a more characteristic and consistent signal, preventing ambiguity (Tinbergen, 1959; Huxley, 1966).

In other cases, there is a more marked shift in motivational control of behaviour as one pattern becomes used for an entirely different function (the process of exaptation: Gould and Vrba, 1982). A well-known example is the adoption of the young's begging response into courtship feeding in birds

(Chapter 8). Eibl-Eibesfeldt (1971) extended this to suggest that where there is feeding of the young, this readily becomes incorporated into adult friendly and courtship gestures. He further speculated that human kissing is derived from ritualized feeding from mouth to mouth, which can be observed in some human societies and also in the great apes.

Ambrose (1966) applied ethological concepts including ritualization to the non-verbal communication shown in the context of mother–infant inter-actions. He viewed smiling as an evolved species-specific form whose function is to promote the strong affective bond between mother and infant. In evolutionary terms, he suggested that smiling is a ritualized form of commun- ication derived from a lower-intensity movement similar to laughing.

More extensive comparative treatments of the possible evolutionary history of human expressions, based on ethological research on displays, have been provided by Andrew and van Hooff. Andrew (1962, 1963a) was initially concerned with the origin of primate vocalizations, which could be understood as being derived from certain non-social responses. Thus exhalation of air may have originally accompanied the sudden presence of an unexpected or frightening stimulus, either as an involuntary movement (Darwin, 1872) or as a protective response (Andrew, 1962): this then became associated with a vocalization which other animals could hear. If the vocalization was given when approaching a social companion, it would provide a source of informa-tion about non-aggressive intentions.

Andrew (1963a, b, 1965) considered facial expressions within the same framework of emphasizing their derivation from non-social responses. For example, many mammals flatten their ears and narrow their eyes when startled. Such protective responses would inform other animals of the actor's internal state and may form the basis for a greeting display indicating lack of confidence. In primates there is less scope for moving the ears, and therefore ear-flattening has become less important, although scalp retraction is present in some animals. In the great apes and humans this is lost, but eyebrow-raising occurs when surprised. Eibl-Eibesfeldt (1972) has suggested that a range of human expressions have evolved from eyebrow-raising, although he proposed that these are derived from eye-opening accompanying attention rather than from protective scalp-retraction (Figure 9.1).

Andrew therefore argued that primate facial expressions and vocal displays originated from responses evoked by broadly similar non-social situations. He characterized these situations as varying along a single dimension, stimulus contrast (Andrew, 1962, 1963a, 1964, 1972). This explanation was primarily intended for vocalizations, but even here it appears oversimplified (Hinde, 1972; van Hooff, 1972), and when applied to facial expressions may obscure qualitative differences, for example, between laughter and smiling. The use of such a general dimension also seems inconsistent with Andrew's emphasis on explaining displays in terms of specific components rather than major

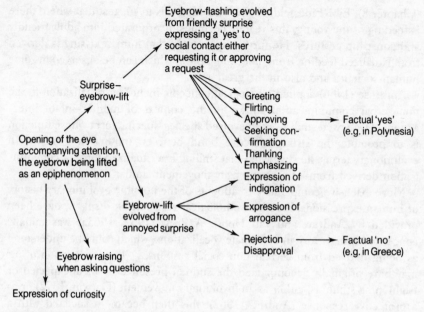

Figure 9.1 The evolution of human signals from eyebrow movements, according to Eibl-Eibesfeldt (1972, Figure 1).

intervening variables (see following section), and with his criticism of the related concept of arousal (Andrew, 1974).

Andrew (1963a, b, 1965) suggested that the grin has two different origins, one of which is protective, a grimace-like reaction derived from the drawing back of the lips prior to biting or expelling a noxious substance from the mouth; the other one is the grin-like expression accompanying high-pitched vocalizations, found in primitive mammals (van Hooff, 1972). In many advanced primates, the vocalization is omitted, producing a grin shown when frightened by another animal. Andrew suggested that the human smile is derived from the grin: in the case of the ingratiating human smile given to someone of higher status, the similarity is clear. What is more difficult to explain is the more relaxed smile of pleasure. Andrew used his stimulus contrast hypothesis to explain such smiles, and also laughter, arguing that small changes in stimulation evoke pleasurable sensations, leading to smiling and laughing, whereas larger ones evoke unpleasant ones, producing the grimace-like grin.

The view that laughing and smiling are evoked by similar situations, differing in intensity, has been proposed by others, including Darwin and Lorenz. van Hooff (1967, 1972) has questioned this, arguing that in some situations smiling is appropriate whereas laughing is not. He argued that they

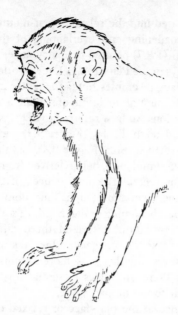

Figure 9.2 Relaxed open-mouth display in the crab-eating monkey (from van Hooff, 1972, Figure 4).

are qualitatively different in both phylogenetic origin and motivational control, although they have come to overlap in humans.

van Hooff (1967, 1972) advanced the following hypothesis concerning their origins. Laughter was derived mainly from a playful expression, the relaxed open-mouth display (Figure 9.2; see also Figure 8.4), and smiling from a combination of this and the grin described by Andrew, which van Hooff called the bared teeth display (Figure 9.3). In chimpanzees the two forms are separate, but in humans they overlap considerably, with the bared teeth

Figure 9.3 Silent bared-teeth display in the crab-eating monkey (from van Hooff, 1972, Figure 1).

display being incorporated into the relaxed open-mouth or play-face (shown in Figure 8.4), by broadening and overlapping of the motivational range (Figure 9.5). van Hooff (1967) pointed to analogous evolution of overlapping between the two displays in the Platyrrhines (New World monkeys), where the relaxed, open-mouth face resembles human laughter more closely.

van Hooff's (1972) account of the origin of smiling is similar to Andrew's. It involves the two expressions Andrew referred to as grins. van Hooff described them as the silent bared-teeth display (Figure 9.3) and the vocalized bared-teeth display or bared-teeth scream (Figure 9.4). Both occur in conditions of threat or strong aversive stimulation, being derived from protective responses, intention movements or secondary consequences of the vocalization. They came to be shown in social situations, signalling submission or non-hostility, with the teeth-baring part becoming exaggerated. In some species the friendly signal predominates. van Hooff described three different types of silent bared-teeth display in the chimpanzee. One was more associated with mutually friendly partners, another was more submissive, and the third a casual display used by dominant males to soothe smaller animals. The first type is the most similar to the human smile.

It is in the importance of the play-face or relaxed open-mouthed display (Figure 9.2) that van Hooff's account differs from that of Andrew. This display accompanies social play (Chapter 8, Figure 8.4), and also involves shallow staccato breathing, which may be vocalized in chimpanzees. Its possible origin is a ritualized intention movement for gnawing which forms part of the rough-and-tumble play of many mammals (Chapter 8). In chimpanzees, the play-face can also be evoked by tickling, again suggesting a parallel with human laughter.

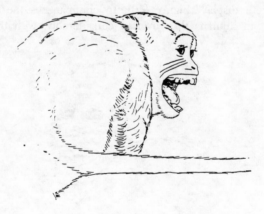

Figure 9.4 Bared-teeth scream display in the crab-eating monkey (from van Hooff, 1972, Figure 2).

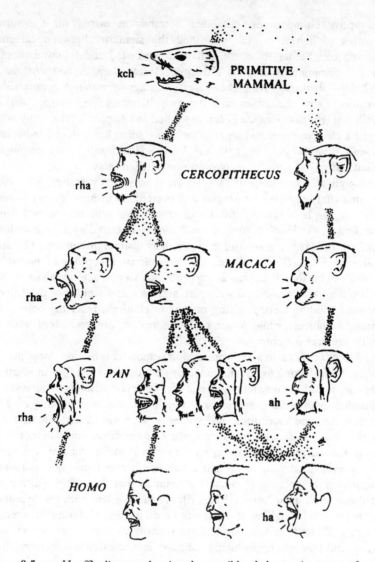

Figure 9.5 van Hooff's diagram showing the possible phylogenetic course of laughter and smiling, based on homologous expressions in living primates. On the left are the silent bared-teeth and bared-teeth scream displays. The former, originally submissive, later became a friendly response as well, and converged in humans with the relaxed open-mouth display, on the right, a play signal. Please note that the model does not imply a linear genaelogical relationship between these present-day genera.(from van Hooff, 1972, Figure 13).

In most primates the two displays appear to be motivationally distinct. van Hooff (1972) carried out a sequential analysis (Chapter 2) on the behaviour of semi-captive chimpanzees, obtaining a transition matrix for the various categories of behaviour. He examined the similarity between categories according to whether the same behaviour preceded and followed them. A principal components analysis (Chapter 2) was then carried out on the correlations obtained. Five higher-level groupings were found, comparable to the results of similar analyses carried out on bitterlings (Wiepkema, 1961) and on children (Blurton Jones, 1972c), described in Chapter 2. The analysis also showed a clear motivational separation for the silent bared-teeth and relaxed open-mouth displays. The first was loaded significantly on a component labelled 'affinitive' and the second on one labelled 'play'.

Although the two displays are separate in other primates, van Hooff suggested that they have converged and overlapped in humans to produce a variety of displays ranging from the submissive grin to the full laugh. Nevertheless, van Hooff argued, the behaviour associated with the pure forms of smiling and laughing are still motivationally distinct in humans. The study by Blurton Jones (1972c, d) of the motivational groupings of pre-school children's behaviour (Chapter 2) supports this view. Factor analysis showed that laughing was associated with play activities and smiling with affiliative activities including talking, giving objects to children, receiving objects and pointing at objects while looking. These results are consistent with van Hooff's findings for chimpanzees.

van Hooff (1972) also asked young adult respondents to rate a large number of adjectives referring to a social mood or attitude along the four motivational groupings found in the chimpanzee study, i.e. play, affinitive, aggression or submission. Most adjectives were given high or low scores, i.e. they could be classified into the categories. Respondents were also asked whether each adjective *could* be accompanied by smiling or laughing, and whether it was *typically* accompanied by these expressions. van Hooff found that smiling was typically associated with an affiliative mood, whereas laughing was typically associated with a playful mood. He concluded that these findings, together with those of Blurton Jones (1972c, d), are inconsistent with the hypothesis that smiling and laughing are variants of each other differing in intensity. Instead, van Hooff argued, smiling is primarily used for overcoming social tension, and laughter for inducing cohesion in a social atmosphere relatively free of tension.

Nevertheless, emphasis on the motivational differences between the pure forms of smiling and laughing should not detract from the various intermediate forms, whose variations can be accounted for in terms of different combinations of the affinitive and playful tendencies. To appreciate this point, it is necessary to consider ethological analyses of the motivational bases of displays.

The motivational bases of displays

In this section, I am concerned with the causal factors underlying displays in their present form. As indicated above, changes in motivational control can occur through the course of evolution. Ritualization involves a change in causal factors from those controlling the ancestral behaviour to those associated with the current display. Differences between similar displays in related species may reflect slight differences in causal factors that can be understood in terms of a shift in the relative strength of a small number of motivational variables (Baerends, 1975). In many species, a range of similar displays are found, and these too can be understood in terms of changes in motivational balance. Thus a consideration of the motivational control of displays in a single species has often been linked with explaining the micro-evolution of displays in related species.

The traditional way of explaining the causation of displays in ethology has been to view them in terms of the activation of competing tendencies or motivational systems: for threat displays these are aggression and fear, and for courtship displays they are aggression, fear and sexual motivation (Hinde, 1952, 1953a; Tinbergen, 1952b). This explanation forms part of the answer to the more general question of what controls the behavioural outcome when causal factors for more than one motivational system are present (Hinde, 1979, Ch. 17). In the case of displays, behaviour intermediate between the two 'pure' forms occurs. They are therefore viewed as being controlled by both the competing underlying motivational systems. Evidence for this hypothesis was originally derived from similarities of threat displays to overt attack or flight, and courtship displays to these two activities and sexual behaviour. Displays also occurred in situations which were likely to evoke attack or flight, or attack, flight and sexual motivation. These conclusions were based on a number of very detailed observational studies of birds, such as the great tit (Hinde, 1952), the chaffinch (Hinde, 1953a), several European gull species (Moyni-han, 1955; Tinbergen, 1959; see also Groothius, 1989a, b), two North American gulls (Moynihan, 1958) and a wide variety of South American gulls (Moynihan, 1962). Mammalian displays were also explained in this way (e.g. dogs: Lorenz, 1953; cats: Leyhausen, 1956).

Figure 9.6 shows the variation in facial expressions shown by cats (Leyhausen, 1956, 1979), which can be explained in terms of the relative activation of different levels of the systems controlling aggression and fear. Figure 9.7 shows a graphical representation of this view of the causation of aggressive displays.

One of the best-known examples of this approach is Tinbergen's (1959) study of gull displays. This was referred to briefly in Chapter 8 to illustrate variations on the same basic sequence in two related species (Figure 8.1). Tinbergen used three sources of evidence to conclude that threat displays

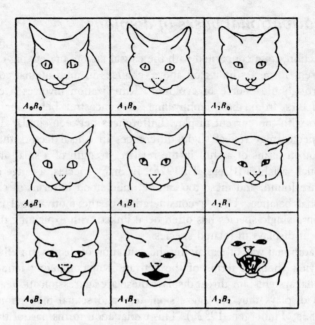

Figure 9.6 Facial expressions shown by domestic cats under the influence of aggressive (A) and fear (B) motivation. A increases from left to right, and B from top to bottom (from Archer, 1988a, Figure 10.1, modified from Leyhausen, 1956, 1979).

were the outcome of the simultaneous arousal of the motivation to flee and to attack. These sources were first, the form of the display, second, temporal

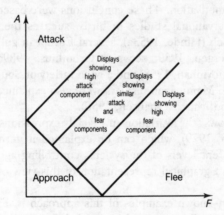

Figure 9.7 Graphical representation of interaction between aggression (A) and fear (F) motivation, to produce a series of displays differing in emotional state (from Archer, 1988a, Figure 10.2, from a diagram by Felicity Huntingford).

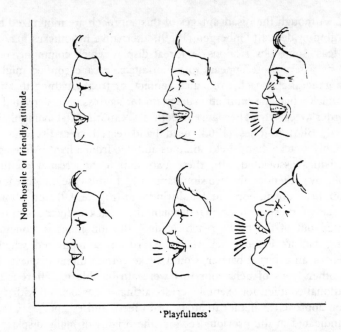

Non-hostile or friendly attitude

'Playfulness'

Figure 9.8 The motivational–interaction hypothesis applied to the origin of human smiling and laughing. Increasing playful motivation from left to right and increasing affiliative motivation up the page (from van Hooff, 1972, Figure 12).

associations with behaviour indicative of attack or fleeing, and third, occurrence in similar situations. From this evidence, Tinbergen inferred that variations in the displays could be explained in terms of fluctuations in the relative strengths of the two tendencies.

The conflict hypothesis has been used in some of the descriptive studies of human expressions: for example, Brannigan and Humphries (1972) remarked that the oblong mouth shape (Figure 2.3a) is shown by nursery school children who are motivated both to flee and to attack. A more systematic use was that of van Hooff (1972), who applied the conflict explanation to human laughing and smiling. As indicated earlier, there is evidence that these are associated with play and affiliation respectively. van Hooff used one of Tinbergen's three sources of evidence, similarity of form, to suggest that different degrees of relative activation of two systems, one controlling play and the other affiliation, produce a variety of forms intermediate between pure laughing and smiling (Figure 9.8).

In reviewing the evidence for the conflict hypothesis, Baerends (1975) cautioned against assuming that it has general applicability. For example, it would not necessarily apply where emancipation from the original source of motivational control has occurred. The evidence for the hypothesis found in earlier studies was based on inferences derived from uncontrolled observations. Although the disadvantages of this approach are minimized by using converging evidence (Tinbergen, 1959), alternative hypotheses may account for at least some observations. A threat display which commonly occurs in situations where there appears to be an attack–escape conflict might result from a general approach–avoidance conflict, or from anything that prevents overt attack when the motivational system for aggression is activated.

In order to test such alternative hypotheses, experimental manipulations are required. Blurton Jones (1968) used hand-reared great tits which would predictably attack a hand-held stimulus and flee from a light. After observing the activities associated with these two stimuli, he created conflicts, for example, by presenting the two simultaneously. In this case, the threat displays head up, head down, horizontal and wings out (Figure 9.9) were shown. The last three of these also occurred when the attack-inducing stimulus was presented out of the bird's reach, leading Blurton Jones to conclude that anything that prevented attack when the bird was so motivated, whether this was fear or an external barrier, would evoke certain threat displays. He also found other types of behaviour that were attributable to different types of motivational conflict: for example, crest-raising was associated with a conflict between approach (whether to attack or to feed) and escape.

As indicated in the previous section, the origins of many displays can be explained in terms of non-social behaviour such as protective responses, which have become ritualized during the course of evolution to convey information. Andrew (1956, 1963a, 1972) extended this emphasis on specific responses – rather than motivational systems – to the causation of displays. He argued that the causal factors for the original non-social response will be shared by the existing social situation, and that many aspects of displays can be understood in terms of these more specific reactions, leaving it unnecessary to invoke higher-level variables such as aggression and fear.

Andrew (1972) examined the immediate causal factors involved in activities commonly used in displays. These were grouped into a number of categories, such as protective responses, locomotion and alert responses. It is apparent that this level of analysis can readily account for the origins of display components, as indicated in the previous section: for example, similarities between many hostile and friendly displays can be accounted for in terms of their both involving components of protective responses. Andrew argued that it is simpler to explain the present causation of such display components in terms of social situations also evoking protective responses. However, as was acknowledged, it is not clear to what extent the present display components maintain the same causation as in the original case. Again, the issue of emancipation of displays is raised, in this case at the lower level of specific display components.

As Blurton Jones (1972d) commented, one advantage of Andrew's approach is that it directs the observer to begin with a more detailed level of analysis (Chapter 2). A higher-level analysis can subsequently be applied to

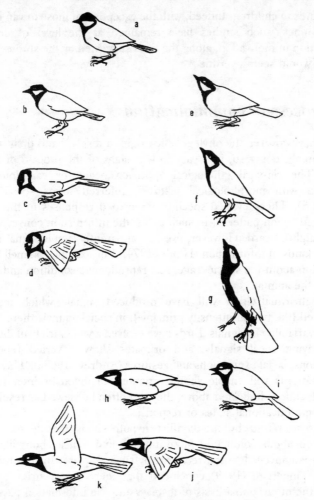

Figure 9.9 Threat displays of the great tit (a) identified by Blurton Jones (1968, Figure 1), showing: (b–d) head down; (e–g) head-up; (h–k) horizontal. These show variations in erectness of the body. Wings out varies down the page.

the data using techniques such as factor analysis (Chapter 2). In his study of great tits, Blurton Jones (1968) found that one activity – turning – was evoked by any conflict to approach and to avoid, whatever the motivation: in this case, an explanation in terms of conflicts between specific responses would appear better suited to the evidence. As Hinde (1972, 1974) remarked, the level of explanation that is best suited to explaining a specific instance remains an empirical issue.

These alternatives to the conflicting motivation hypothesis of display causation have had little impact on ethological studies of facial expressions and gestures in children. Indeed, with the exception of those of van Hooff and Blurton Jones, such studies have remained at the level of description. Investigation of motivation, along the lines suggested by the studies of animal displays, would seem overdue.

The process of communication

So far I have covered the phylogenetic origin of displays and their underlying motivation. In doing so, it is easy to lose sight of the process of communication. The classical ethological approach began by examining signals associated with morphological features, referred to as social releasers (Chapter 5). These evoked specific stereotyped responses in the recipient, called fixed action patterns. In such cases, the information conveyed appears to be straightforward. However, even an apparently simple signal may carry different kinds of information (Hinde, 1974). For example, a smell may carry information about the species, age, sex, reproductive condition and territorial status of the animal.

Although ritualization will have produced signals which tend to be stereotyped (the typical intensity principle), in social animals there is also the need for variability in signals. Birds have evolved a wide variety of displays and accompanying vocal signals, and primates show a varied repertoire of vocalizations, facial expressions and gestures (Andrew, 1963a). These variable display patterns will enable subtle variations in mood or intentions to be conveyed, and, as indicated above, they can often be viewed as resulting from conflicting motivational states or responses.

One issue raised by the conflict hypothesis is the degree to which information about conflicting motivations – and hence about likely future actions – is conveyed to the recipient by such displays. In his study of gull displays, Tinbergen (1959) concluded that there was a striking similarity between the motivational basis of displays and the information passed to the recipients.

One way of assessing the meaning of a display is to determine the likelihood that it will be followed by specific behaviour in the displayer. For example, the likelihood of attack following a particular threat display is information which would be available to the opponent. Stokes (1962) used this method to assess the probability that different threat displays shown by blue tits at a winter feeding station would be followed by attack, staying or escaping. He found that individual threat components only provide a poor prediction of future behaviour, with the exception of one display (raising the crest) which predicted fleeing on 90 per cent of occasions. Partly, this poor predictability reflected the level of analysis: often the meaning of a specific component depended on the others that occurred with it. Combinations of components gave better predictions of subsequent behaviour than individual ones: the highest values were 48 per cent for attack, 94 per cent for escape and 79 per cent for staying. It should be noted that these figures have to be compared with the probability of showing that response in the absence of the threat posture (0, 35 and 66 per cent respectively: i.e. staying was highly likely anyway, but the other two were substantially increased by the displays).

As Hinde (1974) pointed out, there is bound to be some uncertainty in what follows a display, since this will depend on the behaviour of the other animal: there would be little point in signalling that attack was going to follow in 100 per cent of cases irrespective of what the opponent does. An effective threat signal should indicate a conditional message: attack is highly likely if the opponent does not withdraw. This highlights the weakness of examining only intra-individual sequences, which has arisen because classical ethology tended to concentrate on the signaller, rather than the interaction between signaller and respondent (Hinde, 1974). It is therefore important to examine the behaviour shown by the respondent to a particular display.

Stokes (1962) also examined the subsequent behaviour of the opponent in his study of blue tit threat displays. Various postures, which were associated with aggressive behaviour in the signaller, such as raising the wings and facing the opponent, reduced the likelihood of the opponent attacking. Others, such as raising the crest, which were not associated with attacking, did not affect the opponent's likelihood of attacking, but did increase the likelihood that it would stay (with the proviso that this was high anyway). Another display, the open beak, reduced both the likelihood of attack and fleeing by the opponent.

One widespread type of animal signal is that which indicates submission or appeasement in the face of an attack or potential attack. As indicated in the next section, it is selectively advantageous for such signals to be clear and distinct. The postures involved tend to be the opposite of those used for aggressive threat (Darwin, 1872; Eibl-Eibesfeldt, 1970; Hinde, 1974), including a hunched body posture which decreases apparent body size. The specific suggestion that adopting such a posture inhibits attack by another individual (Eibl-Eibesfeldt, 1970, from Darwin, 1872) was investigated in children by Ginsburg *et al.* (1977). They found that behaviour such as bowing and shoe-tying was common immediately prior to the cessation of aggressive behaviour among 8–12-year-old boys. A follow-up study (Ginsburg, 1980) showed that most instances of a third party coming to the aid of a child who was being attacked were preceded by the attacker failing to respond to a decrease in stature by the child under attack.

In pre-school children, Strayer and Strayer (1976) identified a wider group of 'appeasement' behaviour, including flinch, cringe, withdraw, and cover with their hands, which preceded the end of a conflict. Sackin and Thelin (1984) distinguished between these, which were followed by separation of the two children, and conciliatory behaviour, such as offering a toy, sharing, grooming or apologizing, which were followed by continued but peaceful associations between the two children.

A broadly comparable method was used by Camras (1977) to study whether children's facial expressions when engaged in conflicts over objects predicted the behaviour of an opponent. She observed the facial expressions accompanying the possession of objects which could only be held by one child at a time, in children aged 5–6½ years. Using the categories devised by Blurton Jones (1971), she classified these expressions into aggressive and non-aggressive ones. The former were found to be associated with persistent attempts by the owner to keep the object. Although recipients of these expressions were hesitant in making an attempt to take the object from the possessor, such hesitancy also occurred following non-aggressive expressions. Camras noted that apparently aggressive expressions did not necessarily predict the probability of attack, and regarded this finding as incompatible with early ethological views (e.g. Tinbergen, 1953). However, as indicated above, the likelihood that a display will be followed by attack or fleeing cannot be assessed from its underlying motivation: it is also dependent on the behaviour of the recipient.

The recipient's response to a display is also variable. This is because it depends not only on the type of display but also the context in which it is given. W. J. Smith (1965) distinguished between 'message' and 'meaning' in animal communication: message refers to information about the communicator which is common to all situations in which the signal is given, whereas the meaning to the recipient also depends on other sources of information such as the context and the recipient itself. In the examples discussed so far, message would correspond more closely to the motivational state of the signaller, and meaning to how this is interpreted by the recipient.

Smith (1965) offered an example from his own study of the Eastern kingbird. One type of call occurs when approach or locomotion is prevented, and is given whether this involves approaching a mate, a rival or a perch. The recipient has to assess its meaning in terms of the context in which it is given. Smith also showed that many of the gull displays studied by Tinbergen (1959) and Moynihan (1958, 1962) also occurred in various contexts. For example, Tinbergen (1959) identified hostile interactions, and nest-site selection, nest relief and sexual interactions as circumstances in which the 'choking' display occurs. The message would be that there is a motivational conflict between approach (for different reasons, often involving aggressive motivation) and escape. The meaning would be variable, depending on the context. This analysis – in terms of specific responses conveying different meanings in different motivational contexts – converges with Andrew's emphasis on understanding display components at the level of the individual response (see above).

Context is even more important when considering human non-verbal communication (Hinde, 1974). Camras (1980) applied Smith's distinction to her earlier study of aggressive expressions (see above): she concluded that although some expressions do have intimidating effects, context is taken into account by another child interpreting the expression. From this perspective, the use of photographs of expressive movements to elicit ratings of their meanings involves taking the expressions out of context, and hence removes an important contribution to their meanings. The usefulness of this approach would be restricted to instances where the expression closely corresponds to the 'releaser' of classical ethology, for example, in the case of the baby features discussed in Chapter 5.

Part of the context of a message is the interaction sequence in which it is embedded. This sequence may have a structure which influences how a particular message is viewed at a particular time. For example, the sequence of displays between two animals engaged in an aggressive encounter often involves an escalation of aggressive activities (Archer and Huntingford, in press). Fights tend to begin with the opponents at a distance from one another exchanging low-level displays, which do not entail much risk of damage or energy expenditure. If these do not result in one contestant withdrawing, they become progressively replaced by higher-level displays, which are both more risky and more energy-consuming. Studies of fish show that one aspect of such exchanges is that the behaviour of the winner and the loser are similar until near the end of the encounter (e.g. Simpson, 1968; Dow *et al.*, 1976; Jakobsson *et al.*, 1979). These findings can be understood in terms of the animals matching their level of escalation to that of the opponent (Simpson, 1968; Archer, 1988a). However, at the giving-up point, the eventual loser rapidly reverts to flight or submissive behaviour.

In discussing the results of his study of Siamese fighting fish displays, Simpson (1968) raised the question of whether such an exchange can be viewed in terms of the influence of a series of individual moves or whether it is the cumulative effect of all preceding moves. He inferred that the pattern of escalation could best be understood in terms of the fish drawing on its previous experience of the partner's displays, and using this to evaluate the current display level.

In Chapter 2, I described some of the methods used by ethologists to analyse sequences of behaviour within an individual. A major problem in applying methods involving first-order Markov chain analysis to interactions between individuals is that they only take account of the influence of preceding actions. Analysis of sequences where earlier activities are likely to have had an influence on current behaviour requires a different approach. As mentioned briefly in that chapter, S. A. Altmann (1965) applied an information theory method to analysing sequences of behaviour in rhesus monkeys from a two-year field study. He categorized the animals' social behaviour, and then compared the data against a number of mathematical models representing null hypotheses.

First, it was established that a small number of behavioural categories occurred much more frequently than the majority of the 120 categories eventually used. Second, it was established that much of the behaviour recorded was dependent on the immediately preceding event. The extent to which behaviour was dependent on the previous two events, then the previous three, and so on, was calculated. As longer sequences of preceding events were used, the current behaviour was predicted to a greater extent. In information theory terms, uncertainty decreased. Although this method is potentially very useful for analysing the influence of preceding sequences on current behaviour (cf. Simpson, 1968), there are a number of problems with its application in Altmann's study (Hinde, 1974). Foremost among these is the mixture of intra-individual and inter-individual sequences of behaviour (S. A. Altmann, 1965, p. 96). The study is therefore partly a motivational analysis and partly a study of interaction sequences.

The function of displays

Classical ethologists were not concerned with making direct inferences from the theory of natural selection about the selective advantage of particular displays. The main emphasis was placed on how displays had changed through the course of evolution, and their causation. In some cases, researchers interested in the process of communication assumed that this involved mutual benefit for the performer and recipient alike. But generally, there was little or no direct interest in the selective advantage of communication.

Following the advent of the functional approach (Chapter 6), Dawkins and Krebs (1978) argued that the earlier ethological analyses of displays could be characterized as follows: because researchers had analysed displays in terms of conflicting motivational tendencies, it was implied that the recipient would receive an accurate view of the performer's internal state. This 'ethological view' of the function of displays was then contrasted with predictions derived more directly from the theory of natural selection. When viewed from this perspective, behaviour is seen as having evolved to enhance the individual's fitness; any benefits to others would have to arise through their being relatives (inclusive fitness) or through mutual benefit. Dawkins and Krebs argued that it follows that the general function of communication is to manipulate the reactor rather than to transfer accurate information about the performer's internal state.

Krebs and Dawkins (1984) argued that manipulation of another animal will be most effective if it exploits any regular behavioural dispositions. As they put it, effective manipulation of a recipient will involve 'mind-reading'. They characterized animal communication as involving a process analogous to advertising rather than the exchange of accurate information. For example, larger-sized animals are generally able to beat smaller ones in fights, and the smaller of two opponents will often withdraw without fighting (Archer, 1988a). Displays which involve artificially enlarging the body exploit this tendency to withdraw from a larger opponent. Such signals will lead to the co-evolution of strategies to counter their effectiveness, for example, to ignore the bluff and evaluate real size.

This view predicts that animal signals will involve manipulation whenever there is a conflict of interests between categories of individuals. The communicators need to be viewed in terms of their 'roles', male and female, parent and offspring, competitors over a resource, to understand the degree to which their interests conflict (Krebs and Dawkins, 1984).

Caryl (1979, 1981) and Maynard Smith (1982) extended these general arguments about the function of animal signals by drawing inferences from one specific functional model. This model was part of the application of the game theory approach to the evolution of animal fighting (Maynard Smith, 1982; Archer, 1988a; Archer and Huntingford, in press). As indicated in Chapter 7, this involves examining the consequences of different strategies by depicting them in a pay-off matrix involving different costs and benefits. Its usefulness lies in being able to calculate the relative fitness of the different strategies (and hence their frequencies in future generations) when these depend on the nature and frequencies of other strategies available in the population. It is possible to calculate an evolutionarily stable strategy (ESS), one that cannot be replaced by an alternative given the current conditions of the population (Maynard Smith, 1982).

The 'War of Attrition' model (Maynard Smith, 1974; Norman *et al.*, 1977; Bishop and Cannings, 1978) involves two animals displaying to one another, but not attacking. The one that persists longer wins the encounter. The important conclusion derived from this model was that selection would oppose any tendency for the display to reveal either the time until giving up (Maynard Smith, 1974) or the cost to be incurred before doing so (Norman *et al.*, 1977; Caryl, 1979). A more general conclusion was also drawn: this was that it would not be selectively advantageous for animals to communicate their intentions about the point at which they would give up. Caryl (1979, 1981) and Maynard Smith (1982) argued that this was at variance with the ethological view of the function of displays, which had been portrayed by Dawkins and Krebs (1978) as involving accurate exchange of information about motivational state. Caryl (1981) reassessed earlier studies of threat displays, including that of Stokes (see above), to show that attack was not readily predicted from the type of display shown (although escape was fairly predictable). Maynard Smith (1982) also cited several studies of fish aggressive encounters, including that of Simpson (1968), to show that the eventual winner and loser could not be predicted until near the end of the exchange.

A number of criticisms have been made of these analyses. The first is that their characterization of the ethological view as implying accurate exchange of information is incorrect or at least oversimplified (Hinde, 1981). In earlier sections, we saw that the conflicting motivation hypothesis did not always explain the causation of displays. Emancipation from the original motivational control often occurred, and displays could occur at a typical intensity (which would fit the functional view of concealing precise motivational state: Hinde, 1981). As indicated at the beginning of this section, the ethological view is best characterized as being concerned with other issues rather than having a rival viewpoint on the function of displays.

Hinde (1981) also criticized the inference that lack of predictability is necessarily incompatible with a causal analysis involving conflicting motivations. As indicated in the previous section, the message of a display is not the same as its underlying motivation. The message is conditional. For example, if a highly aggressive animal gives a threat display, the message is not 'I will attack' but 'I will attack if you stay'. Accuracy in predicting the displayer's subsequent behaviour cannot be used to indicate whether the display contains accurate information since in many circumstances a highly aggressive display will not lead to subsequent attack because it has been effective in making the opponent flee.

A third criticism concerns the relevance of the War of Attrition model. As M. S. Dawkins (1986) pointed out, the original version of this model applies to two equally matched animals which simply display to one another, neither one escalating the display to a fight. Although a later version (Bishop and Cannings, 1978; Caryl, 1981) extended this slightly to include some circumstances in which injury occurs, it still remains very restricted. In practice, most conflicts are settled by prior or sequential assessment of fighting ability and resource value (Archer and Huntingford, in press), not by seeking to spend longer in an innocuous display.

Such criticisms have led Hinde (1981) to argue that the ethological and functional views of animal communication are not as incompatible as was claimed. In seeking to integrate the two viewpoints, Hinde (1985b) argued that animal and human signals range on a continuum between expression and negotiation, the former being more compatible with the motivational analyses of classical ethology and the latter with the implications of the functional approach. Camras (1984) also suggested that children's communication patterns can be understood as negotiations, in explaining the finding that dominant children obtained a valued resource without using aggression or threats. Emphasis on negotiations leads us to consider cognitive factors in non-verbal communication (Hinde, 1985b), a subject which will be dealt with in the next chapter.

The main value of the functional approach has been to identify the types of signal which are favoured by selection. It has raised the important question of under what circumstances do animal signals provide accurate information to a recipient. Game theory analyses led to a distinction being drawn between displays indicating behavioural dispositions (such as the threat displays discussed in this chapter) and signals which indicate the animal's quality, for example, its fighting ability. The first type is transient features, and hence deceptive signalling would incur little cost. The second type involves relatively permanent features, such as size, possession of weapons or ability to vocalize loudly and at a certain pitch. These are relatively permanent features, which would be difficult to mimic. It was argued that such signals would generally be accurate or 'honest' (e.g. Maynard Smith, 1982; Clutton-Brock and Albon, 1979).

In practice, the distinction between the two may not be straightforward. An animal's assessment of its chances of winning a fight is likely to influence its motivational balance (Archer, 1988a). In addition, Dawkins and Guilford (1991) have argued that the emphasis on 'honesty' in signals of an animal's quality has neglected the high costs of engaging in such signals for the recipient and sender alike: in red deer, for example, there are energy-consuming roaring contests which gradually become escalated. Dawkins and Guilford argued that where the costs to both animals are very high, it will pay them to settle for less costly – but less reliable – signals of quality. These will take the form of conventional signals, ones whose meaning is derived from a generalized association and not from the process of individual assessment.

Most of the discussion in this section has concerned threat displays, since the game theory approach has been applied mainly to the evolution of fighting strategies (Archer, 1988a), and also because these displays were the subject of the earlier ethological investigations. Animal signals are of course emitted in a much wider range of circumstances. Following the functional analyses, Cheney and Seyfarth (1991) argued that animals will seldom communicate accurately about their intentions unless in a co-operative environment. Much interest has been focused on the extent to which social animals show flexible forms of deception, and the criteria by which one might infer intent to deceive. This issue is discussed in the next chapter.

The functional issues outlined in this section have hardly touched studies of non-verbal communication in children, which have mainly been influenced by the older ethological tradition. As indicated in Chapter 6, the functional approach can enrich the more proximate or immediate level of analysis by providing an explanation of why certain patterns of behaviour occur, in terms of fitness advantages conferred during their evolution. As is apparent from this section, this may be a complex matter.

Conclusions

Only a few existing studies of non-verbal communication and emotional expressions in children have been influenced by ethological research on animal displays. In those that have, the concepts used have mainly been derived from classical ethology. There is little recognition of the complexities and subtleties shown in animal communication. There is also no awareness of the possible implications of the game theory analysis of animal conflicts for the information likely to be communicated in children's threat displays.

These are two ways in which ethology might enhance studies of children's emotional expressions. Another lies in supplying the possible phylogenetic origins of the common facial expressions, through comparative studies such as those of Andrew (1963a, b) and van Hooff (1967, 1972). As indicated earlier, these can be linked with the detailed descriptive studies carried out by child ethologists such as Blurton Jones (1967, 1971) and Brannigan and Humphries (1972).

The study of facial expressions is, however, one area where a detailed descriptive base has been generated from within psychology. The Facial Action Coding System of Ekman and Friesen (1978) and the similar system derived by Izard (1979) both analyse facial expressions at a very fine-grained level (Chapter 2). The research using these methods has concentrated on issues such as the universality of facial expressions and their meaning, and the relation between expression and the experience of emotion (Izard, 1990). The potential contribution of ethological research from the perspective of evolved displays is to raise new questions and to provide a different perspective to psychological research.

Chapter 10

Cognitive ethology: the mental experiences of animals

Introduction

We all take for granted the mental continuity between adults and children. Each one of us was once a child, and we have, to varying degrees, access to our childhood memories. It is therefore relatively straightforward to assume gradual development from an unaware pre-conscious state through intermediate forms to the type of awareness experienced in adulthood. There may be differences of opinion about the precise ages at which different types of awareness begin. But we can agree that at some stage general feelings of comfort, discomfort and pain begin to be experienced, at another, awareness of self emerges, and that thinking progresses from simpler to more complex levels of understanding.

In animals, we find forms of behaviour similar to those that indicate mental experiences in children. These include the emotional expressions discussed in the previous chapter, self-directed responses to their mirror-image, and behaviour that suggests the ability to view others as having intentions. In animals, there is no developmental continuity with adult humans and no possibility of retrospective introspection. Nevertheless, the concept of evolutionary continuity can be used to consider their mental experiences. Darwin himself began the comparison of mental processes in humans and animals. After many decades of avoiding inferences about animals' mental experiences, this approach has received a new lease of life during the last ten to twenty years, in the form of 'cognitive ethology'.

Cognitive ethology: historical background

In *The Descent of Man*, Darwin (1871) wrote: 'The difference in mind between man and higher animals, great as it is, certainly is one of degree and not kind.'

The conclusion that there is continuity between the minds of non-human and human primates followed from an acceptance of physical continuity. Darwin (1877) observed the reactions of great apes to their mirror-images, to investigate not only their facial expressions (Chapter 9), but also their awareness of self.

In the years following the publication of *The Descent of Man*, a number of exaggerated claims were made for the mental capacities of animals. For example, Lewis Henry Morgan viewed the dams built by beavers as evidence of conscious planning and self-awareness. Based on a variety of anecdotes from those in contact with animals, George Romanes published, in 1882, a grand theory of mental evolution: sexual passion first arose in molluscs, jealousy in fish and artistic feelings in birds. Dogs possessed a sense of humour (Sparks, 1982).

Against this background, it is understandable that the behaviourists rejected mental explanations and adopted Lloyd Morgan's canon: 'In no case may we interpret an action as the outcome of the exercise of a higher psychical faculty, if it can be interpreted as the outcome of the exercise of one which stands lower on the psychological scale' (Lloyd Morgan, 1894, p. 53). This approach was paralleled in zoological studies of animal behaviour by the rejection of concepts such as free will and mind, notably by Loeb, who saw animals as mindless mechanisms pushed and pulled by environmental influences (Fraenkel and Gunn, 1940).

Within the tradition that gave rise to ethology, there were still those who were interested in studying the mental processes of animals, albeit in a cautious way. The famous essay by Jakob von Uexküll (1934) concerned the *Umwelt*, or self-world of animals, and included inferences about their subjective experience of time, movement and space. However, von Uexküll warned against assuming that animals acted on the basis of the sorts of goal understood by humans as plans for action.

Nevertheless, most of the researchers in the classical ethological tradition concentrated exclusively on the study of behaviour, and constructed motivational models of the mechanisms controlling behaviour (Chapter 5). This approach paid little attention to the structure of mental processes underlying behaviour, which was the concern of cognitive models in psychology, or to the question of whether animals share the forms of awareness and consciousness experienced by humans. Both issues have aroused considerable interest over the last twenty years, the impetus arising from a variety of sources, including a sub-branch of ethology referred to as cognitive ethology. This research links up with a more cognitive emphasis in contemporary animal learning studies, with studies of language capabilities in apes, and with renewed interest in the understanding of mental processes in young children.

Intelligence and cognition: complexity or consciousness?

The most influential restatement of the case for considering mental processes in animals was Griffin's (1976), although the contributions of Crook (1980), Gardner and Gardner (1975), Humphrey (1976) and Jolly (1972) were also important for the emergence of cognitive ethology. Griffin's interest grew from research on the orientation and navigation of bats and birds (Griffin, 1976, 1981). He claimed that scientists working in these fields had minimized the complexity of the mental processes involved, as a result of the zoological tradition of emphasizing mechanical reactions to stimuli (see above). Research carried out in the 1950s and 1960s revealed the following about orientation and navigation. Birds are able to make approximate corrections for the movements of the sun and the stars across the sky. Bats are able to hunt insects by echo-location, which is also found in whales, dolphins and porpoises, where it is used for communication as well as navigation. Griffin argued that in order to mediate between incoming signals and such complex patterns of behaviour, there must be elaborate representations in the central nervous system. He inferred from this that conscious thinking might be present in these animals. He argued that conscious thinking is an efficient way to use the CNS for solving complex and challenging problems, and even suggested that this may be particularly important in animals with relatively simple nervous systems whose patterns of communication are complex, such as the honeybee.

These inferences have been strongly disputed by others. Gould and Gould (1986) have argued that complexity in a communication system, such as that of the honeybee, does not imply a certain type of mechanism. Because an animal has solved a complex problem, it does not follow that it has awareness or understanding of the nature of the problem. McFarland (1989) argued that Griffin had confused intelligence, which describes adaptive processes involving a sophisticated and complex rule-guided system, with the means through which intelligent behaviour is achieved: he had confused the performance of the system with the mechanism for achieving this performance. A system may be sophisticated and complex, yet require no conscious thought. Indeed, there are human abilities which are of this sort: the way in which spatial orientation and visual perception are controlled involves complex processes, but they are not accessible to conscious awareness.

Nevertheless, the term 'cognitive' has often been used to denote the existence of complex rules and constraints (implying 'knowledge'), for example, when referring to the generation of characteristic biological forms (Goodwin, 1978). This would seem to be a misuse of the term. As Gould and Gould (1986) pointed out, it confuses the 'intelligence' of evolution (the sense in which McFarland uses the term) with conscious 'intelligence'.

Confusion between a complex performance and the means by which it is achieved is reminiscent of the controversy surrounding the Turing test in artificial intelligence. Here it was argued that if a programme results in a performance indistinguishable from that of a person, the programme constitutes a mental process. Critics (e.g. Searle, 1980) have pointed out that simulation is not the same as duplication, i.e. performance criteria should not be confused with the means by which the performance is achieved. The same point applies to Griffin's inferences from the complexity of animal behaviour.

Folk psychology and cognitive psychology

Griffin's inference of mental processes in animals is also derived from commonsense attributions about mental states in humans. If we are prepared to attribute a state such as conscious thought, or belief or intention in other humans on the basis of their behaviour, we should make the same attribution when similar behaviour occurs in an animal. This way of explaining behaviour is referred to as 'folk psychology', and it has been the subject of considerable critical scrutiny.

In humans, attributions are known to be influenced by social beliefs and biases. As McFarland (1989) remarked, this applies not only to attributions made about others but also to those made about one's own intentions. Michel (1991) has questioned the legitimacy of *explaining* behaviour, whether human or animal, through attributions of intention, pointing out that these are very different from the logical inferences which underlie scientific explanations. He argued that the 'cognitive illusions' inherent in everyday reasoning will only impede our understanding of mental processes if applied to animals. It is clear that this *can* happen, as shown by the nineteenth-century accounts of the animal mind, and the attributions made about the behaviour of pets by their owners. The important point is whether cognitive ethologists have been led astray. Critics such as Gould and Gould (1986) and McFarland (1989) would argue that they have. Others, such as Premack and Woodruff (1978), Dennett (1983) and Whiten and Byrne (1988), have defended the cautious use of folk psychology, and have sought to build a systematic explanatory framework on it. Their work is considered in later sections.

A further philosophical problem raised by folk psychology is that the terminology for understanding human mental states is rooted in a network of meanings derived from human contexts and language. Beer (1991) and others (e.g. Kummer et al., 1990) have argued that these meanings become lost when the terms are applied to animals. This may apply more to certain mental terms than to others. It is, for example, possible to operationalize thinking with reference to the empirical methodology derived from the Piagetian framework, or from human cognitive psychology (cf. Yoerg and Kamil, 1991). Inferences about intentions in animals are more likely to remain as inferences, although as indicated above there have been suggestions for using folk psychology in a more rigorous way to study intentions.

Others have criticized Griffin's cognitive ethology for its emphasis on conscious awareness. Yoerg and Kamil (1991) remind us that cognition is not the same as consciousness, and that much human cognitive processing occurs unconsciously. Human cognitive psychology is based on an information-processing analogy, which led to experimental investigations of specific hypotheses about the nature of representations and the processing of incoming information. Yoerg and Kamil argued that Griffin's cognitive psychology lacks empirical rigour and theoretical cohesion precisely because it has neglected cognition, in the sense used by psychologists, in favour of conscious experiences, which present the problems of inference outlined above. They advocated an ethological study of animal cognition which is more integrated with cognitive sciences such as artificial intelligence, animal learning and cognitive psychology. Ethologists' specific contributions would be to provide the evolutionary and naturalistic perspective absent elsewhere.

Several points can be made in response to this particular criticism. First, the evolution of consciousness is a topic of major biological significance, about which systematic inferences can be made from studies of complex behaviour. Second, because human cognition does not necessarily involve conscious thought, this does not detract from the *capability* of conscious thought in humans. It is the capacity for consciousness that is particularly interesting from an evolutionary viewpoint. Third, cognitive ethology is now broader than the emphasis on consciousness apparent in Griffin's work. Several researchers have sought to integrate cognitive ethology with psychological studies of animal and human cognition. For example, Pepperberg (1990, 1991) has drawn on both animal learning and an ethological approach to teach a parrot limited aspects of human language, and Jolly (1972) began the integration of animal cognition into the Piagetian perspective, which has been continued since by Etienne (1984) and others.

Animal communication and thought

Griffin (1976) followed Darwin in viewing animal communication as the key to studying animal awareness. As indicated in Chapter 9, communication can provide information about the species, age, sex and behavioural state of an animal. An earlier view of animal signals was that they are only tied to the existing situation and are closely linked with emotional state. Griffin argued that there are many cases where communication is about events which are not in the present: this property is called 'displacement'. Signals refer to or convey information about objects or events removed in time or space.

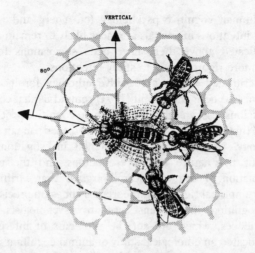

Figure 10.1 Diagram from Gould and Gould (1986, Figure 1), showing aspects of the zig-zag dance of the honeybee. Location of the food source is communicated by the figure 8-shaped zig-zag dance performed by a forager on the vertical sheets of comb. During the straight (middle) portion, the body is vibrated from side to side. The angle of the straight run relative to vertical shows the angle of the food source relative to the sun: in this case, the food is 80 degrees to the left of the sun. The number of vibrations in the straight part shows the distance from the food.

Griffin suggested that communication of this sort would be most highly developed among members of specialized and integrated animal societies, such as the social insects. The workers (non-reproductive females) of the honeybee give a figure eight-shaped dance when foraging. This communicates information about the distance, direction and quality of food or potential hive sites (von Frisch, 1967). Direction is encoded by movements on a vertical piece of comb in the hive. The degrees to the left and right of the vertical reveal the outside angle between the food source and the sun (Figure 10.1, from Gould and Gould, 1986). Distance is encoded by the number of waggles of the body in the straight portion of the dance.

Griffin (1976) argued that this type of communication shows displacement, and that its properties and complexity have been underestimated because it occurs in an insect with a relatively simple nervous system. Had it been found in a mammal, Griffin argued, it would be attributed to a more advanced mental state. This argument again confuses complexity with the means by which it is achieved. As Gould and Gould (1986) remarked: 'Even though this abstract, symbolic communication system is second only in complexity and information capacity to human speech, it is wholly innate.' In other words, the bee is able to understand the communication without previous experience.

Rather than using abstract properties of the communication system, such as displacement, as indications of the animals' mental state, the emphasis in cognitive ethology has shifted to inferring intentional states by devising critical tests using communication signals, and often involving deception. This approach, which converges with developmental psychologists' current interest in young children's understanding of others' minds, is discussed later in the chapter.

Studies of the language capabilities of apes have also contributed to the renewed interest in the cognitive structures of animals. Communication – in this case an artificially taught system – can be used as a means of making inferences about the capacity for logical thought. Although this aim has been overshadowed by the debate over whether animals can truly be said to learn human language, it has emerged as an important issue since Premack (1983) sought to identify the specific abilities which are enhanced by language-training in chimpanzees. He concluded, necessarily from a very small sample, that a range of abilities that require an 'abstract code' are found in the language-trained animals but not in those that were untrained. Specific abilities consisted of same or different judgements, analogies, matching like proportions of physically unlike exemplars, and completing incomplete representations of actions.

A more detailed consideration of the implications of ape language studies for investigating the cognitive abilities of animals is beyond the scope of the present book. Instead, I shall describe the research of Pepperberg (1990, 1991), who investigated the cognitive capacities of an African Grey parrot through language training. Her research adopted more of an ethological approach than was the case in the ape language studies. Pepperberg's training method was based on the bird's natural method of communication, involving dueting and turn-taking. Her choice of species reflected a desire to get away from human-centred comparisons with our nearest living animal relatives.

Pepperberg's research involves a single parrot, called Alex. Previous attempts to teach a parrot the meaning of words by conventional operant techniques had been unsuccessful, apparently supporting the popular belief that parrots could only imitate sounds. Pepperberg's training method took account of the social context in which the bird would learn vocalizations, using a 'model/rival' method. This involved two humans showing the bird the types of interactions which were desired: thus the one who is taking the part intended for the bird is both a model (in the sense used in imitation research) and also a rival for the attention of the human who is asking the questions. The protocol also involved reversing the trainer-model roles and involving the parrot in the interactions. The method used intrinsic reinforcers, rather than arbitrary ones unrelated to the object of the interaction. Thus when conversing about wooden lollipop ('popsicle') sticks, Alex would be reinforced by being given the sticks. In order to obtain food, such as a banana, Alex would have to request it, by saying: 'I want banana.'

Over a period of years, Alex has achieved a vocabulary of over 30 objects, 7 colours, 5 shapes, 5 numbers (2–6), and functional phrases such as 'I want' and 'come here'. He also learnt phrases such as 'What's this?' and 'What colour?' This represents his basic vocabulary. Of more interest in terms of his cognitive ability is the evidence of category formation. Alex was able to distinguish four categories: colour, shape, material and quantity. He could recognize these as different attributes of the same object. He was able to answer 'What colour?' and 'What shape?' for objects in which both shape and colour differed. Pepperberg commented that this involved reclassification of objects: he was required to use colour at one time and shape at another. This ability is found in 2–3-year-old children (e.g. Rice, 1980).

The ability to understand more abstract concepts, such as same and different, is found in 3-year-old children (e.g. Brown and Scott, 1972). According to previous research, it is restricted to primates, although in monkeys considerable training is necessary (e.g. Wright *et al.*, 1990). Premack (1983) argued that it is most readily shown in apes who have undergone language training because of the symbolic representation involved in testing the concepts. Pepperberg designed a task which was equivalent to those used by Premack for chimpanzees. Alex was given two objects differing in three categories, and was asked a series of questions about what was the same or different about them. The results indicated that Alex could successfully answer these questions for both familiar objects which had not been used in training and for novel objects.

Perhaps this demonstration provides further evidence that it is the availability of an abstract code, as Premack called it, rather than the general level of ability in the species, that is important for these sorts of task. One of the commentaries on Premack's (1983) article (Bickerton, 1983) pointed out that there is considerable evidence that humans provided with explicit verbal labels for objects perform considerably better on certain tasks than those without the verbal labels. On the other hand, Pepperberg (1990) argued that language merely enabled the animal to perform a task which made its abilities more accessible to the experimenter. She presented evidence from studies of both children and animals that while some forms of learning may be helped by language, tasks such as same/difference, object permanence and Piagetian sorting can all be completed successfully without language.

Pepperberg (1990) also used the abstract same/difference task to determine whether Alex could distinguish the *absence* of same or different, which represents a further level of abstraction. He was able to do this. Finally, Alex showed some degree of numerical competence, responding to different collections of familiar objects in familiar and unfamiliar patterns, to novel objects in familiar patterns, and to heterogeneous collections of objects.

Pepperberg's research indicates a range of abilities which match those of a child during the earlier part of Piaget's pre-operational period. However, none of the tests considered so far is based on the Piagetian tradition. In the next section, I examine studies applying Piagetian tests to other species.

Thinking: the comparative study of cognitive structures

Piaget's research provides an empirical framework for describing different levels of thinking based on careful observations and inferences from behaviour in test situations designed to answer particular questions about the development of thought. Inferring the existence and nature of thought in non-human animals presents similar problems to those encountered in studying very young children.

Jolly (1972) was the first ethologist to realize the usefulness of Piaget's detailed description of the ontogeny of cognitive structures for comparing humans with other species. As she pointed out, the helplessness of the human infant ensures a longer period before active manipulation of objects can occur than is the case in the development of other primates. For example, rhesus monkeys begin manipulating objects at about 16 days of age, which represents the end of stage 2 of the sensorimotor period in the human infant. In stage 3, external objects have little identity except as part of the current action: similar reactions have been found in young infant lemurs and rhesus monkeys. During stage 4, hidden objects are uncovered, and Piaget argued that they have a continuous existence in time, but not in space. Jolly compared this ability with the delayed response learning tests, on which adult primates are known to perform well. Piaget's fifth sensorimotor stage involves a trial-and-error approach to problems, which Jolly argued is characteristic of adult primates including lemurs.

Reviews of later research confirm the attainment of stage 4 of the sensorimotor period in a variety of monkeys, and in cats, dogs and wolves, but question the evidence for claims that these animals progress through the last two stages (Doré and Dumas, 1987; but see Dumas and Doré, 1989). Although early cognitive development is broadly comparable with the Piagetian description, there are some structural differences, and social interactions appear to play a more important part in non-human primates and in cats.

The final sensorimotor stage involves the full attainment of object permanence, the realization that objects exist independently of their current perception, which forms the basis of subsequent symbolic representation. This is indicated by the ability to take into account sequential invisible displacements. Object permanence develops gradually from the third sensorimotor stage, when there is searching for objects hidden in front of the individual.

Most of the existing studies of object permanence in non-human species have concentrated on primates, but there are some using other mammalian species and birds (Doré and Dumas, 1987; Dumas and Doré, 1989; Pepperberg and Funk, 1990). Etienne (1984) adopted a comparative approach to animals' reactions to the disappearance of objects, contrasting the stereotyped reactions characteristic of invertebrates with the ability to show place learning, but not to generalize this ability, shown by many vertebrates. Etienne suggested that the ability to adjust searching in a way that indicates object permanence occurs in birds from the family Corvidae, some mammalian carnivores, and in primates. Doré and Dumas (1987) reached a more cautious conclusion in their review: there is clear evidence that degrees of object permanence from stage 4 onwards are found in these animals, but only in the great apes is there conclusive evidence of stage 6 performance. There is more recent evidence (Dumas and Doré, 1989) that cats reach stage 5b (multiple visual displacements) at 7 weeks, and remain at this level during adulthood. There is doubt as to whether studies on three species of monkey show evidence of the more advanced sensorimotor stages, despite claims that stage 6 was reached. The problem of interpretation centres on the possibility that behaviour indicative of the later stages may have been learned (cf. Pepperberg and Funk, 1990).

A generally similar developmental sequence to humans, including object permanence, has been shown for gorillas and chimpanzees. Nevertheless, Spinozzi and Natale (1989) question the applicability of the common method of testing, the scales of Uzgiris and Hunt (1975), which are used in humans to assess the conformity of infants to already known developmental norms. Spinozzi and Natale argued that the clinical method of Piaget is more suitable for investigating another species, as the scales may mask important differences. Using the clinical method to study the development of a single gorilla to the age of 15 months, they concluded that, despite initial similarity with a human infant, the gorilla had only reached stage 4 by this time. This was comparable to a 10-month-old child. Nevertheless, earlier studies did indicate that the gorilla eventually reaches stage 6, the completion of object permanence (Doré and Dumas, 1987).

Two more recent studies have found evidence for stage 6 in birds from the Psittacine group, the African Grey parrot, macaw, cockatiel and parakeet. Pepperberg and Kozak (1986) studied the language-trained African Grey parrot, Alex. They used the scales of Uzgiris and Hunt (1975), which as indicated above were designed for human infants. They involve a progressive sequence of fifteen tasks beginning with straightforward visible displacements and ending up with the more difficult invisible ones, the last of which involves deception. Pepperberg and Kozak found that Alex did fulfil all the criteria for object permanence, including stage 6. Pepperberg and Funk (1990) replicated these findings with an African Grey parrot which had not been language-trained, and with individuals from the three other species referred to above. They defended use of the standard scales, pointing out that since these were measuring attainment of object permanence in adult animals, the issue of comparability with human development did not arise. They also took great care to eliminate the possibility that the birds were able to learn the correct responses, either incidentally or as a result of the progressive procedure involved. Pepperberg and Funk also noted that observational studies show many examples of behaviour which would seem to indicate object perman-ence, such as hiding and retrieving food, in specific species of birds (see also Etienne, 1984), for example, jays, nutcrackers and marsh tits. There is, however, always the problem of alternative interpretations, based on specific learning, with these field observations.

Stage 6 of the sensorimotor period also involves the beginnings of representational symbolic intelligence: in human infants, object permanence develops just prior to displacement in language learning, the ability to refer to an object not immediately present in space or time. Pepperberg and Kozak (1986) pointed out that Alex does show displacement in language use, for example, when saying 'Alex want banana'.

Early pre-operational thinking is still characterized by concrete and static images of the external world, a form of thought which is irreversible and centred: reasoning cannot be followed back to where it began, and attention is directed to a single feature, neglecting other important aspects (Doré and Dumas, 1987). Is there evidence of anything more than the most rudimentary forms of pre-operational thought in other species?

Doré and Dumas (1987) reviewed the studies on conservation tasks, and concluded that in two studies of squirrel monkeys, there was evidence for prerequisite skills only after extensive training: for example, discriminating between two objects of different volumes required many trials, and a subsequent same–different task took some hundreds of trials (see previous section). It would seem that such skills are not spontaneously learned during the course of development, as they are with human children. There was, however, evidence for two types of quantity conservation, liquid and solid, despite transformation of shape, in one language-trained chimpanzee. As indicated in Chapter 8, chimpanzees brought up as human children also show symbolic play, which Piaget and others regarded as a uniquely human characteristic, involving pre-operational thinking.

In tests of classification and seriation, the limited evidence suggests that chimpanzees fare less well. The first appears doubtful from the two studies reviewed by Doré and Dumas (1987), although the interpretation is not entirely clear. There was no evidence for seriation from the single available study, but it did indicate that the chimpanzees understood notions of tall and small, i.e. that they operate at the level of a 3–4-year-old pre-operational child (see, for example, Brown and Scott, 1972, for evidence of the ability to understand relative size in 3- and 4-year-old children). Nevertheless, as Doré and Dumas (1987) caution, it is possible that the abilities of chimpanzees have been underestimated in these tests, which were built around verbal exchanges with young children. Training procedures have to be substituted instead for the ape tests, which complicates the interpretation of the results.

Summing up their review of Piagetian studies of animals, Doré and Dumas (1987) caution against transferring methodology from the animal learning tradition. Piagetian studies are more concerned with investigating cognitive capacities which are used spontaneously in different situations rather than determining what an animal *can* learn as a result of extensive training. In this sense, they are well suited to the ethological approach with its emphasis on the observation of behaviour, and simple tests which fit the animals' social context and behavioural capabilities.

In addition to providing comparative information, the Piagetian approach can provide a framework for understanding the nature of animal thought. According to Piaget (1936), the basis of pre-operational thinking lies in the young child's ability to evaluate the appropriateness of a possible action without testing it out in the world. Thought consists of internalized actions. Likewise, Griffin (1991) defined thinking in animals as the ability to attend to internal images of objects and events, so as to form representations of the probable results of alternative actions and to choose the one most likely to achieve a desired result. The only added emphasis is the role of thinking in decision-making, and the role of the desired result in controlling action. Griffin regarded this type of thinking as a simple form of mental state, on which more complex forms such as self-awareness and reflective thought could be built. Again, this broadly parallels the Piagetian framework.

Beer (1991) suggested that there are two forms of desired states in animals. Referents may be 'opaque', when they do not clearly specify an object. In this case, they represent forms of awareness that are equivalent to the sensori-motor level. Alternatively, referents may specify an object or individual, in which case they reflect thinking at a pre-operational level, after object permanence has been achieved.

Sensorimotor awareness may be characterized as awareness restricted to feelings rather than the manipulation of internalized actions involving representations of objects. Awareness of a bodily state, coupled with a desire to remain in this state, or to seek an alternative state, such as absence of pain, or lack of hunger, would be an example of this type of awareness. Major (1906) noted that the sensations accompanying the earliest expressions of pleasant and unpleasant feelings in human infants occur in the absence of clear referents, and are clearly separable from thinking. Besides applying to young infants, this form of awareness would be found in a wide range of animals. It represents a motivating state, but not the directing role presumed to accompany thought at a pre-operational level.

In discussing animal suffering, Singer (1976) used the term 'sentience' to indicate a simple form of mental experience comparable to that identified here as sensorimotor awareness. He argued that we can reasonably infer that a non-human animal is suffering or in pain if it shows a comparable reaction to the human case. Since such forms of awareness are not dependent on thought at a pre-operational level or above, they can be inferred in a wide range of animals and in young infants. The issue that is raised is: At what point in the evolution of nervous systems is it reasonable to assume the presence of such feelings? A similar problem presents itself in relation to the point at which we can assume feelings in human development.

Gallup (1985) has argued that there can be no awareness prior to self-awareness (discussed in a later section). He argued that animals without this ability, demonstrated by self-recognition in a mirror, are in a state similar to that of a human sleepwalker or a blindsight patient: they are able to respond to their environments but show no immediate or reflective awareness. Gallup referred to this as 'unconscious sensation'. He also argued that the lack of childhood recollections before the time when self-awareness develops (1½–2 years) supports this view. The implications are that cats, dogs, monkeys and one-year-old infants do not show any form of awareness. The alternative, more usual, interpretation is that there is a transient form of awareness which is not available to reflection or integration into a consistent notion of self (e.g. Duval and Wicklund, 1972), and which corresponds to sensorimotor awareness. It is the 'I' or self as knower, as opposed to the self as known (James, 1892) or the 'existential' rather than the 'categorical' self (Lewis and Brooks-Gunn, 1979). Our legal framework regarding cruelty towards animals and young infants is based on an implicit acknowledgement of this view.

Intentions, goals and the function of consciousness

Although we can operationalize thought by using the Piagetian framework, it has been remarked that the process of thought by itself cannot provide an explanatory framework for animal or human action. Additional 'intentional' concepts, such as beliefs and desires have to be introduced (e.g. Dennett, 1983; Bennett, 1991). While pre-operational thought may be characterized as involving the representations of objects, intentional concepts involve additional features: for example, a belief involves the certainty that a representation does represent the outside world (Ristau, 1991); a desire involves a representation that is linked with a sought-after state (Bennett, 1991). Adopting a functional view, Beer (1991) suggested that desires represent states that are important to the individual's interests, i.e. its fitness. Behavioural action represents the achievement of a desired state, or goal, in this case one related to fitness. The sequence belief–desire–behaviour is the essence of the explanatory framework of folk psychology (Ristau, 1991).

McFarland (1989) has questioned the assumption that behaviour can necessarily be explained in terms of goal direction involving the belief–desire–action sequence. This implies that the conscious representation of the desired end-point guides behaviour. He argued that behaviour is not necessarily *controlled* by goal-directed cognitive processes, but instead involves trade-off considerations of the perceived benefits and costs of alternative actions. Cognitive processes provide an input into the trade-off calculation. He suggested that it is a mistake to conclude that behaviour is goal-directed just because it is often goal-achieving: the human observer has a predilection to assume goal-directed cognitive behaviour, even when it is not there (see also Gould and Gould, 1986).

McFarland's emphasis on decision processes involving trade-off considerations was derived from his functional framework for considering animal motivation. A number of cognitive ethologists have adopted views rather similar to this in considering the function of conscious thought in animals. Griffin (1991) speculated that the ability to consider alternative actions and to choose the one most likely to achieve a desired result would be valuable where the animal faces an unpredictable problem. However, this still emphasizes intentionality. Instead, McFarland argued that novel responses will be required in unpredictable circumstances, and the importance of consciousness lies in monitoring their consequences.

Crook (1983) also suggested that consciousness had evolved because it aids decision-making. He speculated that where information of several different types has to be integrated, it would aid fitness for a rapid decision-making process to be available when there is a mismatch between expectancy and the incoming signals. Under such circumstances, some pictorial representation which can rapidly be shifted would provide an overall scanning function. Crook suggested that consciousness is the subjective manifestation of this overall pictorial representation. It can take one of several forms, from simpler forms of transient pictures in the head, to self-awareness and the ability for self-reflection. This view of consciousness is nearer to McFarland's depiction of cognitive processes as part of a complex input into a decision-making process, and yet recognizes that consciousness has an important part to play in directing behaviour.

The view of consciousness as a form of overriding control in a complex decision-process is difficult to reconcile with the simpler functional view (Beer, 1991), based on folk psychology, that desires represent sought-after states which enhance fitness. It may be possible to reconcile the two by suggesting a gradation of states of awareness: the simplest would be when feelings motivate but do not direct behaviour, i.e. the referents are opaque (see previous section); pre-operational awareness would occur where the referents are specified, and these actions could be described in terms of the belief–desire–behaviour sequence; where there is more than one type of competing motivation, or where the consequences of behaviour are not clear, the sequence of internalized actions becomes more complex, and less readily described in terms of attaining a sought-after goal: in this case, the role of conscious thought in deciding between alternative actions becomes paramount.

Self-awareness and self-recognition

It is well known that many animals will respond to a mirror-image as if another animal were present. Major (1906) commented on the Aesop's fable in which a dog mistook its image in the water for another dog and jumped into the water. Darwin's observations of animals' responses to their mirror-images suggested that they reacted to them as companions or rivals (Darwin, 1877). Naive humans also respond in this way (Gallup, 1979), indicating that learning is necessary for viewing a mirror-image as a self-reflection.

Gallup (1970) tested the possibility that chimpanzees might also be able to learn mirror-image self-recognition. He exposed individual chimpanzees to a mirror-image once a day for ten days. For the first few days, they reacted, as expected, as if a companion were present. Between 6 and 10 days, this reaction was replaced by self-directed responses, such as grooming the top of the head and pulling faces. After the tenth day, Gallup anaesthetized each chimpanzee, and applied an odourless bright red dye to the eyebrow ridge opposite the ear, where it could only be viewed in the mirror. When the mirror was reintroduced, behaviour directed towards the mark greatly increased, and the time the chimp spent viewing itself increased. It would also attempt to smell its fingers after these had touched the dyed part. Control animals, which had not had prior experience with the mirror, did not show these self-directed responses when anaesthetized and applied with the dye.

Gallup's results have been replicated with other samples of chimpanzees and with orang-utans (Gallup, 1979, 1985), but not with gorillas, a wide variety of monkey species or with elephants (Povinelli, 1987, 1989; see also Gallup, 1991). Interestingly, other primates – and elephants – can use mirrors to respond to reflections of objects or of humans, but not to their own reflections as coherent wholes (Gallup, 1979, 1991). Gallup has argued that the concept of self is necessary for correct recognition of oneself in a mirror, and that such self-awareness is restricted to humans and the two great apes referred to above. This view relies heavily on the mirror test as an indication of self-awareness. It is always possible that other types of testing may be more suited to other species: here I am thinking of animals such as cetaceans and Psittacine birds.

Besides using mirrors to study the emotional expressions of animals, Darwin also studied the beginnings of mirror-recognition in his own child's development: 'When four and a half months old, he repeatedly smiled at my image and his own in a mirror, and no doubt mistook them for real objects. . . . In less than two months [he] perfectly understood that it was an image; for if I made quite silently any odd grimace he would suddenly turn around to look at me' (Darwin, 1877, p. 470). Darwin also noted the contrast between this recognition and the initial reaction shown by the great apes he observed: 'The higher apes which I tried with a small looking-glass behaved differently; they placed their hands behind the glass, and in doing so showed their sense, but far from taking pleasure in looking at themselves they got angry and would look no more.' Gallup's studies have now shown that these reactions are typical of the initial reaction shown by both animals and humans to their mirror-image. They also indicate that recognition of another person or object in a mirror, as described by Darwin, is not the same as recognition of oneself, and occurs more widely in primates.

Darwin noted a further development in his son's reaction to the mirror: 'when a few days under nine months he associated his own name with his image in the looking-glass, and when called by name would turn towards the glass even at some distance from it' (1877, p. 470). Later studies suggest that this was a conditioned response rather than true self-recognition.

In a later baby biography, Major (1906) also observed the behaviour of his child before a mirror. In this case, the observations were begun during the 15th month. On first seeing the image, the child reacted as if to another baby, leaning over to try to kiss the image, and crying 'babee'. Three days later, the same response was shown. When retested at 28 months, the child looked bewildered or alarmed at first, but after 10 seconds or more, seemed to recognize the image as himself. When asked who it was, he gave his own name.

Later studies, such as those of Bertenthal and Fischer (1978), and Lewis and Brooks-Gunn (1979), have shown that the development of self-recognition appears gradually, as a progressive sequence, during the first two years of life, at a time when the child is developing many skills (for a review of earlier studies, see Lewis and Brooks-Gunn, 1979). Full self-recognition is attained towards the end of the second year, and coincides with object permanence, indicating that Darwin did not observe a true recognition of self. Bertenthal and Fischer used a range of criteria for mirror recognition, including the ability to recognize objects in the mirror. In view of the ability of monkeys to achieve this without self-recognition, we should be wary of this measure (Gallup, 1979). Both Bertenthal and Fischer and Lewis and Brooks-Gunn also looked for the infant's ability to respond to a dot of rouge applied to the tip of the nose, which is similar to the mirror test used by Gallup (but note the reservations of Gallup, 1979). A number of other researchers have used responses to marks which are surreptitiously placed when the infant is not looking in the mirror (Anderson, 1984). These studies generally find that self-directed responses begin in some infants at around 15 months and are shown by most at 24 months.

Other researchers (e.g. Lewis and Brooks-Gunn, 1979; Johnson, 1983) have investigated children's reactions to themselves and other children on a TV monitor. Johnson compared reactions to the self and to another infant in five different age groups, from 12 to 26 months of age. Again, they investigated behaviour before and after the application of a mark, in this case applied to the infant's nose by the mother while she was wiping its face with a tissue. They also observed the infants' reactions to objects (such as a toy rabbit) appearing on the TV screen, either in front or above or behind the child on the screen (but presented in such a way that they were not directly visible to the infant). When viewing a TV image of their current behaviour, infants of 18 months or older showed considerably more mark-directed responses than those of younger ages. They were also more likely to look for an object that was behind rather than in front of or above them.

When viewing the (pre-recorded) image of another infant, mark-directed behaviour was infrequent at all the ages tested, and looking at objects was unrelated to their position relative to the infant. Johnson concluded that mark-directed behaviour was the clearest indication of self-recognition, although noting that the two conditions would have differed in terms of the type of feedback provided by their respective images, one being contingent and the other non-contingent. In this case, contingent play and attempts to imitate representations of oneself provide useful additional measures of early self-recognition.

Very similar behaviour has been shown by chimpanzees confronted with an image of themselves on a video monitor (Savage-Rumbaugh, 1986). Upon recognizing himself, the chimpanzee Austin stared at the screen, making faces at it. He then continued to watch the monitor for about 20 minutes, as he tried out various postures, facial expressions and ways of eating. He later used the video camera and monitor to carry out activities not possible with a mirror, such as looking down his throat.

Gallup (1985) has argued that self-recognition in the mirror is a crucial test of awareness of oneself, and that self-awareness is necessary for understanding others as intentional agents (see following sections). It is necessary for being able to take another's perspective, and its development in humans coincides with a period of rapid growth in the frontal cortex (15–24 months). As indicated earlier, Gallup regards self-awareness as signifying the crucial distinction between animals with consciousness and those without.

Other researchers have stressed the limitations of the simple forms of self-awareness found in apes and at young ages in humans. As Dunn pointed out: 'Although they understand that mental entities are different from physical ones, and that human action is governed by wishes, beliefs, and attitudes, they do not have a concept of mind as an interpreting, mediating processor of information. ... They have made a critical first step toward understanding this sense of mind, but it is still only a first step' (Dunn, 1988, p. 175).

Dunn argued that the use of tests such as the mirror and TV monitor involve a restricted view of self-awareness: 'Changes in children's responses to self-in-mirror or to adult interferences are usually described in stage terms, for a mythical child who grows up alone. The implications are that the cognitive abilities of the child simply emerge with age' (Dunn, 1988, p. 78). Instead, she argued that development of a sense of self is linked to two other considerations, the first being awareness of others, and the second emotional experiences.

This view of self-awareness as arising from affectively charged social relationships is not, however, inconsistent with that proposed by Gallup (1979) in discussing mirror-image studies on chimpanzees and children. He rejected stage accounts (e.g. Bertenthal and Fischer, 1978), and emphasized the importance of early social interactions for the development of a self-concept. He argued that knowledge of others precedes knowledge of the self. Similarly, Dunn (1988) argued that during the second and third years of life, children are sensitive to how others respond to them and to other children, and it is this sensitivity that is central to the continuing development of self-awareness. Dunn commented that cross-cultural data on children of these ages show that they are sensitive to their culture in a way that supports the tenets of Mead (1934) that the development of self is bound up with the social exchanges he or she has with others, which in turn reflect the cultural context of development. Similarly, Hobson (1990a, b) argued that infants develop a sense of others as persons with mental processes through their early social interactions, their own sense of self developing from this. He criticized one aspect of Leslie's (1987) 'theory of mind' hypothesis (Chapter 5), the assumption that the sense of self emerged prior to the understanding of others. A similar disagreement is apparent in the writings of theorists concerned with the emergence of self-awareness (e.g. Mead, 1934; Piaget, 1924; Duval and Wicklund, 1972). Although this issue is important, the major implication of the 'theory of mind' hypothesis for the present discussion is that it indicates an important step beyond the simpler form of self-awareness revealed by the mirror test.

Imputing mental states to others

Darwin's interest in mental continuity through evolution was extended by modern ethologists in the form of hypotheses about the evolution of human consciousness. Of course, they had available a large amount of field and laboratory research on the cognitive abilities and social behaviour of primates, as well as detailed investigations of their cognitive abilities. Supporting earlier suggestions that primate intelligence had evolved in a social context (e.g. Jolly, 1966), Humphrey (1976) argued that primate, and in particular human, consciousness had evolved because it was useful in *social* relations: it provided a way of understanding other individual's motives. In Humphrey's terminology, evolution has made human beings effective intuitive psychologists. We can picture how others feel and think by understanding their non-verbal and verbal signals. This ability began to evolve in our primate ancestors, and is therefore shared, to a lesser degree, by our primate relatives.

In their influential paper, Premack and Woodruff (1978) posed the question: 'Does the chimpanzee have a theory of mind?' By this phrase they meant imputing mental states to oneself and to others. As Premack and Woodruff indicated, we generally impute intentions to other human and non-human animals who are said to possess minds. The researchers derived an affirmative answer to their question through a series of experiments with Sarah, a language-trained chimpanzee. She was shown a series of videotapes of a human actor struggling to complete various problems of different complexities. Some involved obtaining inaccessible food with a stick, as in Kohler's earlier studies of insight learning. Others involved the actor trying to get out of a locked cage, or shivering because the heater was not working, or unable to play a record player because it was unplugged. Associated with each videotaped scene was a series of photographs, one of which depicted the solution to the problem: for example, there was a stick for the inaccessible food, a key for the locked cage, and a lighted wick for the heater. The chimpanzee showed a consistent choice of the correct photograph. The inference from this was that she recognized the videotape as presenting a problem, understood the actor's thwarted intentions, and chose alternatives compatible with those intentions. Different numbers of correct responses were found with two different actors, which Premack and Woodruff related to Sarah's liking one but not the other.

Towards the end of their article, Premack and Woodruff remarked that the same videotapes had been used with normal and retarded children, and they posed the question of whether some retarded children are specifically deficient in the ability to understand another individual as a mental agent, i.e. lack a 'theory of mind'. This comment foreshadowed the later research on the so-called 'theory of mind' deficit hypothesis of childhood autism (Chapter 5). Some of the commentaries on Premack and Woodruff's paper emphasized the following important point: a clearer test of whether a chimpanzee could understand that another individual had a mental state different from its own would involve the notion of false belief (Butterworth *et al.*, 1991). Simple intentions or purposes could be understood with reference to one's own intentions or purposes, but the understanding that others could have beliefs different from one's own provides a crucial test of the ability to understand the other's mind. This realization led to the development of false belief tests used in research on children's 'theory of mind'.

As indicated in Chapter 5, this research is concerned with the development of the ability to understand the beliefs, knowledge and intentions of others in young children (e.g. Hobson, 1981; Baron-Cohen *et al.*, 1985; Astington and Gopnick, 1991). Dennett (1983) referred to the understanding of, and reaction to, others on the basis of their assumed beliefs, and desires, as 'the intentional stance', and he devised a system for assessing different complexities of intentional states in animals. Whiten and Byrne (1988) have extended this general approach by proposing an empirically-based classification of intentional (or 'tactical') deception in primates. In the remaining sections, I consider intentions and deception in animals, and discuss parallels with the development of a 'theory of mind' in humans.

Intentions

In considering intentions, we come back to the problems with folk psychology encountered earlier. The essential difficulty is that inferring intentions solely from behaviour involves assuming a belief–desire–action sequence which may not be applicable in every case; even if it is, there is no guarantee that our particular sequence is the correct one.

The first point applies to complex thought, where a decision-making model is more appropriate than goal direction. It also applies to simple forms of behavioural control where again goal direction may be inappropriate. In an earlier section, I discussed these points in relation to the difference between consciousness and a non-conscious but intelligently designed system controlling animal behaviour. Michel (1991) made a similar point in relation to inferring intentions from the behaviour of a very young infant on the basis of the temporal order of behaviour. Butterworth (1986) reported that day-old infants show the intention to place their hands in their mouths because they open their mouths in advance of the hand movement. Michel offered an alternative, mechanistic, explanation in terms of motor actions and their physiological control. As indicated in Chapter 2, descriptions of behaviour are possible in terms of either motor acts or consequences. The question raised here, as in many other instances, is whether this is a complementary description or whether a genuine alternative is being introduced. Intentions would appear to add the notion of higher-level control, which is lacking in a description involving motor acts. Michel (1991) argued that intentional explanations may make unwarranted inferences about the goal-directed control of the behaviour.

We are left with the question of how to decide when intentional explanations are warranted. Bennett (1991) has argued that by adding sensory input to the belief–desire–action sequence, we can at least tie intentionality to an event in the animal's surroundings. This is in effect the approach that many cognitive ethologists have adopted to rescue the subject from endless speculation. In most cases the sensory input is a complex one involving communication, and this can potentially enable a distinction to be made between competing possibilities regarding the animal's motives. Essentially, this involves devising a test to rule out alternative simpler or 'lower-level' explanations (Dennett, 1983; Bennett, 1991).

This approach was developed by Dennett (1983), a philosopher who became interested in cognitive ethology because it raised similar problems to those posed by interpreting the actions of an alien human community without an interpreter. In particular, Dennett considered the research of Seyfarth *et al.*

(1980) on the alarm calls of vervet monkeys. Different alarm calls are given for three different types of predator: leopards, snakes and eagles, and each call is associated with a different form of anti-predator behaviour in the recipient. Dennett adopted what he called 'the intentional stance', the use of terms such as belief, desire and other mentalistic notions, to describe and explain behaviour.

Although Dennett used folk psychology as a starting point, he went on to examine different types of intentional systems in terms of their logical content, and classified them accordingly. A zero-order system would lack intentionality, utterances merely reflecting the animal's current internal state. Differences in the vervet anti-predator calls would reflect different internal states induced by the different predators. First-order intentional systems refer to simple statements about beliefs and desires. In the case of the vervets, X wants Y to run to the trees or look in the grass. This is achieved on the basis of a routine action which produced this result on previous occasions. It is also demonstrated when an animal physically prevents a competitor from achieving a reward.

Second-order systems contain intentional states such as beliefs about intentional states in others. This is where the possibility of intended deception arises. In the vervet example, X wants Y to believe there is a leopard or a snake. It is achieved by a flexible response which is tailored to this specific aim. A third-order system extends this further: individual A wants B to believe that A is in a particular state. X wants Y to believe that X wants Y to run to the trees.

In theory the progression can be extended further with the addition of ever more complex links to the chain, but even in the human case, it soon becomes difficult to follow. The important question is the extent to which animals are capable of intentionality beyond the zero- and first-order levels. Dennett argued that this is an empirical question, answered by inferences from the animals' behaviour. If an isolated vervet monkey does not make these calls on seeing a predator, but simply takes anti-predator action itself, this rules out the zero-order interpretation. If behaviour underlying apparent intentionality fails to show flexibility in a novel situation, a first-order interpretation is most likely; if it is flexible and occurs in a novel situation, a second-order interpretation is likely. As indicated above, Dennett argued that such distinctions could be made by devising a crucial test which would reveal the animal's understanding of the situation.

Deception

Dennett identified 'second-order intentional systems' as those that indicate that an individual shows understanding of beliefs and desires in others. The same distinction has assumed crucial importance in research on 'theory of mind' in children (Wimmer and Perner, 1983; Sodian, 1991). In animal research, it led to interest in deliberate deception. If this could be demonstrated, the animal would not only possess a mind, but would be capable of attributing a mind to others (Kummer *et al.*, 1990).

There are functional reasons why deceptive communication should have evolved in animals (Chapters 6 and 9), but the use of the term 'deception' in a functional sense does not necessarily imply conscious deception. There are many examples of apparently deceptive behaviour by animals from field and laboratory studies; for example, the use of alarm calls as decoys in several bird species (Whiten and Byrne, 1988), feigned broken wing displays by birds, which distract predators from their nests (Ristau, 1986), and death feigning in hognose snakes (Burghardt, 1991). However, in seeking examples where deliberate intent is apparent, most attention has been directed to primates: for example, female hamadryas baboons, which are guarded by a much larger male, show deceptive copulations; chimpanzees may deceive others about the location of food (Ristau, 1986).

In deciding whether deception is based on an understanding of another's mental state, or on a simpler and less flexible mechanism (Dennett's zero- or first-order systems), Whiten and Byrne (1988) used the following criteria to examine information supplied to them by 115 primatologists: they defined deliberate or 'tactical' deception as an act which is usually shown in one context and produces a predictable response from familiar individuals, but is used in a different context to gain an advantage for the actor due to misinterpretation by the recipient.

Whiten and Byrne offered a classification of tactical deception found in primates, on the basis of the information supplied to them. Their specific categories were as follows: concealment, where the agent's behaviour had the intent of concealing something from the target; distraction, where it was intended to direct the target's behaviour away from something; creating an image, which seeks to present the agent's behaviour in a misleading manner; manipulation of a target using a social tool, which involves the use of another animal to affect the target to the agent's advantage; and finally, deflection of the target to fall guy, which seeks to divert the target's behaviour to a third party, so as to enable the actor to gain some resource which was prevented by the target.

Whiten and Byrne found that chimpanzees showed evidence of most of their categories of deception. Jolly (1991) considered such incidents in more detail. Concealment was inferred from the behaviour of a language-taught chimpanzee who was signed to look for the lost key to its cage. The chimpanzee went ahead looking even though it had hidden the key itself. Jolly referred to several examples of suppressing vocalizations in the self or others when these would result in a dominant animal interrupting a sought-after activity, such as copulating or eating a banana. Giving the appearance of not attending to a sought-after object was another strategy used to obtain the same ends. de Waal (1982) provided many other examples from the behaviour of the chimpanzee colony at Arnhem Zoo, and Cheney and Seyfarth (1991) give examples of withholding information in vervet monkeys.

Distraction is regarded as more active than concealment (Whiten and Byrne, 1988). False or confusing messages are sent to others while still retaining the original goal. In chimpanzees this is inferred from the apparent use of social grooming, or leading away and vocalizing, to distract another individual (Jolly, 1991). For example, Jane Goodall observed that a young male led older males away by purposefully striding into the woods, most likely to a real food source. When they disappeared, he circled back and was able to eat bananas undisturbed by them. Chimpanzee mothers also distract troublesome young by grooming or tickling them.

Use of alarm calls to distract others was reported in the study of Seyfarth *et al.* (1980) described in the previous section. Vervet monkeys would call and act as if they had spotted a specific predator when in conflict with another band of monkeys. Jane Goodall observed comparable behaviour by two chimpanzees at the time of weaning, which resulted in their being carried by their mothers (Jolly, 1991). Several other examples are apparent in language-trained chimpanzees: one animal used the sign for a food item apparently to achieve the goal of being near to other chimpanzees who were located on the way to the food (Jolly, 1991).

Whiten and Byrne's category 'creating an image' involves the use of behaviour to present a 'front' to another animal in order to conceal the nature of the social interaction. Jolly refers to an example from the study of de Waal (1982): a male who had sustained an injury exaggeratedly limped in front of the dominant male, but only this male, for some days. Jolly also refers to chimpanzees luring humans near to them by friendly gestures only to spit on or bite them. (Here I am reminded of the following story about a caged chimpanzee in a zoo: when confronted by a crowd of people he would urinate on those nearest to him, but always retain sufficient for a repeat performance on people who struggled to the front to find out what the fuss was about.)

Whiten and Byrne's final two categories involve relations between more than two animals. For example, if a threatened young chimpanzee exaggerates its vocal responses so as to elicit aid from an older 'protector' (Jolly, 1991), the latter is said to have been used as a 'social tool'. There are also many examples of using animals as social tools in the Old World monkeys (Whiten and Byrne, 1988; Cheney and Seyfarth, 1991).

The approach advocated by Whiten and Byrne, and endorsed by others such as Jolly, de Waal and Gallup, has attracted criticism. Kummer *et al.* (1990) lament the preference for anecdote over experiment, stating that accepted rules are being disregarded in this field. They attributed this partly to the teleological labelling apparent in sociobiology and modern primate ethology, for example, terms such as 'tactical deception', altruism and cheating, but also to the theorizing of Griffin and Dennett. They argued that in seeking to attribute knowledge of other minds to primates, we may readily misinterpret their behaviour as we are ignorant of their social world. In the opinion of Kummer *et al.*, such ignorance makes reliance on the anecdote, as Whiten and Byrne advocated, a flawed method. Nevertheless, when a number of anecdotal examples, each with a possible alternative explanation, collectively point to the likelihood of intentional deception, and this is supported by more rigorous tests in the laboratory (see below), I would argue that it adds up to a strong case. This represents the current state of knowledge regarding the chimpanzee. In other instances of apparent deception, the caution advocated by Kummer *et al.* is more justified – for the time being at least.

The observational evidence for tactical deception in chimpanzees is supported by an experimental study carried out by Woodruff and Premack (1979). They set up a situation in which a human–chimpanzee pair were required to exchange information about a hidden reward. When the two were required to compete, rather than co-operate, the chimpanzee partner would withhold vital information or even misinform the human partner about the location of the reward, and also discount or act against the sender's misleading information.

A very similar method was later used by Sodian (1991) to study the ability of 3–5-year-old children to deceive a competitor in a hiding game. The youngest children were unable to show deception even under the most favourable conditions; yet they were able to manipulate another's behaviour by strategic interaction, i.e. by physically preventing them from obtaining a reward. This indicates that they were operating at Dennett's first level. These results support previous studies (e.g. Wimmer and Perner, 1983) showing that 3-year-old children are unable to understand false beliefs and hence practise deception, but that this ability is shown by 4 year olds. Although some studies (Chandler *et al.*, 1989; Sullivan and Winner, 1991) have found evidence of deception at a slightly earlier age, Sodian *et al.* (1991) showed that 3 year olds use deceptive ploys indiscriminately, for example, whether they are asked to mislead a competitor or to inform a collaborator.

The identification of the point at which the understanding of false beliefs develops in children, and its appearance in the social exchanges of animals, is centrally important for the 'theory of mind'. Yet it is not the same as awareness that others possess mental states. Several studies (see Astington and Gopnik, 1991; Sodian, 1991) indicate that children younger than 3 years do understand that people think of objects and events, and that this is related to their actions. They can even understand that what other people are thinking can differ from their own viewpoint. But they rarely anticipate the impact of their own actions on another's beliefs (Sodian *et al.*, 1991). Therefore awareness of the self and others as causal agents occurs some time prior to the understanding of beliefs, probably coinciding with recognition of a mirror-image during stage 6 of the sensorimotor period (see above).

Conclusions: A comparative perspective on mental processes

A comparative perspective has been used to consider a variety of different approaches to mental processes in animals and in young humans. The evidence has been derived from several sources, in particular a Piagetian perspective on thinking in animals, studies of self-awareness using mirror reactions, and research on intentions and deception. It is possible to draw the following conclusions from the existing evidence.

The most widespread form of awareness in animals, which also occurs in very young infants, is the capacity to experience suffering or pleasure, referred to as sentience by Singer (1976). The referents of any desired state are 'opaque', i.e. they do not clearly specify an object (Beer, 1991). At this level, thinking is tied to the consequences of actions in the outside world. It is at the sensorimotor level.

From both field and laboratory studies, it is apparent that a number of birds and mammals show evidence of object permanence, although there is some dispute about how widespread achievement of Piaget's stage 6 is in the animal world. In humans, this stage coincides with the development of self-awareness in mirror tests. Among other species, this has only been demonstrated for chimpanzees and orang-utans, prompting Gallup to speculate that only these species show self-awareness. He argued that this is the crucial test of whether an animal is conscious, regarding what I referred to as sensorimotor awareness as no more than unconscious responses to sensations, similar to sleepwalking. Infants only emerge from this state in the second half of their second year. The implications of such a view would be that cats, dogs, monkeys and one-year-old infants do not show any form of awareness. The more usual view is that there is a form of non-reflective awareness prior to this.

If some form of awareness of the self and of others as objects in the world develops towards the end of the second year of life in humans, it marks the beginning of understanding others as thinking beings and the link between thought and action, i.e. the basis for the intentional stance or folk psychology. Nevertheless, it is only later, in the third year of life, that false beliefs, the key to Dennett's level two intentionality and to the acquisition of a 'theory of mind', are understood. This is shown in chimpanzees, and forms the basis of the many examples of tactical deception found in the social interactions of these animals.

Even so, the level of conceptual thought, the understanding of the self and others, and the degree of intentional thinking that underlies the behaviour of our nearest animal relatives is soon outstripped by a normally developing child as she or he progresses through the pre-operational period. Apes only show rudimentary symbolic play, and their language learning is limited compared with that of a human child. Nevertheless such human superiority should not blind us to the constant reconstruction of these abilities during development in the human child, and the extent to which humans do share at least some aspects of awareness and thought with other species.

References

Abbott, D. and Barrett, J. (1990) 'Physiology of socially-induced fertility in subordinate female marmoset monkeys', presented at Meeting of the Association for the Study of Animal Behaviour, London, 6–7 December.

Abramovitch, R. (1976) 'The relation of attention and proximity to rank in preschool children', in M.R.A. Chance and R.R. Larsen (eds.), *The Social Structure of Attention*, pp. 153–76, New York & London: Wiley.

Ainsworth, M.D.S. (1979) 'Attachment as related to mother–infant interaction', *Advances in the Study of Behavior*, 9, 2–51.

Alcock, J. (1975) *Animal Behavior: An evolutionary approach*, Sunderland, MA: Sinauer.

Aldis, O. (1975) *Play Fighting*, New York: Academic Press.

Allee, W.C. (1938) *The Social Life of Animals*, New York: W.W. Norton.

Allee, W.C. (1942) 'Social dominance and subordination among vertebrates', *Biological Symposia*, 8, 139–62.

Alley, T.R. (1983) 'Infantile shape as an elicitor of adult protection', *Merrill Palmer Quarterly*, 29, 411–27.

Altmann, J. (1974) 'Observational study of behavior: sampling methods', *Behaviour*, 49, 227–67.

Altmann, J. (1980) *Baboon Mothers and Infants*, Cambridge, MA: Harvard University Press.

Altmann, S.A. (1962) 'A field study of the sociobiology of rhesus monkeys, *Macaca mulatta*', *Annals of the New York Academy of Sciences*, 102, 338–435.

Altmann, S.A. (1965) 'Sociobiology of rhesus monkeys. II: Stochastics of social communication', *Journal of Theoretical Biology*, 8, 490–522.

Ambrose, J.A. (1966) 'Ritualization in the human infant–mother bond', *Philosophical Transactions of the Royal Society, London, Series B*, 251, 359–62.

Ambrose, J.A. (1968) 'The comparative approach to early child development: the data of ethology', in E. Miller (ed.), *Foundations of Child Psychiatry*, pp. 183–232, Oxford & New York: Pergamon.

Anastasi, A. (1958) 'Heredity, environment, and the question "How?" ', *Psychological Review*, 65, 197–208.

Anderson, J.R. (1984) 'The development of self-recognition: A review', *Developmental Psychobiology*, 17, 35–49.

Andrew, R.J. (1956) 'Some remarks on behaviour in conflict situations, with special reference to *Emberiza* spp.', *British Journal of Animal Behaviour*, *4*, 41–5.

Andrew, R.J. (1962) 'The situations that evoke vocalization in primates', *Annals of the New York Academy of Sciences*, *102*, 296–315.

Andrew, R.J. (1963a) 'The origin and evolution of the calls and facial expressions of the primates', *Behaviour*, *20*, 1–109.

Andrew, R.J. (1963b) 'Evolution of facial expressions', *Science*, *142*, 1034–41.

Andrew, R.J. (1964) 'Vocalisation in chicks and the concept of stimulus contrast', *Animal Behaviour*, *12*, 64–76.

Andrew, R.J. (1965) 'The origins of facial expressions', *Scientific American*, *213*, 88–94.

Andrew, R.J. (1972) 'The information potentially available in mammal displays', in R.A. Hinde (ed.), *Non-verbal Communication*, pp. 179–206, London & New York: Cambridge University Press.

Andrew, R.J. (1974) 'Arousal and the causation of behaviour', *Behaviour*, *51*, 135–65.

Appleby, M.C. (1983) 'The probability of linearity in hierarchies', *Animal Behaviour*, *31*, 600–8.

Appleby, M.C. (1985) 'Hawks, doves . . . and chickens', *New Scientist*, *105*, no. 1438, 16–18.

Archer, J. (1973) 'Tests for emotionality in rats and mice: A review', *Animal Behaviour*, *21*, 205–35.

Archer, J. (1976) 'The organization of aggression and fear in vertebrates', in P.P.G. Bateson and P. Klopfer (eds.), *Perspectives in Ethology 2*, pp. 231–98, New York: Plenum.

Archer, J. (1979) 'Behavioural aspects of fear', in W. Sluckin (ed.), *Fear in Animals and Man*, pp. 56–85, Wokingham, Van Nostrand.

Archer, J. (1984) 'Gender roles as developmental pathways', *British Journal of Social Psychology*, *23*, 245–56.

Archer, J. (1986a) 'Animal sociobiology and comparative psychology: A review', *Current Psychological Research and Reviews*, *5*, 48–61.

Archer, J. (1986b) 'Game theoretic models and respect for ownership', *The Behavioral and Brain Sciences*, *9*, 740–4.

Archer, J. (1988a) *The Behavioural Biology of Aggression*, Cambridge & New York: Cambridge University Press.

Archer, J. (1988b) 'The sociobiology of bereavement: A reply to Littlefield & Rushton', *Journal of Personality and Social Psychology*, *55*, 272–8.

Archer, J. (1989) 'Childhood gender roles: structure and development', *The Psychologist: Bulletin of the British Psychological Society*, *2* (9), 367–70.

Archer, J. (1989/90) 'Pain-induced aggression: An ethological perspective', *Current Psychology Research and Reviews*, *8*, 298–306.

Archer, J. (1990) 'Have animal models contributed to studies of loss and separation?', *The Psychologist: Bulletin of the British Psychological Society*, *3* (7), 298–301.

Archer, J. (1991) 'Sociobiology and psychology: problems and prospects', *Journal of Social Issues*, *47*, 11–26.

Archer, J. (1992) 'Childhood gender roles: Social context and organization', in H. McGurk (ed.), *Childhood Social Development: Contemporary perspectives*, pp. 31–61, London & Hillsdale, NJ: Lawrence Erlbaum.

Archer, J. and Browne, K. (1989) 'Concepts and approaches to the study of aggression', in J. Archer and K. Browne (eds.), *Human Aggression: Naturalistic approaches*, pp. 3–24, London & New York: Routledge.

Archer, J. and Huntingford, F.A. (in press) 'Game theory models and escalation of animal fights', in M. Potegal and J. Knutson (eds.), *The Escalation of Aggression: Biological and social processes*, Hillsdale, NJ: Lawrence Erlbaum.

Archer, J. and Lloyd, B.B. (1985) *Sex and Gender*, 2nd edn, New York: Cambridge University Press.

Archer, J., Pearson, N.P. and Westeman, K.E. (1988) 'Aggressive behaviour of children aged 6–11: gender differences and their magnitude', *British Journal of Social Psychology*, *27*, 371–84.

Ardrey, R. (1967) *The Territorial Imperative*, London: Collins.

Astington, J.W. and Gopnik, A. (1991) 'Theoretical explanations of children's understanding of the mind', *British Journal of Developmental Psychology*, *9*, 7–31.

Attili, G. (1985) 'Concomitants and factors influencing children's aggression', *Aggressive Behavior*, *11*, 291–301.

Attili, G. and Hinde, R.A. (1986) 'Categories of aggression and their motivational heterogeneity', *Ethology and Sociobiology*, *7*, 17–27.

Atz, J.W. (1970) 'The application of the idea of homology to behavior', in L.R. Aronson, E. Tobach, D.S. Lehrman and J.S. Rosenblatt (eds.), *Development and Evolution of Behavior: Essays in memory of T.C. Schneirla*, pp. 53–74, San Francisco: W.H. Freeman.

Baerends, G.P. (1941) 'Fortpflanzungsverhalten und Orientierung der Grabwespe *Ammophila campestris* Jur', *Tijdschrift voor Entomologie*, *84*, 68–275.

Baerends, G.P. (1970) 'A model of the functional organisation of incubation behaviour', in G.P. Baerends and R.H. Drent (eds.), *The Herring Gull and its Egg. Behaviour*, Supplement 17, 263–312.

Baerends, G.P. (1975) 'An evaluation of the conflict hypothesis as an explanatory principle for the evolution of displays', in G.P. Baerends, C. Beer and A. Manning (eds.), *Function and Evolution of Behaviour*, pp. 187–227, Oxford: Clarendon Press.

Baerends, G.P. (1976) 'The functional organization of behaviour', *Animal Behaviour*, *24*, 726–38.

Baerends, G.P. (1985) 'Do the dummy experiments with sticklebacks support the IRM concept?', *Behaviour*, *93*, 258–77.

Baerends, G.P. and Baerends-van Roon, J.M. (1950) 'An introduction to the study of the ethology of cichlid fishes', *Behaviour*, Supplement 1, 1–242.

Bakeman, R. and Gottman, J.M. (1986) *Observing Interaction: An introduction to sequential analysis*, Cambridge & New York: Cambridge University Press.

Bandura, A., Ross, D. and Ross, S.A. (1961) 'Transmission of aggression through imitation of aggressive models', *Journal of Abnormal and Social Psychology*, *63*, 575–82.

Bandura, A., Ross, D. and Ross, S.A. (1963) 'Imitation of film-mediated aggressive models', *Journal of Abnormal and Social Psychology*, *66*, 3–11.

Barash, D.P. (1977) *Sociobiology and Behavior*, New York: Elsevier.

Barash, D.P. (1982) *Sociobiology and Behavior*, 2nd edn, New York: Elsevier.

Barber, N. (1991) 'Play and energy regulation in mammals', *The Quarterly Review of Biology*, *66*, 129–47.

Barlow, G.W. (1977) 'Modal action patterns', in T.A. Sebeok (ed.), *How Animals Communicate*, pp. 98–134, Bloomington & London: Indiana University Press.

Barlow, G.W. (1989) 'Has sociobiology killed ethology or revitalized it?', in P.P.G. Bateson and P. Klopfer (eds.), *Perspectives in Ethology 8: Whither ethology?*, pp. 1–45, New York: Plenum.

Barnard, C.J. and Burk, T. (1979) 'Dominance hierarchies and the evolution of "individual recognition" ', *Journal of Theoretical Biology*, *81*, 65–73.

Baron-Cohen, S. (1992) 'The theory of mind hypothesis of autism: history and prospects of the idea', *The Psychologist: Bulletin of the British Psychological Society*, *5*, 9–12.

Baron-Cohen, S., Leslie, A.M. and Frith, U. (1985) 'Does the autistic child have a "theory of mind"?', *Cognition*, *21*, 37–46.

Barrett, P. and Bateson, P.P.G. (1978) 'The development of play in cats', *Behaviour*, *66*, 106–20.

Bateman, A.J. (1948) 'Intrasexual selection in *Drosophila*', *Heredity*, *2*, 349–68.

Bateson, P.P.G. (1976a) 'Specificity and the origins of behavior', *Advances in the Study of Behavior*, *6*, 1–20.

Bateson, P.P.G. (1976b) 'Rules and reciprocity in behavioural development', in P.P.G. Bateson and R.A. Hinde (eds.), *Growing Points in Ethology*, pp. 401–21, Cambridge: Cambridge University Press.

Bateson, P.P.G. (1978a) 'Sexual imprinting and optimal outbreeding', *Nature*, *273*, 659.

Bateson, P.P.G. (1978b) 'Early experience and sexual preferences', in J.B. Hutchison (ed.), *Biological Determinants of Sexual Behavior*, pp. 29–53, New York: Wiley.

Bateson, P.P.G. (1978c) 'How does behavior develop?', in P.P.G. Bateson and P. Klopfer (eds.), *Perspectives in Ethology 3*, pp. 55–66, New York: Plenum.

Bateson, P.P.G. (1979) 'How do sensitive periods arise and what are they for?', *Animal Behaviour*, *27*, 470–86.

Bateson, P.P.G. (1980a) 'Optimal outbreeding and the development of sexual preferences in Japanese Quail', *Zeitschrift für Tierpsychologie*, *53*, 231–44.

Bateson, P.P.G. (1980b) 'How do we decide whether or not to experiment with animals?', presented at Association for the Study of Animal Behaviour Conference on The Ethics of Animal Experimentation, Durham, 19–20 March.

Bateson, P.P.G. (1981) 'Ontogeny', in D. McFarland (ed.), *The Oxford Companion to Animal Behaviour*, pp. 414–26, Oxford & New York: Oxford University Press.

Bateson, P.P.G. (1982) 'Preferences for cousins in Japanese Quail', *Nature*, *295*, 236–7.

Bateson, P.P.G. (1983a) 'Genes, environment and the development of behaviour', in T.R. Halliday and P.J.B. Slater (eds.), *Animal Behaviour. 3. Genes, development and learning*, pp. 52–81, Oxford: Blackwell.

Bateson, P.P.G. (1983b) 'The interpretation of sensitive periods', in A. Oliverio and M. Zappella (eds.), *The Behavior of Human Infants*, pp. 57–70, New York: Plenum.

Bateson, P.P.G. (1984) 'Genes, environment and learning', in P. Marler and H. Terrace (eds.), *The Biology of Learning*, pp. 75–88, Berlin & New York: Springer-Verlag.

Bateson, P.P.G. (1985) 'Problems and possibilities in fusing developmental and evolutionary thought', in G. Butterworth, J. Rutkowska and M. Scaife (eds.), *Evolution and Developmental Psychology*, pp. 3–21, Brighton: Harvester Press.

Bateson, P.P.G. (1986) 'When to experiment on animals', *New Scientist*, *109* (1496), 30–2.

Bateson, P.P.G. (1987) 'Biological approaches to the study of behavioural development', *International Journal of Behavioural Development*, 10, 1–22.

Bateson, P.P.G. (1989) 'Obituary of Konrad Lorenz', *The Independent*, 4 March.

Bateson, P.P.G. (1991) 'Are there principles of development?', in P.P.G. Bateson (ed.), *The Development and Integration of Behaviour. Essays in honour of Robert Hinde*, pp. 19–39, Cambridge & New York: Cambridge University Press.

Beach, F.A. (1950) 'The snark was a boojum', *American Psychologist*, 5, 115–24.

Beer, C.G. (1991) 'From folk psychology to cognitive psychology', in C.A. Ristau (ed.), *Cognitive Ethology: the minds of other animals. Essays in honor of Donald R. Griffin*, pp. 19–33, Hillsdale, N.J.: Lawrence Erlbaum.

Bekoff, M. (1984) 'Social play behavior', *Bioscience*, 34, 228–33.

Belsky, J., Steinberg, L. and Draper, P. (1991) 'Childhood experience, interpersonal development, and reproductive strategy: An evolutionary theory of socialization', *Child Development*, 62, 647–70.

Bennett, J. (1991) 'How is cognitive ethology possible?', in C.A. Ristau (ed.), *Cognitive Ethology: the minds of other animals. Essays in honor of Donald R. Griffin*, pp. 35–49, Hillsdale, NJ: Lawrence Erlbaum.

Bernstein, I.S. (1981) 'Dominance: the baby and the bathwater', *The Behavioral and Brain Sciences*, 4, 419–57 (including commentaries).

Bernstein, I.S. and Sharpe, L.G. (1966) 'Social roles in a rhesus monkey group', *Behaviour*, 26, 91–104.

Berry, D.S. and McArthur, L.Z. (1985) 'Some components and consequences of a babyface', *Journal of Personality and Social Psychology*, 48, 312–23.

Bertenthal, B.I. and Fischer, K.W. (1978) 'Development of self–recognition in the infant', *Developmental Psychology*, 14, 44–50.

Bickerton, D. (1983) 'The last of Clever Hans?', *The Behavioral and Brain Sciences*, 6, 141–2 (commentary on Premack, 1983).

Bischof, H.-J. and Clayton, N. (1991) 'Stabilization of sexual preferences by sexual experience in male zebra finches Taeniopygia guttata castanotis', *Behaviour*, 118, 144–55.

Bishop, D.T. and Cannings, C. (1978) 'A generalized War of Attrition', *Journal of Theoretical Biology*, 70, 85–124.

Blanchard, D.C. and Blanchard, R.J. (1989) 'Experimental animal models of aggression: What do they say about human behaviour?', in J. Archer and K. Browne (eds.), *Human Aggression: Naturalistic approaches*, pp. 94–121, London & New York: Routledge.

Blest, D. (1961) 'The concept of ritualization', in W.H. Thorpe and O.L. Zangwill (eds.), *Current Problems in Animal Behaviour*, pp. 102–24, London & New York: Cambridge University Press.

Block, N. (1979) 'A confusion about innateness', *The Behavioral and Brain Sciences*, 2, 27–9.

Blurton Jones, N. (1967) 'An ethological study of some aspects of social behaviour of children in nursery school', in D. Morris (ed.), *Primate Ethology*, pp. 347–68, London: Weidenfeld and Nicolson.

Blurton Jones, N. (1968) 'Observations and experiments on causation of threat displays of the great tit (*Parus major*)', *Animal Behaviour Monographs*, 1, 75–158.

Blurton Jones, N. (1971) 'Criteria for use in describing facial expressions of children', *Human Biology*, 43, 365–413.

Blurton Jones, N. (1972a) 'Characteristics of ethological studies of human behaviour', in N. Blurton Jones (ed.), *Ethological Studies of Child Behaviour*, pp. 3–33, London & New York: Cambridge University Press.

Blurton Jones, N. (1972b) 'Comparative aspects of mother–child contact', in N. Blurton Jones (ed.), *Ethological Studies of Child Behaviour*, pp. 305–28, London & New York: Cambridge University Press.

Blurton Jones, N. (1972c) 'Categories of child–child interaction', in N. Blurton Jones (ed.), *Ethological Studies of Child Behaviour*, pp. 97–127, London & New York: Cambridge University Press.

Blurton Jones, N. (1972d) 'Non-verbal communication in children', in R.A. Hinde (ed.), *Non-verbal Communication*, pp. 271–96, London & New York: Cambridge University Press.

Blurton Jones, N.G. (1986) 'Bushman birth-spacing: A test for optimal interbirth intervals', *Ethology and Sociobiology*, 7, 91–106.

Blurton Jones, N.G. (1989) 'The costs of children and the adaptive scheduling of births: Towards a sociobiological perspective on demography', in A.E. Rasa, C. Vogel and E. Voland (eds.), *The Sociobiology of Sexual and Reproductive Strategies*, pp. 265–82, London & New York: Chapman & Hall.

Blurton Jones, N. and Konner, M.J. (1973) 'Sex differences in the behaviour of London and Bushman children', in R.P. Michael and J.H. Crook (eds.), *Comparative Ecology and Behaviour of Primates*, pp. 689–750, London & New York: Academic Press.

Blurton Jones, N. and Leach, G.M. (1972) 'Behaviour of children and their mothers at separation and greeting', in N. Blurton Jones (ed.), *Ethological Studies of Child Behaviour*, pp. 217–47, London & New York: Cambridge University Press.

Boakes, R. (1984) *From Darwin to Behaviourism: Psychology and the minds of animals*, Cambridge & New York: Cambridge University Press.

Bolles, R.C. (1979) 'The functional significance of behavior', *The Behavioral and Brain Sciences*, 2, 29–30.

Bornstein, M.H. (1989) 'Sensitive periods in development: Structural characteristics and causal interpretations', *Psychological Bulletin*, 105, 179–97.

Boulton, M.J. (1988) 'A multi-methodological investigation of rough-and-tumble play, aggression, and social relationships in middle school', unpublished doctoral thesis, University of Sheffield.

Boulton, M.J. (1991a) 'A comparison of structural and contextual features of middle school children's playful and aggressive fighting', *Ethology and Sociobiology*, 12, 119–45.

Boulton, M.J. (1991b) 'Partner preferences in middle school children's playful fighting and chasing: A test of some competing functional hypotheses', *Ethology and Sociobiology*, 12, 117–93.

Boulton, M.J. and Smith, P.K. (1989) 'Issues in the study of children's rough-and-tumble play', in M.N. Bloch and A. Pellegrini (eds.), *The Ecological Context of Children's Play*, pp. 57–83, Norwood NJ: Ablex.

Boulton, M.J. and Smith, P.K. (in press) 'The social nature of play fighting and play chasing: mechanisms and strategies underlying co-operation and compromise', in J. Barkow, L. Cosmides and J. Tooby (eds.), *The Adapted Mind*, Oxford: Oxford University Press.

Bowlby, J. (1953a) *Child Care and the Growth of Love*, Harmondsworth: Penguin Books.

Bowlby, J. (1953b) 'Critical phases in the development of social responses in man and other animals', *New Biology*, *14*, 25–32.

Bowlby, J. (1969) *Attachment and Loss: Vol. 1 Attachment*, London: Hogarth Press.

Bowlby, J. (1973) *Attachment and Loss: Vol. 2. Separation: Anxiety and anger*, London: Hogarth Press.

Bowlby, J. (1980a) 'By ethology out of psychoanalysis: an experiment in interbreeding', *Animal Behaviour*, *28*, 649–56.

Bowlby, J. (1980b) *Attachment and Loss: Vol. 3. Sadness and depression*, London: Hogarth Press.

Bradshaw, J.L. (1991) 'Animal asymmetry and human heredity: Dextrality, tool use and language in evolution – 10 years after Walker (1980)', *British Journal of Psychology*, *82*, 39–59.

Brannigan, C. and Humphries, D.A. (1972) 'Human non-verbal behaviour as a means of communication', in N. Blurton Jones (ed.), *Ethological Studies of Child Behaviour*, pp. 37–64, London & New York: Cambridge University Press.

Bronfenbrenner, U. (1973) 'A theoretical perspective for research on human development', in H.P. Dreitzel (ed.), *Childhood and Socialization*, pp. 337–63, London: Collier-Macmillan.

Brown, A.L. and Scott, M.S. (1972) 'Transfer between the oddity and relative size concept: reversal and extradimensional shifts', *Journal of Experimental Child Psychology*, *13*, 350–67.

Brown, J.L. (1964) 'The evolution of diversity in avian territorial systems', *Wilson Bulletin*, *6*, 160–9.

Browne, K.D. (1989) 'The naturalistic context of family violence and child abuse', in J. Archer and K.D. Browne (eds.), *Human Aggression: Naturalistic approaches*, pp. 182–216, London & New York: Routledge.

Browne, K.D. and Madeley, R. (1985) 'ETHOGRAM (Software package)', *Journal of Child Psychology and Psychiatry*, *26*, 111.

Browne, K.D. and Saqi, S. (1987) 'Parent–child interaction in abusing families: its possible causes and consequences', in P. Maher (ed.), *Child Abuse: The educational perspective*, pp. 77–104, Oxford: Blackwell.

Bruner, J.S. (1972) 'Nature and uses of immaturity', *American Psychologist*, *27*, 687–708.

Burghardt, G.M. (1991) 'Cognitive ethology and critical anthropomorphism: A snake with two heads and hognose snakes that play dead', in C. Ristau (ed.), *Cognitive Ethology: The minds of other animals. Essays in honor of Donald R. Griffin*, pp. 53–90, Hillsdale, NJ: Lawrence Erlbaum.

Burkhardt, R.W. (1987) 'The *Journal of Animal Behavior* and the early history of animal behavior studies in America', *Journal of Comparative Psychology*, *101*, 223–30.

Buss, A.H., Plomin, R. and Willerman, L. (1973) 'The inheritance of temperaments', *Journal of Personality*, *41*, 513–24.

Butterworth, G. (1986) 'Some problems in explaining the origins of movement control', in M.G. Wade and H.T.A. Whiting (eds.), *Motor Development in Children: Aspects of coordination and control*, pp. 23–32, Dordrecht & Boston: Martinus Nijhoff.

Butterworth, G., Harris, P., Leslie, A. and Wellman, H. (1991) 'Editorial preface to Special issue: Perspectives on the child's theory of mind, Part 1', *British Journal of Developmental Psychology*, *9*, 1–4.

Camras, L.A. (1977) 'Facial expressions used by children in a conflict situation', *Child Development*, *48*, 1431–5.

Camras, L.A. (1980) 'Animal threat displays and children's facial expressions: A comparison', in D.R. Omark, F.F. Strayer and D.G. Freedman (eds.), *Dominance Relations: An ethological view of human conflict and social interaction*, pp. 121–36, New York & London: Garland STPM Press.

Camras, L.A. (1984) 'Children's verbal and nonverbal communication in a conflict situation', *Ethology and Sociobiology*, 5, 257–68.

Capitanio, J.P., Rasmussen, K.L.R., Snyder, D.S., Laudenslager, M. and Reite, M. (1986) 'Long-term follow-up of previously separated pigtail macaques: group and individual differences in response to novel situations', *Journal of Child Psychology and Psychiatry*, 27, 531–8.

Carlstead, K. (1981) 'Motivational influences on individual and species differences in responses to conspecifics in three *Haplochromis* species (Pisces: Cichlidae)', PhD thesis, Rijksuniversiteit Groningen.

Caro, T.M. (1981) 'Predatory behaviour and social play in kittens', *Behaviour*, 76, 1–24.

Caro, T.M. and Borgerhoff Mulder, M. (1987) 'The problem of adaptation in the study of human behavior', *Ethology and Sociobiology*, 8, 61–72.

Caro, T.M., Roper, R., Young, M. and Dank, G.R. (1979) 'Inter-observer reliability', *Behaviour*, 69, 303–15.

Carthy, J.D. (1951) 'Instinct', *New Biology*, 10, 95–105.

Caryl, P.G. (1979) 'Communication by agonistic displays: What can game theory contribute to ethology?', *Behaviour*, 68, 136–69.

Caryl, P.G. (1981) 'Escalated fighting and the war of nerves: Games theory and animal combat', in P.P.G. Bateson and P. Klopfer (eds.), *Perspectives in Ethology 4*, pp. 199–224, New York & London: Plenum.

Caspi, A., Elder, G.H. Jr and Bem, D.J. (1987) 'Moving against the world: life-course patterns of explosive children', *Developmental Psychology*, 23, 308–13.

Caspi, A., Elder, G.H. Jr and Bem, D.J. (1988) 'Moving away from the world: life-course patterns of shy children', *Developmental Psychology*, 24, 824–31.

Chalmers, N.R. (1987) 'Developmental pathways of behaviour', *Animal Behaviour*, 35, 659–74.

Chalmers, N.R. and Locke-Haydon, J. (1986) 'Effects on the behavior of infant common marmosets (*Callithrix jacchus*) of separation from caregivers and of drug-induced reduction of caregiver responsiveness', *Developmental Psychobiology*, 19, 399–411.

Chance, M.R.A. (1967) 'Attention structure as the basis of primate rank orders', *Man*, 2, 503–18.

Chandler, M., Fritz, A. and Hala, S. (1989) 'Small-scale deceit: Deception as a marker of two-, three-, and four-year-olds' early theories of mind', *Child Development*, 60, 1263–77.

Charlesworth, W.R. (1979) 'An ethological approach to studying intelligence', *Human Development*, 22, 212–16.

Charlesworth, W.R. (1982) 'An ethological approach to research on facial expressions', in C.E. Izard (ed.), *Measuring Emotions in Infants and Children*, pp. 317–34, New York & Cambridge: Cambridge University Press.

Charlesworth, W.R. (1983) 'An ethological approach to cognitive development', in C.J. Brainerd (ed.), *Recent Advances in Cognitive Developmental Theory: Progress in cognitive developmental research*, pp. 237–58, New York: Springer-Verlag.

Chase, I.D. (1974) 'Models of hierarchy formation in animal societies', *Behavioral Science, 19,* 374–82.

Chase, I.D. (1980) 'Social processes and hierarchy formation in small groups: A comparative perspective', *American Sociological Review, 45,* 905–24.

Chase, I.D. (1985) 'The sequential analysis of aggressive acts during hierarchy formation: An application of the "jigsaw" approach', *Animal Behaviour, 33,* 86–100.

Chase, I.D. (1986) 'Explanations of hierarchy structure', *Animal Behaviour, 34,* 1265–7.

Cheney, D.L. and Seyfarth, R.M. (1991) 'Truth and deception in animal communication', in C.A. Ristau (ed.), *Cognitive Ethology: The minds of other animals. Essays in honor of Donald R. Griffin,* pp. 127–51, Hillsdale, NJ: Lawrence Erlbaum.

Chisholm, J.S. (1983) *Navajo Infancy: An ethological study of child development,* New York: Aldine.

Chisholm, J.S. (1987) 'Towards a developmental evolutionary ecology of humans', in K.B. MacDonald (ed.), *Sociobiological Perspectives on Human Development,* pp. 78–102, New York & Berlin: Springer-Verlag.

Clarke, A.D.B. and Clarke, A.M. (1984) 'Constancy and change in the growth of human characteristics', *Journal of Child Psychiatry, 25,* 191–210.

Clarke, A.M. and Clarke, A.D.B. (1976) 'The formative years?', in A.M. Clarke and A.D.B. Clarke (eds.), *Early Experience: Myth and evidence,* pp. 3–24, London: Open Books.

Clausen, C.P. (1940) *Entomophagous Insects,* New York: McGraw-Hill.

Clutton-Brock, T.H. and Albon, S.D. (1979) 'The roaring of red deer and the evolution of honest advertisement', *Behaviour, 69,* 145–70.

Clutton-Brock T.H. and Harvey, P.H. (1976) 'Evolutionary rules and primate societies', in P.P.G. Bateson and R.A. Hinde (eds.), *Growing Points in Ethology,* pp. 195–237, Cambridge: Cambridge University Press.

Clutton-Brock, T.H. and Harvey, P.H. (1977) 'Primate ecology and social organization', *Journal of Zoology, 183,* 1–39.

Cohen, J. (1960) 'A coefficient of agreement for nominal values', *Educational and Psychological Measurement, 20,* 37–46.

Cohn, J.F. and Tronick, E.Z. (1983) 'Three-month-old infants' reactions to simulated maternal depression', *Child Development, 54,* 185–93.

Collias, N.E. (1991) 'The role of American zoologists and behavioural ecologists in the development of animal sociology 1934–1964', *Animal Behaviour, 41,* 613–32.

Costabile, A., Smith, P.K., Matheson, L., Aston, J., Hunter, T. and Boulton, M. (1991) 'Cross-national comparison of how children distinguish serious and play fighting', *Developmental Psychology, 27,* 881–7.

Craig, W. (1918) 'Appetites and aversions as constituents of instincts', *Biological Bulletin, 34,* 91–107.

Crawford, C.B. (1989) 'The theory of evolution: of what value to comparative psychology?', *Journal of Comparative Psychology, 103,* 4–22.

Crook, J.H. (1960) 'Studies of the social behaviour of *Quelea q. quelea* (Linn.) in French West Africa', *Behaviour, 16,* 1–55.

Crook, J.H. (1964) 'The evolution of social organisation and visual communication in the weaver birds (Ploceinae)', *Behaviour,* Supplement 10, 1–178.

Crook, J.H. (1966) 'Gelada baboon herd structure and movement: a comparative report', *Symposia of the Zoological Society of London, 18,* 237–58.

Crook, J.H. (1970a) 'Social organization and the environment: aspects of contemporary social ethology', *Animal Behaviour*, *18*, 197–209.

Crook, J.H. (1970b) 'The socio-ecology of primates', in J.H. Crook (ed.), *Social Behaviour in Birds and Mammals*, pp. 103–66, London & New York: Academic Press.

Crook, J.H. (1970c) 'Introduction – social behaviour and ethology', in J.H. Crook (ed.), *Social Behaviour in Birds and Mammals*, pp. xxi–xl, London & New York: Academic Press.

Crook, J.H. (1980) *The Evolution of Human Consciousness*, New York & Oxford: Oxford University Press.

Crook, J.H. (1983) 'On attributing consciousness to animals', *Nature*, *303*, 11–14.

Crook, J.H. and Crook, S.J. (1988) 'Tibetan polyandry: problems of adaptation and fitness', in L. Betzig, M. Borgerhoff Mulder and P. Turke (eds.), *Human Reproductive Behaviour*, pp. 97–114, Cambridge & New York: Cambridge University Press.

Crook, J.H. and Gartlan, J.S. (1966) 'Evolution of primate societies', *Nature*, *210*, 1200–3.

Cullen, E. (1957) 'Adaptations in the kittiwake to cliff-nesting', *The Ibis*, *99*, 275–302.

Cunningham, M.R., Barbee, A.P. and Pike, C.L. (1990) 'What do women want? Facialmetric assessment of multiple motives in the perception of male facial physical attractiveness', *Journal of Personality and Social Psychology*, *59*, 61–72.

Daly, M. and Wilson, M. (1981) 'Abuse and neglect of children in evolutionary perspective', in R.D. Alexander and D.W. Tinkle (eds.), *Natural Selection and Social Behavior*, pp. 405–16, New York: Chiron Press.

Daly, M. and Wilson, M. (1985) 'Child abuse and other risks of not living with both parents', *Ethology and Sociobiology*, *6*, 197–210.

Daly, M. and Wilson, M. (1987) 'Evolutionary psychology and family violence', in C. Crawford, M. Smith and D. Krebs (eds.), *Sociobiology and psychology: Ideas, issues and applications*, pp. 293–309, Hillsdale, NJ & London: Lawrence Erlbaum.

Daly, M. and Wilson, M. (1988a) *Homicide*, New York: Aldine de Gruyter.

Daly, M. and Wilson, M. (1988b) 'Evolutionary social psychology and family homicide', *Science*, *242*, 519–24.

Darling, F.F. (1937) *A Herd of Red Deer*, London: Oxford University Press.

Darwin, C. (1859) *On the Origin of Species*, London: John Murray.

Darwin, C. (1871) *The Descent of Man and Selection in Relation to Sex*, London: John Murray.

Darwin, C. (1872) *The Expression of the Emotions in Man and Animals* (1904 edn), London: John Murray.

Darwin, C. (1877) 'A biographical sketch of an infant', *Mind*, *2*, 285–94.

Datta, S. (1988) 'The acquisition of dominance among free-ranging rhesus monkey siblings', *Animal Behaviour*, *36*, 754–72.

Davie, C.E., Hutt, S.J., Vincent, E. and Mason, M. (1984) *The Young Child at Home*, London: NFER-Nelson.

Davies, N.B. and de Brooke, M. (1988) 'Cuckoos versus reed warblers: adaptations and counteradaptations', *Animal Behaviour*, *36*, 262–84.

Davies, N.B. and Lundberg, A. (1984) 'Food distribution and a variable mating system in the dunnock, *Prunella modularis*', *Journal of Animal Ecology*, *53*, 895–912.

Dawkins, M.S. (1986) *Unravelling Animal Behaviour*, Harlow: Longman.

Dawkins, M.S. and Guilford, T. (1991) 'The corruption of honest signalling', *Animal Behaviour*, *41*, 865–73.

Dawkins, R. (1971) 'A cheap method of recording behavioural events, for direct computer access', *Behaviour*, *40*, 162–73.

Dawkins, R. (1976) *The Selfish Gene*, Oxford & New York: Oxford University Press.

Dawkins, R. and Krebs, J.R. (1978) 'Animal signals: Information and manipulation', in J.R. Krebs and N.B. Davies (eds.), *Behavioural Ecology: An evolutionary approach*, pp. 282–309, Oxford: Blackwell.

de Waal, F.B.M. (1982) *Chimpanzee Politics*, London: Jonathan Cape.

de Waal, F.B.M. (1986) 'The integration of dominance and social bonding in primates', *The Quarterly Review of Biology*, *61*, 459–79.

de Waal, F.B.M. (1989a) 'Dominance "style" and primate social organization', in V. Standen and R.A. Foley (eds.), *Comparative Socioecology: the behavioural ecology of humans and other mammals* (special publications of the British Ecological Society No. 8), pp. 243–63, Oxford: Blackwell Scientific Publications.

de Waal, F.B.M. (1989b) *Peacemaking among Primates*, Cambridge, MA: Harvard University Press.

de Waal, F.B.M. (1990) 'Sociosexual behavior used for tension regulation in all age and sex combinations among bonobos', in J.R. Fierman (ed.), *Pedophilia: Biosocial dimensions*, pp. 378–93, New York & Berlin: Springer-Verlag.

de Waal, F.B.M. and van Roosmalen, A. (1979) 'Reconciliation and consolation among chimpanzees', *Behavioral Ecology and Sociobiology*, *5*, 55–66.

de Waal, F.B.M. and Yoshihara, D. (1983) 'Reconciliation and redirected affection in rhesus monkeys', *Behaviour*, *85*, 224–41.

Denenberg, V.H. (1973) 'Developmental factors in aggression', in J.F. Knutson (ed.), *The Control of Aggression*, pp. 41–57, Chicago: Aldine.

Dennett, D.C. (1983) 'Intentional systems in cognitive ethology: The "Panglossian paradigm" defended', *The Behavioral and Brain Sciences*, *6*, 343–90 (including commentaries).

Dewsbury, D.A. (1984) *Comparative Psychology in the Twentieth Century*, Stroudsburg, PA: Hutchinson Ross.

Dewsbury, D.A. (1988) 'The comparative psychology of monogamy', in R. Dienstbier (series ed.) and D.W. Leger (volume ed.), *Nebraska Symposium on Motivation 1987, Comparative perspectives in modern psychology*, pp. 1–50, Lincoln, NA: University of Nebraska Press.

Diamond, M. (1965) 'A critical evaluation of the ontogeny of human sexual behavior', *Quarterly Review of Biology*, *40*, 147–73.

Dienske, H. (1984) 'The identity of human ethology', *Human Ethology Newsletter*, *4*, (4), 4.

DiPietro, J.A. (1981) 'Rough and tumble play: a function of gender', *Developmental Psychology*, *17*, 50–8.

Dissanayake, C. and Crossley, S.A. (1989) 'Behaviour in children with early infantile autism: Responsiveness to people', in P. Lovibond and P. Wilson (eds.), *Clinical and Abnormal Psychology*, pp. 221–32, Amsterdam & New York: Elsevier/North-Holland.

Dominey, W.J. (1984) 'Alternative mating tactics and evolutionarily stable strategies', *American Zoologist*, *24*, 385–96.

Doré, F.Y. and Dumas, C. (1987) 'Psychology of animal cognition: Piagetian studies', *Psychological Bulletin, 102,* 219–33.

Dow, M., Ewing, A.W. and Sutherland, I. (1976) 'Studies on the behaviour of Cyprinodont fish. III. The temporal patterning of aggression in *Aphyosemion striatum* (Boulenger)', *Behaviour, 59,* 252–68.

Draper, P. and Harpending, H. (1982) 'Father absence and reproductive strategy: An evolutionary perspective', *Journal of Anthropology Research, 38,* 255–73.

Draper, P. and Harpending, H. (1987) 'A sociobiological perspective on the development of human reproductive strategies', in K.B. MacDonald (ed.), *Sociobiological Perspectives on Human Development,* pp. 340–72, New York & Berlin: Springer-Verlag.

Driscoll, J.W. and Bateson, P.P.G. (1988) 'Animals in behavioural research', *Animal Behaviour, 36,* 1569–74.

Dumas, C. and Doré, F.Y. (1989) 'Cognitive development in kittens (*Felis cattus*): A cross-sectional study of object permanence', *Journal of Comparative Psychology, 103,* 191–200.

Dunn, J. (1988) *The Beginnings of Social Understanding,* Oxford: Blackwell.

Duval, S. and Wicklund, R.A. (1972) *A Theory of Objective Self-awareness,* London & New York: Academic Press.

Eagly, A.H. (1987) *Sex Differences in Social Behavior: A social role interpretation,* Hillsdale, NJ: Lawrence Erlbaum.

Eales, L. (1985) 'Song learning in zebra finches: Some effects of song model availability on what is learnt and when', *Animal Behaviour, 33,* 1293–300.

Eales, L. (1987) 'Song learning in female-raised zebra finches: Another look at the sensitive phase', *Animal Behaviour, 35,* 1356–65.

Edelman, M.S. and Omark, D.R. (1973) 'Dominance hierarchies in young children', *Social Science Information, 12,* 103–10.

Eibl-Eibesfeldt, I. (1961) 'The fighting behavior of animals', *Scientific American, 205,* 112–22.

Eibl-Eibesfeldt, I. (1967) 'Concepts of ethology and their significance in the study of human behavior', in H.W. Stevenson, E.H. Hess and H.L. Rheingold (eds.), *Early Behavior: comparative and developmental approaches,* pp. 127–46, New York: Kreiger.

Eibl-Eibesfeldt, I. (1968) 'Zur Ethologie des menschlichen Grußverhaltens. 1. Beobachtungen an Balinesen, Papuas und Samoanern nebst vergleichenden Bemerkungen', *Zeitschrift für Tierpsychologie, 25,* 727–44.

Eibl-Eibesfeldt, I. (1970) *Ethology: the biology of behavior,* New York: Holt, Rinehart & Winston.

Eibl-Eibesfeldt, I. (1971) *Love and Hate,* London: Methuen.

Eibl-Eibesfeldt, I. (1972) 'Similarities and differences between cultures in expressive movements', in R.A. Hinde (ed.), *Non-verbal Communication,* pp. 297–314, Cambridge: Cambridge University Press.

Eibl-Eibesfeldt, I. (1973) 'The expressive behaviour of the deaf-and-blind born', in M. von Cranach and I. Vine (eds.), *Social Communication and Movement: Studies of interaction and expression in man and chimpanzee,* pp. 163–94, London & New York: Academic Press.

Eibl-Eibesfeldt, I. (1975) *Ethology: The biology of behavior* (2nd edn), New York: Holt, Rinehart & Winston.

Eibl-Eibesfeldt, I. (1979) 'Human ethology: concepts and implications for the science of man', *The Behavioral and Brain Sciences*, 2, 1–57 (including commentaries).

Eibl-Eibesfeldt, I. (1989) *Human Ethology*, New York: Aldine de Gruyter.

Einon, D.F. (1980) 'The purpose of play', in J. Cherfas and R. Lewin (eds.), *Not Work Alone*, pp. 21–32, London: Temple Smith.

Einon, D.F. (1983) 'Play and exploration', in J. Archer and L.I.A. Birke (eds.), *Exploration in Animals and Humans*, pp. 210–29, Wokingham: Van Nostrand.

Einon D.F., Humphreys, A.P., Chivers, S.M., Field, S. and Naylor, V. (1981) 'Isolation has permanent effects upon the behavior of the rat, but not the mouse, gerbil or guinea pig', *Developmental Psychobiology*, 14, 343–55.

Einon, D.F., Morgan, M.J. and Kibbler, C.C. (1978) 'Brief periods of socialization and later behavior in the rat', *Developmental Psychobiology*, 11, 213–25.

Einon, D.F. and Potegal, M. (1991) 'Enhanced defense in adult rats deprived of playfighting experiences as juveniles', *Aggressive Behavior*, 17, 27–40.

Ekman, P. (1973) 'Cross-cultural studies of facial expression', in P. Ekman (ed.), *Darwin and Facial Expression*, pp. 169–222, New York & London: Academic Press.

Ekman, P.W. and Friesen, W. (1978) *Manual for the Facial Action Coding System*, Palo Alto, CA: Consulting Psychologist Press.

Ellis, H. (1926) *Studies in the Psychology of Sex. Vol 2. Sexual Inversion* (3rd edn, revised and enlarged), Philadelphia, PA: F.A. Davis.

Etienne, A.S. (1984) 'The meaning of object permanence at different zoological levels', *Human Development*, 27, 309–20.

Fagen, R.M. (1976) 'Exercise, play, and physical training in animals', in P.P.G. Bateson and P. Klopfer (eds.), *Perspectives in Ethology 2*, pp. 189–219, New York: Plenum.

Fagen, R.M. (1977) 'Selection for optimal age-dependent schedules of play behavior', *American Naturalist*, 111, 395–414.

Fagen, R.M. (1981) *Animal Play Behavior*, New York and Oxford: Oxford University Press.

Fantz, R.L. (1967) 'Visual perception and experience in early infancy: A look at the hidden side of behavior development', in H.W. Stevenson, E.H. Hess and H.L. Rheingold (eds.), *Early Behavior: Comparative and developmental approaches*, pp. 181–224, New York: Kreiger.

Fassnacht, G. (1982) *Theory and Practice of Observing Behaviour*, London: Academic Press.

Faulkes, C., Abbott, D., Barrett, J. and Smith, T.E. (1990) 'Endocrine mechanisms underlying the social control of reproduction in naked mole rats', paper presented at Meeting of the Association for the Study of Animal Behaviour, London, 6–7 December.

Fein, D., Pennington, B., Markowitz, P., Braverman, M. and Waterhouse, L. (1986) 'Toward a neuropsychological model of infantile autism: Are the social deficits primary?', *Journal of the American Academy of Child Psychiatry*, 25, 198–212.

Feirman, J.R. and Feirman, L.A. (1989) 'Behavioural pathology', presented at 21st International Ethological Conference, Utrecht, 9–17 August.

Ficken, M.S. (1977) 'Avian play', *Auk*, 94, 573–82.

Field, T., Vega-Lahr, N., Scaffidi, F. and Goldstein, S. (1986) 'Effects of maternal unavailability on mother–infant interactions', *Infant Behavior and Development*, 9, 473–8.

Fisher, R.A. (1930) *The Genetical Theory of Natural Selection*, Oxford: Clarendon Press.

Ford, C.S. and Beach, F.A. (1951) *Patterns of Sexual Behavior*, New York: Harper.

Forest, M.G., Sizonenko, P.C., Caithiard, A.M. and Bertrand, J. (1974) 'Hypophyso-gonadal function in humans during the first year of life. 1. Evidence for testicular activity in early infancy', *Journal of Clinical Investigation*, 53, 819–28.

Fraenkel, G.S. and Gunn, D.L. (1940) *The Orientation of Animals*, Oxford: Clarendon Press.

Francis, R.C. (1988) 'On the relationship between aggression and social dominance', *Ethology*, 78, 223–37.

Freedman, D. (1964) 'Smiling in blind infants and the issue of innate vs. acquired', *Journal of Child Psychology and Psychiatry*, 5, 171–84.

Freedman, D. (1965) 'Hereditary control of early social behavior', in B.M. Foss (ed.), *Determinants of Infant Behaviour. Vol. III*, pp. 149–59, London: Methuen.

Freedman, D.G. (1980) 'Sexual dimorphism and the status hierarchy', in D.R. Omark, F.F. Strayer and D.G. Freedman (eds.), *Dominance Relations: An ethological view of human conflict and social interaction*, pp. 261–71, New York & London: Garland STPM Press.

Fry, D.P. (1987) 'Differences between playfighting and serious fighting among Zapotec children', *Ethology and Sociobiology*, 8, 285–306.

Fullard, W. and Reiling, A.M. (1976) 'An investigation of Lorenz's "babyness" ', *Child Development*, 47, 1191–3.

Galef, B.G. Jr (1987) 'Comparative psychology is dead! Long live comparative psychology', *Journal of Comparative Psychology*, 101, 259–61.

Gallagher, J.E. (1976) 'Sexual imprinting: effects of various regimens of social experience on mate preference in Japanese quail *Coturnix coturnix japonica*', *Behaviour*, 47, 91–114.

Gallup, G.G. (1970) 'Chimpanzees: self–recognition', *Science*, 167, 86–7.

Gallup, G.G. (1979) 'Self-recognition in chimpanzees and man: A developmental and comparative perspective', in M. Lewis and L.A. Rosenblum (eds.), *The Child and its Family*, pp. 107–26, London & New York: Plenum.

Gallup, G.G. (1985) 'Do minds exist in species other than our own?', *Neuroscience and Biobehavioral Reviews*, 9, 631–41.

Gallup, G.G. (1991) 'Toward a comparative psychology of self–awareness: Species limitations and cognitive consequences', in G.R. Goethals and J. Strauss (eds.), *The Self: An interdisciplinary approach*, New York: Springer-Verlag.

Gardner, B.T. and Wallach, L. (1965) 'Shapes of figures identified as a baby's head', *Perceptual and Motor Skills*, 20, 135–42.

Gardner, H. (1978) *Developmental Psychology: An introduction*, Boston, MA: Little, Brown.

Gardner, R.A. and Gardner, B.T. (1975) 'Early signs of language in child and chimpanzee', *Science*, 187, 752–3.

Gartlan, J.S. (1968) 'Structure and function in primate society', *Folia Primatologica*, 8, 89–120.

Geist, V. (1978) 'On weapons, combat and ecology', in L. Krames, P. Pliner and T. Alloway (eds.), *Advances in the Study of Communication and Affect. Vol. 4, Aggression dominance and individual spacing*, pp. 1–30, New York: Plenum.

Gesell, A. and Ilg, F.L. (1943) *Infant and Child in the Culture of Today*, New York: Harper (1965 edn, London: Hamilton).

Gewirtz, J.L. (1965) 'The course of infant smiling in four childrearing environments in Israel', in B.M. Foss (ed.), *Determinants of Infant Behaviour. Vol. III*, pp. 205–48, London: Methuen.

Ginsburg, H.J. (1980) 'Playground as laboratory: naturalistic studies of appeasement, altruism, and the omega child', in D.R. Omark, F.F. Strayer and D.G. Freedman (eds.), *Dominance Relations: An ethological view of human conflict and social interaction*, pp. 341–57, New York & London: Garland STPM Press.

Ginsburg, H.J., Pollman, V.I. and Wauson, M.S. (1977) 'An ethological analysis of nonverbal inhibitors of aggressive behavior in male elementary school children', *Developmental Psychology, 13*, 417–18.

Gittleman, J.L. (1989) 'The comparative approach in ethology: Aims and limitations', in P.P.G. Bateson and P. Klopfer (eds.), *Perspectives in Ethology 8*, pp. 55–83, New York: Plenum.

Goodenough, F.L. (1928) 'Measuring behavior traits by means of repeated short samples', *Journal of Juvenile Research, 12*, 230–5.

Goodenough, F.L. (1932) 'Expression of the emotions in a blind-deaf child', *Journal of Abnormal and Social Psychology, 27*, 328–33.

Goodman, R.A. and Whitaker, H.A. (1985) 'Hemispherectomy: A review (1928–1981) with special reference to the linguistic abilities and disabilities of the residual right hemisphere', in C.T. Best (ed.), *Hemispheric Function and Collaboration in the Child*, pp. 121–55, New York: Academic Press.

Goodwin, B.C. (1978) 'A cognitive view of biological process', *Journal of Social and Biological Structures, 1*, 117–25.

Gottlieb, G. (1987) 'The developmental basis of evolutionary change', *Journal of Comparative Psychology, 101*, 262–71.

Gottlieb, G. (1991) 'Experiential canalization of behavioral development: Results', *Developmental Psychology, 27*, 35–9.

Gould, J.L. and Gould, C.G. (1986) 'Invertebrate intelligence', in R.J. Hoage and L. Goldman (eds.), *Animal Intelligence: Insights into the animal mind*, pp. 21–36, Washington, DC & London: Smithsonian Institution Press.

Gould, S.J. (1976) 'Grades and clades revisited', in R.B. Masterton, W. Hodos and H. Jerison (eds.), *Evolution, Brain and Behavior: Persistent problems*, pp. 115–22, Hillsdale, NJ: Lawrence Erlbaum.

Gould, S.J. (1977a) *Ever since Darwin: Reflections on natural history*, New York: Burnett Books. (1980 edition published by Penguin, Harmondsworth).

Gould, S.J. (1977b) *Ontogeny and Phylogeny*, Cambridge, MA & London: Belknap Press of Harvard University Press.

Gould, S.J. (1980) *The Panda's Thumb*, New York: W.W. Norton (1983 edition published by Penguin, Harmondsworth).

Gould, S.J. and Lewontin, R.C. (1979) 'The spandrels of San Marco and the Panglossian paradigm: A critique of the adaptationist programme', *Proceedings of the Royal Society of London B, 205*, 581–98.

Gould, S.J. and Vrba, E.S. (1982) 'Exaptation – a missing term in the science of form', *Paleobiology, 8*, 4–15.

Goy, R.W., Bercovitch, F.B. and McBrair, M.C. (1988) 'Behavioral masculinization is independent of genital masculinization in prenatally androgenized female rhesus monkeys', *Hormones and Behavior, 22*, 552–71.

Goy, R.W. and McEwan, B.S. (1980) *Sexual Differentiation in the Brain*, Cambridge, MA: MIT Press.

Grammer, K. and Stockl, M. (1989) 'Human ethology: r/K selection and the "New Racism" ', *Human Ethology Newsletter*, 5, 2–4.

Grant, E.C. (1965a) 'An ethological description of some schizophrenic patterns of behaviour', in F.A. Jenner (ed.), *Proceedings of the Leeds Symposium on Behavioural Disorders*, pp. 99–113, Dagenham: May & Baker.

Grant, E.C. (1965b) 'The contribution of ethology to child psychiatry', in J.G. Howells (ed.), *Modern Perspectives in Child Psychiatry*, pp. 20–37, Edinburgh & London: Oliver & Boyd.

Grant, E.C. (1968) 'An ethological description of non-verbal behaviour during interviews', *British Journal of Medical Psychology*, 41, 177–84.

Grant, E.C. (1969) 'Human facial expressions', *Man*, 4, 525–36.

Grant, E.C. and Mackintosh, J.H. (1963) 'A comparison of the social postures of some common laboratory rodents', *Behaviour*, 201, 246–59.

Green, R., Roberts, C.W., Williams, K., Goodman, M. and Mixon, A. (1987) 'Specific cross-gender behavior in boyhood and later homosexual orientation', *British Journal of Psychiatry*, 151, 84–8.

Griffin, D.R. (1976) *The Question of Animal Awareness: Evolutionary continuity of mental experience*, New York: Rockefeller University Press.

Griffin, D.R. (1981) *The Question of Animal Awareness: Evolutionary continuity of mental experience*, revised edn, New York: Rockefeller University Press, and Los Altos, CA: Kaufmann.

Griffin, D.R. (1991) 'Progress toward a cognitive ethology', in C.A. Ristau (ed.), *Cognitive Ethology: the minds of other animals. Essays in honor of Donald R. Griffin*, pp. 3–17, Hillsdale, NJ: Lawrence Erlbaum.

Groos, K. (1898) *The Play of Animals*, New York: Appleton.

Groothius, A.G.G. (1989a) 'On the ontogeny of display behaviour in black-headed gulls I: the gradual emergence of adult forms', *Behaviour*, 109, 76–124.

Groothius, A.G.G. (1989b) 'On the ontogeny of display behaviour in black-headed gulls II: causal links between the development of aggression, fear and display behaviour: emancipation reconsidered', *Behaviour*, 110, 161–204.

Gross, M.R. (1985) 'Disruptive selection for alternative life histories in salmon', *Nature*, 313, 47–8.

Guiton, P. (1959) 'Socialisation and imprinting in brown leghorn chicks', *Animal Behaviour*, 7, 26–34.

Guthertz, M. and Field, T. (1989) 'Lap computer or on-line coding and data analysis for laboratory and field observations', *Infant Behavior and Development*, 12, 305–19.

Hailman, J. (1967) 'The ontogeny of an instinct', *Behaviour*, Supplement 15.

Hailman, J. (1979) 'The ethology behind human ethology', *The Behavioral and Brain Sciences*, 2, 35–6.

Hall, K.R.L. (1965) 'Social organization of the old-world monkeys and apes', *Symposia of the Zoological Society of London*, 14, 265–89.

Hamilton, W.D. (1964) 'The genetical evolution of social behavior, I and II', *Journal of Theoretical Biology*, 7, 1–52.

Hamilton, W.D. (1972) 'Altruism and related phenomena, mainly in social insects', *Annual Review of Ecology and Systematics*, 3, 193–232.

Hanfmann, E. (1935) 'Social structure of a group of kindergarten children', *American Journal of Orthopsychiatry*, 5, 407–10.

Harcourt, A.H. and Stewart, K.J. (1981) 'Gorilla male relationships: can differences during immaturity lead to contrasting reproductive tactics in adulthood?', *Animal Behaviour*, 29, 206–10.

Harlow, H.F., Dodsworth and Harlow, M.K. (1965) 'Total social isolation in monkeys', *Proceedings of the National Academy of Sciences*, 54, 90–7.

Harlow, H.F. and Zimmerman, R.R. (1958) 'The development of affectional responses in infant monkeys', *Proceedings of the American Philosophical Society*, 102, 501–9.

Hart, P.J.B. (1986) 'An ecological perspective on factors influencing decision making in urban female *Homo sapiens*', *Bulletin d'Ecologie et Ethologie Humaines*, 5, 119–23.

Hass, H. (1970) *The Human Animal*, New York: Putnam.

Hay, D.F. and Lockwood, R. (1989) 'Girls' and boys' success and strategies on a computer-generated hunting task', *British Journal of Developmental Psychology*, 7, 17–27.

Hebb, D.O. (1953) 'Heredity and environment in mammalian behaviour', *British Journal of Animal Behaviour*, 1, 43–7.

Hemingway, E. (1935) 'Monologue to the maestro: A high seas letter', *Esquire*, October. Reprinted E. Hemingway, *By-Line: Selected articles and dispatches of four decades*, London: Grafton Books, 1989.

Herbert, M., Sluckin, W. and Sluckin, A. (1982) 'Mother-to-infant "bonding"', *Journal of Child Psychology and Psychiatry*, 23, 205–21.

Hess, E.H. (1959) 'Imprinting', *Science*, 130, 133–41.

Hess, E.H. (1967) 'Introduction', in H.W. Stevenson, E.H. Hess and H.L. Rheingold (eds.), *Early Behavior: comparative and developmental approaches*, pp. 1–3, New York: Kreiger.

Hess, E.H. (1970) 'Ethology and developmental psychology', in P.H. Mussen (ed.), *Carmichael's Manual of Child Psychology* (3rd edn): Vol. 1, pp. 1–38. New York: Wiley.

Hess, E.H. and Polt, J.M. (1960) 'Pupil size as related to interest value of visual stimuli', *Science*, 132, 349–50.

Hinde, R.A. (1952) 'The behaviour of the great tit (*Parus major*) and some other related species', *Behaviour*, Supplement, 2, 1–201.

Hinde, R.A. (1953a) 'The conflict between drives in the courtship and copulation of the chaffinch', *Behaviour*, 5, 1–13.

Hinde, R.A. (1953b) 'Appetitive behaviour, consummatory act, and the hierarchical organisation of behaviour – with special reference to the Great Tit (*Parus major*)', *Behaviour*, 5, 189–224.

Hinde, R.A. (1956) 'Ethological models and the concept of drive', *British Journal for the Philosophy of Science*, 6, 321–31.

Hinde, R.A. (1958) 'The nest-building behaviour of domesticated canaries', *Proceedings of the Zoological Society of London*, 131, 1–48.

Hinde, R.A. (1959a) 'Some recent trends in ethology', in S. Koch (ed.), *Psychology, a study of a science*: Vol. 2, pp. 561–610, New York: McGraw-Hill.

Hinde, R.A. (1959b) 'Unitary drives', *Animal Behaviour*, 7, 130–41.

Hinde, R.A. (1960) 'Energy models of motivation', *Symposia of the Society for Experimental Biology*, 14, 199–213.

Hinde, R.A. (1966) *Animal Behaviour: A synthesis of ethology and comparative psychology*, London & New York: McGraw-Hill.

Hinde, R.A. (1970) *Animal Behaviour: A synthesis of ethology and comparative psychology* (2nd edn), London & New York: McGraw-Hill.

Hinde, R.A. (1972) 'Editorial comments' (on Andrew, 1972), in R.A. Hinde (ed.), *Non-verbal Communication*, pp. 204–6, Cambridge & New York: Cambridge University Press.

Hinde, R.A. (1973) 'On the design of check-sheets', *Primates*, *14*, 393–406.

Hinde, R.A. (1974) *Biological Bases of Human Social Behavior*, New York: McGraw-Hill.

Hinde, R.A. (1978) 'Dominance and role – two concepts with dual meanings', *Journal of Social and Biological Structures*, *1*, 27–38.

Hinde, R.A. (1979) *Towards Understanding Relationships*, London & New York: Academic Press.

Hinde, R.A. (1981) 'Animal signals: Ethological and games-theory approaches are not incompatible', *Animal Behaviour*, *29*, 535–42.

Hinde, R.A. (1982) *Ethology: Its nature and relations with other sciences*, Oxford: Oxford University Press.

Hinde, R.A. (1983a) 'Ethology and child development', in P.H. Mussen (series ed.), M.M. Haith and J.J. Campos (volume eds.), *Handbook of Child Psychology: Vol. 2. Infancy and developmental psychobiology*, pp. 27–93, New York: Wiley.

Hinde, R.A. (1983b) 'Dialogue with Jonathan Miller', in J. Miller (ed.), *States of Mind*, pp. 174–90, London: BBC.

Hinde, R.A. (1985a) 'Was "The Expression of the Emotions" a misleading phrase?', *Animal Behaviour*, *33*, 985–92.

Hinde, R.A. (1985b) 'Expression and negotiation', in G. Zivin (ed.), *The Development of Expressive Behavior: Biology–environment interactions*, pp. 103–16, New York & London: Academic Press.

Hinde, R.A. (1985c) 'Categories of behavior and the ontogeny of aggression', *Aggressive Behavior*, *11*, 333–5.

Hinde, R.A. (1986) 'Some implications of evolutionary theory and comparative data for the study of human prosocial and aggressive behavior', in D. Olweus, J. Block and M. Radke-Yarrow (eds.), *Development of Antisocial and Prosocial Behavior*, pp. 13–32, New York & London: Academic Press.

Hinde, R.A. (1987) *Individuals, Relationships and Culture*, Cambridge & New York: Cambridge University Press.

Hinde, R.A. (1989) 'Discussion of Symposium on "Ethology, sociobiology and developmental psychology: in memory of Niko Tinbergen and Konrad Lorenz" ', presented at the British Psychological Society Developmental Section Annual Conference, University of Surrey, 9 September.

Hinde, R.A. (1991) 'When is an evolutionary approach useful?', *Child Development*, *62*, 671–5.

Hinde, R.A. and Barden, L.A. (1985) 'The evolution of the teddy bear', *Animal Behaviour*, *33*, 1371–3.

Hinde, R.A. and Bateson, P.P.G. (1984) 'Discontinuities versus continuities in behavioural development and the neglect of process', *International Journal of Behavioural Development*, *7*, 129–43.

Hinde, R.A. and Datta, S. (1981) 'Dominance: An intervening variable (commentary)', *The Behavioral and Brain Sciences*, *4*, 442.

Hinde, R.A., Leighton-Shapiro, M.E. and McGinnis, L. (1978) 'Effects of various types of separation experience on rhesus monkeys 5 months later', *Journal of Child Psychology and Psychiatry*, *19*, 199–211.

Hinde, R.A. and McGinnis, L. (1977) 'Some factors influencing the effects of temporary mother–infant separation: some experiments with rhesus monkeys', *Psychological Medicine*, *7*, 197–212.

Hinde, R.A. and Spencer-Booth, Y. (1970) 'Individual differences in the responses of rhesus monkeys to a period of separation from their mothers', *Journal of Child Psychology and Psychiatry*, *11*, 159–76.

Hinde, R.A. and Spencer–Booth, Y. (1971) 'Effects of brief separation from mother on rhesus monkeys', *Science*, *173*, 111–18.

Hinde, R.A. and Stevenson-Hinde, J. (1986) 'Relating childhood relationships to individual characteristics', in W.W. Hartup and Z. Rubin (eds.), *Relationships and Development*, pp. 27–50, Hillsdale, NJ: Lawrence Erlbaum.

Hinde, R.A. and Stevenson-Hinde, J. (1987) 'Interpersonal relationships and child development', *Developmental Review*, *7*, 1–21.

Hinde, R.A., Thorpe, W.H. and Vince, M.A. (1956) 'The following response of young coots and moorhens', *Behaviour*, *11*, 214–42.

Hines, M. (1982) 'Prenatal gonadal hormones and sex differences in human behavior', *Psychological Bulletin*, *92*, 56–80.

Hirsch, J. (1970) 'Behavior-genetic analysis and its biosocial consequences', *Seminars in Psychiatry*, *2*, 89–105.

Hobson, R.P. (1981) 'The autistic child's concept of persons', in D. Park (ed.), *Proceedings of the 1981 International Conference on Autism*, pp. 97–102, Washington, DC: National Society for Children and Adults with Autism.

Hobson, R.P. (1990a) 'Concerning knowledge of mental states', *British Journal of Medical Psychology*, *63*, 199–213.

Hobson, R.P. (1990b) 'On acquiring knowledge about people and the capacity to pretend: response to Leslie (1987)', *Psychological Review*, *97*, 114–21.

Hodos, W. and Campbell, C.B.G. (1969) '*Scala naturae*: Why there is no theory in comparative psychology', *Psychological Review*, *76*, 337–50.

Hofer, M.A. (1984) 'Relationships as regulators: A psychobiologic perspective on bereavement', *Psychosomatic Medicine*, *46*, 183–97.

Hoffman, H.S., Searle, J.L., Toffey S. and Kozma Jr F. (1966) 'Behavioral control by an imprinted stimulus', *Journal of the Experimental Analysis of Behavior*, *9*, 177–89.

Hogstad, O. (1987) 'Is it expensive to be dominant?', *Auk*, *104*, 333–6.

Holbrook, M.B. and Schindler, R.M. (1989) 'Some exploratory findings on the development of musical tastes', *Journal of Consumer Research*, *16*, 119–24.

Hold, B.C.L. (1976) 'Attention structure and rank specific behavior in preschool children', in M.R.A. Chance and R.R. Larsen (eds.), *The Social Structure of Attention*, pp. 177–201, New York & London: Wiley.

Hold, B.C.L. (1980) 'Attention-structure and behavior in G/wi San children', *Ethology and Sociobiology*, *1*, 275–90.

Hold-Cavell, B.C.L. (1985), 'Showing-off and aggression in young children', *Aggressive Behavior*, *11*, 303–14.

Hold-Cavell, B.C.L. and Borsutzky, D. (1986) 'Strategies to obtain high regard:

Longitudinal study of a group of preschool children', *Ethology and Sociobiology*, *7*, 39–56.

Hole, G.J. and Einon, D.F. (1984) 'Play in rodents', in P.K. Smith (ed.), *Play in Animals and Humans*, pp. 95–117, Oxford: Blackwell.

Horn, H.S. and Rubenstein, D.I. (1984) 'Behavioural adaptations and life history', in J.R. Krebs and N.B. Davies (eds.), *Behavioural Ecology: An evolutionary approach* (2nd edn), pp. 279–98, Oxford: Blackwell Scientific.

Howlin, P. and Rutter, M. (1987) *Treatment of Autistic Children*, London & New York: Wiley.

Hrdy, S.B. (1981) *The Woman that Never Evolved*, Cambridge, MA & London: Harvard University Press.

Hückstedt, B. (1965) 'Experimentelle Untersuchungen zum "Kindchenschema"', *Zeitschrift für Experimentelle und Angwandte Psychologie*, *12*, 421–50.

Humphrey, N.K. (1976) 'The function of intellect', in P.P.G. Bateson and R.A. Hinde (eds.), *Growing Points in Ethology*, pp. 303–17, Cambridge & New York: Cambridge University Press.

Humphreys, A.P. and Smith, P.K. (1984) 'Rough-and-tumble in preschool and playground', in P.K. Smith (ed.), *Play in Animals and Humans*, pp. 241–66, Oxford: Blackwell Scientific.

Humphreys, A.P. and Smith, P.K. (1987) 'Rough and tumble, friendship, and dominance in schoolchildren: Evidence for continuity and change with age', *Child Development*, *58*, 201–12.

Huntingford, F.A. (1984a) *The Study of Animal Behaviour*, London & New York: Chapman & Hall.

Huntingford, F.A. (1984b) 'Some ethical issues raised by studies of predation and aggression', *Animal Behaviour*, *32*, 210–15.

Hutt, C. (1966) 'Exploration and play in young children', *Symposia of the Zoological Society of London*, *18*, 61–81.

Hutt, C. (1972) *Males and Females*, Harmondsworth: Penguin.

Hutt, C., Hutt, S.J. and Ounsted, C. (1963) 'A method for the study of children's behaviour', *Developmental Medicine and Child Neurology*, *5*, 233–45.

Hutt, C. and Ounsted, C. (1970) 'Gaze aversion and its significance in childhood autism', in S.J. Hutt and C. Hutt (eds.), *Behaviour Studies in Psychiatry*, pp. 103–20, Oxford & New York: Pergamon.

Huxley, J.S. (1914) 'The courtship of the great-crested grebe (*Podiceps cristatus*); with an addition to the theory of sexual selection', *Proceedings of the Zoological Society of London*, *35*, 491–562.

Huxley, J.S. (1958) 'Evolutionary processes and taxonomy with special reference to grades', *University of Uppsala Arsskrift*, 201–39.

Huxley, J.S. (1966) 'Ritualization of behaviour in animals and men', *Philosophical Transactions of the Royal Society of London*, *B251*, 249–71.

Immelmann, K. (1972) 'Sexual and other long-term aspects of imprinting in birds and other species', *Advances in the Study of Behavior*, *4*, 147–74.

Immelmann, K. (1981) 'Sexual imprinting', presented at XVIIth International Ethological Conference, Oxford, 1–9 September.

Immelmann, K., Pröve, R., Lassek, R. and Bischof, H.-J. (1991) 'Influence of adult courtship experience on the development of sexual preferences in zebra finch males', *Animal Behaviour*, *42*, 83–9.

Imperato-McGuinley, J., Paterson, R.E. and Gautier, T. (1976) 'Gender identity and hermaphroditism', *Science*, *191*, 872.

Izard, C.E. (1979) *The Maximally Discriminative Facial Movement Coding System (Max)*, Newark, DE: University of Delaware, Office of Academic Computing and Instructional Technology.

Izard, C.E. (1990) 'Facial expression and the regulation of emotions', *Journal of Personality and Social Psychology*, *58*, 487–98.

Jakobsson, S., Radesater, T. and Jarvi, T. (1979) 'On the fighting behaviour of *Nanacara anomala* (Pisces, Cichlidae) males', *Zeitschrift für Tierpsychologie*, *49*, 210–20.

James, W. (1892) *Psychology: The briefer course*, New York: Henry Holt (Harper Torchbook edn, ed. G. Allport, New York: Harper & Row, 1961).

Jaynes, J. (1969) 'The historical origins of "ethology" and "comparative" psychology', *Animal Behaviour*, *17*, 601–6.

Jensen, A.R. (1973) *Educability and Group Differences*, New York: Harper & Row.

Johanson, D.C. and Edey, M.A. (1981) *Lucy: The beginnings of humankind*, New York: Granada.

Johnson, D.B. (1983) 'Self–recognition in infants', *Infant Behavior and Development*, *6* 211–22.

Johnson, J.A. (1987) 'Dominance rank in juvenile olive baboons, Papio anubis: The influence of gender, size, maternal rank and orphaning', *Animal Behaviour*, *35*, 1694–708.

Johnston, T.D. (1987) 'The persistence of dichotomies in the study of behavioral development', *Developmental Review*, *7*, 149–82.

Johnston, T.D. (1988) 'Developmental explanation and the ontogeny of birdsong: Nature/nurture redux', *The Behavioral and Brain Sciences*, *11*, 617–63 (including commentaries).

Jolly, A. (1966) 'Lemur social behavior and primate intelligence', *Science*, *153*, 501–6.

Jolly, A. (1972) *The Evolution of Primate Behavior*, New York: Macmillan.

Jolly, A. (1991) 'Conscious chimpanzees? A review of recent literature', in C.A. Ristau (ed.), *Cognitive Ethology: the minds of other animals. Essays in honor of Donald R. Griffin*, pp. 231–52, Hillsdale, NJ: Lawrence Erlbaum.

Jones, D.C. (1984) 'Dominance and affiliation as factors in the social organization of same-sex groups of elementary schoolchildren', *Ethology and Sociobiology*, *5*, 193–202.

Kagan, J. (1976) 'Resilience and continuity in psychological development', in A.M. Clarke and A.D.B. Clarke (eds.), *Early Experience: Myth and evidence*, pp. 97–121, London: Open Books.

Kagan, J. (1978) 'Continuity and stage in human development', in P.P.G. Bateson and P. Klopfer (eds.), *Perspectives in Ethology 3*, pp. 67–84, New York: Plenum.

Kaufman, I.C. and Rosenblum, L.A. (1967) 'Depression in infant monkeys separated from their mothers', *Science*, *155*, 1030–1.

Kaufman, I.C. and Rosenblum, L.A. (1969) 'Effects of separation from mother on the emotional behavior of infant monkeys', *Annals of the New York Academy of Sciences*, *159*, 681–95.

Keating, C.F. (1985) 'Human dominance signals: The primate in us', in S.L. Ellyson and J.F. Dovidio (eds.), *Power, Dominance and Nonverbal Behavior*, pp. 89–108, New York & Berlin: Springer-Verlag.

Keenleyside, M.H. (1983) 'Mate desertion in relation to adult sex ratio in the biparental cichlid fish *Herotilapia multispinosa*', *Animal Behaviour, 31*, 683–8.

Kennedy, J.S. (1954) 'Is modern ethology objective?', *British Journal of Animal Behaviour, 2*, 12–19.

Klaus, M.H. and Kennell, J.H. (1976) *Maternal–Infant Bonding*, St Louis: C.V. Mosby.

Kohlberg, L. (1966) 'A cognitive-developmental analysis of children's sex-role concepts and attitudes', in E.E. Maccoby (ed.), *The Development of Sex Differences*, pp. 82–173, Stanford, CA: Stanford University Press.

Kohlberg, L. (1976) 'Moral stages and moralization: The cognitive-developmental approach', in T. Lickona (ed.), *Moral Development and Behavior: Theory, research and social issues*, pp. 31–53, New York: Holt, Rinehart & Winston.

Kramer, D.A., Anderson, R.B. and Westman, J.C. (1984) 'The corrective autistic experience: An application of the models of Tinbergen and Mahler', *Child Psychiatry and Human Development, 15*, 104–20.

Krebs, J.R. and Davies, N.B. (1986) *An Introduction to Behavioral Ecology* (2nd edn), Oxford: Blackwell.

Krebs, J.R. and Dawkins, R. (1984) 'Animal signals: Mind reading and manipulation', in J.R. Krebs and N.B. Davies (eds.), *Behavioural Ecology: an evolutionary approach* (2nd edn), pp. 380–402, Oxford: Blackwell Scientific.

Kroodsma, D.E. and Pickert, R. (1980) 'Environmentally-dependent sensitive periods for avian vocal learning', *Nature, 288*, 477–9.

Kruijt, J.P. (1964) 'Ontogeny of social behaviour in Burmese red junglefowl (*Gallus gallus spadiceus* Bonnaterre)', *Behaviour*, Supplement 12, 1–201.

Kruijt, J.P. and Meeuwissen, G.B. (1991) 'Sexual preferences of male zebra finches: effects of early and adult experience', *Animal Behaviour, 42*, 91–102.

Kummer, H., Dasser, V. and Hoyningen-Huene, P. (1990) 'Exploring primate social cognition: Some critical remarks', *Behaviour, 112*, 84–98.

Kuo, Z.Y. (1967), *The Dynamics of Development: An epigenetic view*, New York: Random House.

Lack, D. (1954) *The Natural Regulation of Animal Numbers*, Oxford: Clarendon.

LaFreniere, P. and Charlesworth, W.R. (1983) 'Dominance, attention, and affiliation in a preschool group: a nine–month longitudinal study', *Ethology and Sociobiology, 4*, 55–67.

Lamb, M.E., Thompson, R.A., Gardner, W. and Charnov, E.L. (1985) *Infant–Mother Attachment*, Hillsdale, NJ: Lawrence Erlbaum.

Lamprecht, J. (1977) 'A comparison of the attachment to parents and siblings in juvenile geese (*Branta canadensis* and *Anser indicus*)', *Zeitschrift für Tierpsychologie, 43*, 415–24.

Landau, H.G. (1951) 'On dominance relations and the structure of animal societies: 1. Effects of inherent characteristics', *Bulletin of Mathematical Biophysics, 13*, 1–19.

Laudenslager, M.L., Held, P.E., Boccia, M.L., Reite, M.L. and Cohen J.J. (1990) 'Behavioral and immunological consequences of brief mother–infant separation: A species comparison', *Developmental Psychobiology, 23*, 247–64.

Le Boeuf, B.J. (1972) 'Sexual behaviour in northern elephant seals', *Behaviour, 41*, 1–26.

Lehrman, D.S. (1953) 'A critique of Konrad Lorenz's theory of instinctive behavior', *Quarterly Review of Biology, 28*, 337–63.

Lehrman, D.S. (1970) 'Semantic and conceptual issues in the nature–nurture problem', in L.R. Aronson, E. Tobach, D.S. Lehrman and J.S. Rosenblatt (eds.), *The Development and Evolution of Behavior*, pp. 17–52, San Francisco: W.H. Freeman.

Lerner, R.M. (1976) *Concepts and Theories of Human Development*, Reading, MA: Addison-Wesley.

Leslie, A.M. (1987) 'Pretense and representation: The origins of "theory of mind" ', *Psychological Review*, *94*, 412–26.

Levine, S., Wiener, S.G., Coe, C.L., Bayart, F.E.S. and Hayashi, K.T. (1987) 'Primate vocalization: A psychobiological approach', *Child Development*, *58*, 1409–19.

Lewis, M. and Brooks-Gunn, J. (1979) *Social Cognition and the Acquisition of Self*, New York & London: Plenum.

Leyhausen, P. (1956), 'Verhaltensstudien bei Katzen', *Zeifschrift für Tierpsychologie*, Beiheft, *2*.

Leyhausen, P. (1979) *Cat Behavior*, New York: Garland STPM Press.

Lickliter, R. and Berry, T.D. (1990) 'The phylogeny fallacy: Developmental psychology's misapplication of evolutionary theory', *Developmental Review*, *10*, 348–64.

Littlefield, C.H. and Rushton, J.P. (1986) 'When a child dies: The sociobiology of bereavement', *Journal of Personality and Social Psychology*, *51*, 797–802.

Lloyd Morgan, C. (1894) *An Introduction to Comparative Psychology*, London: Walter Scott.

Lockard, R.B. (1971) 'Reflections on the fall of comparative psychology: Is there a message for us all?', *American Psychologist*, *26*, 168–79.

Locke, J.L. (1990) 'Structure and stimulation in the ontogeny of spoken language', *Developmental Psychobiology*, *23*, 621–43.

Lorenz, K. (1937) 'A companion in the bird's world', *Auk*, *54*, 245–73.

Lorenz, K. (1941) 'Vergleichende Bewegungsstudien an Anatinen', *Supplement, Journal of Ornithology*, *89*, 194–294.

Lorenz, K. (1943) 'Die angeborenen Formen möglicher Erfahrung', *Zeitschrift für Tierpsychologie*, *5*, 235–409.

Lorenz, K. (1950a) 'Part and parcel in animal and human societies', *Studies in Animal and Human Behavior, Volume II*, translated by R. Martin, pp. 115–95, London: Methuen, 1971.

Lorenz, K. (1950b) 'The comparative method in studying innate behaviour patterns', *Symposia of the Society for Experimental Biology*, *4*, 221–68.

Lorenz, K. (1953) 'Die Gestaltwahrnehmung als Quelle wissenschaftlicher Erkenntnis', *Zeitschrift für Experimentelle und Angewandte Psychologie*, *6*, 118–65.

Lorenz, K. (1965) *Evolution and Modification of Behavior*, Chicago: University of Chicago Press.

Lorenz, K. (1966) *On Aggression*, New York: Harcourt, Brace & World.

Lovejoy, O. (1981) 'The origin of man', *Science*, *211*, 341–50.

Low, B.S. (1989) 'Cross-cultural patterns in the training of children: An evolutionary perspective', *Journal of Comparative Psychology*, *103*, 311–19.

Lunardini, A. (1989) 'Social organization in a confined group of Japanese macaques (*Macaca fuscata*): An application of correspondence analysis', *Primates*, *30*, 175–85.

McArthur, L.Z. and Apatow, K. (1983–4) 'Impressions of baby-faced adults', *Social Cognition*, *2*, 315–42.

McArthur, L.Z. and Berry, D.S. (1987) 'Cross-cultural agreement in perceptions of babyfaced adults', *Journal of Cross-Cultural Psychology*, *18*, 165–92.

McArthur, L. and Montepare, J.M. (1989) 'Contributions of a baby face and a childlike voice to impressions of moving and talking faces', *Journal of Nonverbal Behavior*, *13*, 189–203.

McCance, R.A. (1962) 'Food, growth and time', *The Lancet*, *2* (6 October), 671–6.

Maccoby, E.E. (1988) 'Gender as a social category', *Developmental Psychology*, *24*, 755–65.

MacDonald, K.B. (1987) 'The interfaces between sociobiology and developmental psychology', in K.B. MacDonald (ed.), *Sociobiological Perspectives on Human Development*, pp. 3–23, New York & Berlin: Springer-Verlag.

McFarland, D.J. (1989) *Problems of Animal Behavior*, New York: Wiley.

McGrew, W.C. (1969) 'An ethological study of agonistic behaviour in preschool children', in C.R. Carpenter (ed.), *Proceedings of the Second International Congress of Primatology, Atlanta, Georgia, Vol. 1*, pp. 149–59, Basel & New York: Karger.

McGrew, W.C. (1972a) *An Ethological Study of Children's Behavior*, New York & London: Academic Press.

McGrew, W.C. (1972b) 'Aspects of social development in nursery school children with emphasis on the introduction to the group', in N. Blurton Jones (ed.), *Ethological Studies of Child Behaviour*, pp. 129–56, London: Cambridge University Press.

Machlis, L., Dodd, P.W. and Fentress, J.C. (1985) 'The pooling fallacy: problems arising when individuals contribute more than one observation to a data set', *Zeitschrift für Tierpsychologie*, *68*, 201–14.

Main, M. (1990) 'Cross-cultural studies of attachment organization: Recent studies, changing methodologies and the concept of conditional strategies', *Human Development*, *33*, 48–61.

Major, D.R. (1906) *First Steps in Mental Growth*, New York & London: Macmillan.

Mann, J., ten Have, T., Plunkett, J.W. and Meisels, S.J. (1991) 'Time sampling: A methodological critique', *Child Development*, *62*, 227–41.

Manning, M., Heron, J. and Marshall, T. (1978) 'Styles of hostility and school interactions at nursery, at school, and at home. An extended study of children', in L.A. Hersov, M. Berger and D. Shaffer (eds.), *Aggression and Anti-social Behaviour in Childhood and Adolescence*, pp. 29–58, Oxford & New York: Pergamon Press.

Manning, M. and Herrmann, J. (1981) 'The relationships of problem children in nursery school', in S. Duck and R. Gilmour (eds.), *Personal Relationships 3. Personal relationships in disorder*, pp. 143–67, London & New York: Academic Press.

Manning, M. and Sluckin, A.M. (1984) 'The function of aggression in the pre-school and primary school years', in N. Frude and H. Gault (eds.), *Disruptive Behaviour in Schools*, pp. 43–56, London & New York: Wiley.

Marler, P. (1952) 'Variation in the song of the chaffinch *Fringilla coelebs*', *The Ibis*, *94*, 458–72.

Marler, P. (1956) 'Behaviour of the chaffinch, *Fringilla coelebs*, *Behaviour*, Supplement 5, 1–184.

Marler, P. (1976) 'An ethological theory of the origin of vocal learning', *Annals of the New York Academy of Sciences*, *280*, 386–95. (S.R. Harnad, H.D. Steklis and J. Lancaster (eds.), *Origins and evolution of language and speech*, New York Academy of Sciences).

Marler, P. (1990) 'Innate learning preferences: Signals for communication', *Developmental Psychobiology*, *23*, 557–68.

Marler, P. and Tamura, M. (1964) 'Culturally transmitted patterns of vocal behavior in sparrows', *Science*, *146*, 1483–6.

Martin, M.K. and Voorhies, B. (1975) *The Female of the Species*, New York & London: Macmillan.

Martin, P. (1984) 'The time and energy costs of play behaviour in the cat', *Zeitschrift für Tierpsychologie*, *64*, 298–312.

Martin, P. and Bateson, P.P.G. (1986) *Measuring Behaviour*, Cambridge: Cambridge University Press.

Martin, P. and Caro, T. (1985) 'On the functions of play and its role in behavioral development', *Advances in the Study of Behavior*, *15*, 59–103.

Martin, R. (1975) 'Strategies of reproduction', *Natural History*, November, 48–57.

Masataka, N., Ishida, T., Suzuki, J., Matsumura, S., Udono, S. and Sasaoka, S. (1990) 'Dominance and immunity in chimpanzees (Pan troglodytes)', *Ethology*, *85*, 147–55.

Maslow, A.H. (1936) 'The role of dominance in the social and sexual behavior of infra-human primates: IV. The determination of hierarchy in pairs and in a group', *Journal of Genetic Psychology*, *49*, 161–98.

Mather, K. and Jinks, J.L. (1971) *Biometrical Genetics: The study of continuous variation* (2nd edn), London: Chapman & Hall.

Maynard Smith, J. (1964) 'Group selection and kin selection', *Nature*, *210*, 1145–7.

Maynard Smith, J. (1974) 'The theory of games and the evolution of animal conflicts', *Journal of Theoretical Biology*, *47*, 209–21.

Maynard Smith, J. (1977) 'Parental investment: A prospective analysis', *Animal Behaviour*, *25*, 1–9.

Maynard Smith, J. (1982) *Evolution and the Theory of Games*, Cambridge & New York: Cambridge University Press.

Mead, G.H. (1934) *Mind, Self and Society from the Standpoint of a Social Behaviorist*, Chicago, Ill. & London: The University of Chicago Press.

Meadows, S. (1986) *Understanding Child Development*, London: Hutchinson.

Mealey, L. (1990) 'Differential use of reproductive strategies by human groups?', *Psychological Science*, *1*, 385–7.

Meddis, R. (1975) 'On the function of sleep', *Animal Behaviour*, *23*, 676–91.

Meddis, R. (1977) *The Sleep Instinct*, London: Routledge & Kegan Paul.

Melson, G.F. and Dyer, D. (1987) 'Dominance and visual attention rank orders in preschool groups', *Perceptual and Motor Skills*, *65*, 570.

Michel, G.F. (1991) 'Human psychology and the minds of other animals', in C. Ristau (ed.), *Cognitive Ethology: The minds of other animals. Essays in honor of Donald R. Griffin*, pp. 253–72, Hillsdale, NJ: Lawrence Erlbaum.

Miller, M.N. and Byers, J.A. (1991) 'Energetic costs of locomotor play in pronghorn fawns', *Animal Behaviour*, *41*, 1007–15.

Miller, P.H. (1983) *Theories of Developmental Psychology*, San Francisco: W.H. Freeman.

Miller, P.H. (1989) *Theories of Developmental Psychology*, (2nd edn), San Francisco: W.H. Freeman.

Milne, A.A. and Shepard E.H. (1926) *Winnie-the-Pooh*, London: Methuen.

Mineka, S. and Suomi, S.J. (1978) 'Social separation in monkeys', *Psychological Bulletin*, *85*, 1376–400.

Mock, D.W. and Fujioka, M. (1990) 'Monogamy and long-term pair bonding in vertebrates', *Trends in Ecology and Evolution*, 5, 39–43.

Money, J. and Ehrhardt, A.A. (1972) *Man and Woman, Boy and Girl*, Baltimore & London: Johns Hopkins University Press.

Money, J., Hampson, J.G. and Hampson, J.L. (1957) 'Imprinting and the establishment of gender role', *Archives of Neurology and Psychiatry*, 77, 333–6.

Morgan, B.J.T., Simpson, M.J.A., Hanby, J.P. and Hall-Craggs, J. (1976) 'Visualizing interaction and sequential data in animal behaviour: theory and application of cluster analysis methods', *Behaviour*, 56, 1–43.

Morgan, P. (1975) *Child Care: sense and fable*, London: Temple Smith.

Morris, D. (1957) ' "Typical intensity" and its relation to the problem of ritualisation', *Behaviour*, 11, 1–12.

Morris, D. (1958) 'The reproductive behaviour of the ten-spined stickleback (*Pygosteus pungitus L.*)', *Behaviour*, Supplement 6, 1–154.

Morris, D. (1967) *The Naked Ape: A zoologist's study of the human animal*, London: Jonathan Cape; New York: McGraw-Hill.

Moynihan, M. (1955) 'Some aspects of reproductive behaviour in the black-headed gull (*Larus ridibundus ridibundus L.*) and related species', *Behaviour*, Supplement 4, 1–201.

Moynihan, M. (1958) 'Notes on the behaviour of some North American gulls. II: Non-aerial hostile behaviour of adults', *Behaviour*, 12, 95–182.

Moynihan, M. (1962) 'Hostile and sexual behaviour patterns of South American and Pacific Laridae', *Behaviour*, Supplement 8, 1–365.

Murray, L. and Stein, A. (1990) 'The effects of postnatal depression on the infant', in M.R. Oates (ed.), *Psychological Disorders in Obstetrics and Gynaecology*, London: Baillière Tindall.

Myers, B.J. (1984) 'Mother–infant bonding: The status of this critical period hypothesis', *Merrill Palmer Quarterly*, 4, 240–74.

Naef, A. (1926) 'Über die Urformen der Anthropomorphen und die Stammesgeschichte des Menschenschädels', *Naturwiss*, 14, 445–52.

Neill, S.R. St J. (1976) 'Aggressive and non-aggressive fighting in 12 to 13 year-old preadolescent boys', *Journal of Child Psychology and Psychiatry*, 17, 213–20.

Neisser, U. (1976) *Cognition and Reality*, San Francisco: W.H. Freeman.

Nelissen, M.H.J. (1985) 'Structure of the dominance hierarchy and dominance determining "group factors" in Melanochromis auratus (Pisces, Cichlidae)', *Behaviour*, 94, 85–107.

Noakes, D.G.L. (1981) 'Comparative aspects of behavioral ontogeny: A philosophy from fishes', in K. Immelmann, G.W. Barlow, L. Petrinovich and M. Main (eds.), *Behavioral Development: The Bielefeld interdisciplinary project*, pp. 491–508, Cambridge and New York: Cambridge University Press.

Norman, R.F., Taylor, P.D. and Robertson, R.J. (1977) 'Stable equilibrium strategies and penalty functions in a game of attrition', *Journal of Theoretical Biology*, 65, 571–8.

Nottebohm, F. (1971) 'Neural lateralization of vocal control in a passerine bird: I. song', *Journal of Experimental Zoology*, 177, 229–62.

Nottebohm, F. (1977) 'Asymmetries in neural control of vocalisation in the canary', in S. Harnad, D.W. Doty, L. Goldstein, J. Jaynes and G. Krauthamer (eds.), *Lateralization in the Nervous System*, pp. 23–44, New York: Academic Press.

Olson, W.C. (1930) 'The incidence of nervous habits in children', *Journal of Abnormal and Social Psychology*, *35*, 75–92.

Omark, D.R. (1980) 'Human ethology: A holistic perspective', in D.R. Omark, F.F. Strayer and D.C. Freedman (eds.), *Dominance Relations: An ethological view of human conflict and social interaction*, pp. 3–20, New York & London: Garland STPM Press.

Ounsted, C. (1955) 'The hyperkinetic syndrome in epileptic children', *The Lancet*, *ii*, 303–11.

Oyama, S. (1979) 'The concept of the sensitive period in developmental studies', *Merrill Palmer Quarterly*, *25*, 83–103.

Parker, G.A. (1970) 'Sperm competition and its evolutionary consequences in the insects', *Biological Reviews*, *45*, 525–67.

Parker, G.A. (1974) 'Assessment strategy and the evolution of fighting behavior', *Journal of Theoretical Biology*, *47*, 223–43.

Parkes, C.M. (1986) *Bereavement: Studies of grief in adult life* (2nd edn), London: Tavistock.

Passingham, R. (1982) *The Human Primate*, Oxford & San Francisco: W.H. Freeman.

Patterson, G.R. and Maerov, S.L. (1978) 'Observation as a mode of investigation', in J.B. Reid (ed.), *A Social Learning Approach to Family Intervention Volume 2: Observation in home settings*, pp. 1–2, Eugene, OR: Castalia.

Patterson, G.R., Reid, J.B. (ed.), and Maerov, S.L. (1978) 'Development of the family interaction coding system (FICS)', in J.B. Reid (ed.), *A Social Learning Approach to Family Intervention Volume 2: Observation in home settings*, pp. 3–9, Eugene, OR: Castalia.

Pearl, M.C. and Schulman, S.R. (1983) 'Techniques for the analysis of social structure in animal societies', *Advances in the Study of Behavior*, *13*, 107–46.

Pellis, S.M. (1981) 'A description of social play by the Australian magpie, *Gymnorhina tibican* based on Eshkol-Wachman notation', *Bird Behaviour*, *3*, 61–79.

Pellis, S.M. (1988) 'Agonistic versus amicable targets of attack and defense: Consequences for the origin, function and descriptive classification of play-fighting', *Aggressive Behavior*, *14*, 85–104.

Pellis, S.M. and Pellis, V.C. (1983) 'Locomotor-rotational movements in the ontogeny and play of the laboratory rat *Rattus norvegicus*', *Developmental Psychobiology*, *16*, 269–86.

Pellis, S.M. & Pellis, V.C. (1987) 'Play-fighting differs from serious fighting in both target of attack and tactics of fighting in the laboratory rat *Rattus norvegicus*', *Aggressive Behavior*, *13*, 227–42.

Pellis, S.M. and Pellis, V.C. (1988) 'Play-fighting in the Syrian golden hamster *Mesocricetus auratus* Waterhouse, and its relationship to serious fighting during postweaning development', *Developmental Psychobiology*, *21*, 323–37.

Pepperberg, I.M. (1990) 'Some cognitive capacities of an African Grey parrot (*Psittacus erithacus*)', *Advances in the study of behavior*, *19*, 357–409.

Pepperberg, I.M. (1991) 'A communicative approach to animal cognition: A study of conceptual abilities of an African Grey parrot', in C.A. Ristau (ed.), *Cognitive Ethology: The minds of other animals. Essays in honor of Donald R. Griffin*, pp. 153–86, Hillsdale, NJ: Lawrence Erlbaum.

Pepperberg, I.M. and Funk, M. (1990) 'Object permanence in four species of Psittacine birds: An African Grey parrot (*Psittacus erithacus*), an Illiger Mini Macaw (*Ara maracana*), a Parakeet (*Melopsittacus undulatus*) and a Cockatiel (*Nymphicus hollandicus*)', *Animal Learning and Behavior*, *18*, 97–108.

Pepperberg, I.M. and Kozak, F.A. (1986) 'Object permanence in the African Grey parrot (*Psittacus erithacus*)', *Animal Learning and Behavior, 14*, 322–30.

Petrinovich, L. and Baptista, L.F. (1987) 'Song development in the white-crowned sparrow. Modification of learned song', *Animal Behaviour, 35*, 961–74.

Pettijohn, T.F. (1979) 'Attachment and separation distress in the guinea pig', *Developmental Psychobiology, 12*, 73–81.

Piaget, J. (1924) *Le Jugement et le raisonnement chez l'enfant*, translated as *Judgement and Reasoning in the Child*, 1928, London: Routledge & Kegan Paul.

Piaget, J. (1936) *La Naissance de l'intelligence chez l'enfant*, translated as *The Origin of Intelligence in the Child*, 1953, London: Routledge & Kegan Paul.

Poole, T.B. and Fish, J. (1976) 'An investigation of individual, age and sexual differences in the play of *Rattus norvegicus* (Mammalia: Rodentia)', *Journal of Zoology, 179*, 249–60.

Porter, R.H., Berryman, J.C. and Fullerton, C. (1973) 'Exploration and attachment in infant guinea pigs', *Behaviour, 45*, 312–22.

Povinelli, D.J. (1987) 'Monkeys, apes, mirrors and minds: The evolution of self-awareness in primates', *Human Evolution, 2*, 493–509.

Povinelli, D.J. (1989) 'Failure to find self-recognition in Asian elephants (*Elephas maximus*) in contrast to their use of mirror cues to discover hidden food', *Journal of Comparative Psychology, 103*, 122–31.

Pöysä, H. (1991) 'Measuring time budgets with instantaneous sampling: a cautionary note', *Animal Behaviour, 42*, 317–18.

Premack, D. (1983) 'The codes of man and beasts', *The Behavioral and Brain Sciences, 6*, 124–67 (including commentaries).

Premack, D. and Woodruff, G. (1978) 'Does the chimpanzee have a theory of mind?', *The Behavioral and Brain Sciences, 4*, 515–26.

Probst, B. (1987) 'Developmental changes in the pituitary–gonadal-axis in male Mongolian gerbils from birth to adulthood', *Experimental Clinical Endocrinology, 90*, 157–66.

Pyke, G.H., Pulliam, H.R. and Charnov, E.L. (1977) 'Optimal foraging: A selective review of theory and tests', *Quarterly Review of Biology, 52*, 137–54.

Rajecki, D.W., Lamb, M.E. and Obmascher, P. (1978) 'Towards a general theory of infantile attachment: A comparative review of aspects of the social bond', *The Behavioral and Brain Sciences, 3*, 417–64 (including commentaries).

Ramsay, A.O. (1951) 'Familial recognition in domestic birds', *Auk, 68*, 1–16.

Reed, G.L. and Leiderman, P.H. (1983) 'Is imprinting an appropriate model for human infant attachment?', *International Journal of Behavioral Development, 6*, 51–69.

Reite, M. (1987) 'Infant abuse and neglect: lessons from the primate laboratory', *Child Abuse and Neglect, 11*, 347–55.

Reite, M., Short, R., Seiler, C. and Pauley, J.D. (1981) 'Attachment, loss and depression', *Journal of Child Psychology and Psychiatry, 22*, 141–69.

Reynolds, P.C. (1982) 'Affect and instrumentality: an alternative view on Eibl-Eibesfeldt's human ethology', *The Behavioral and Brain Sciences, 5*, 267–74 (including author's response).

Rheingold, H.L. (1967) 'A comparative psychology of development', in H.W. Stevenson, E.H. Hess, and H.L. Rheingold (eds.), *Early Behavior: Comparative and developmental approaches*, pp. 279–93, New York: Kreiger.

Rheingold, H.L. and Keene, G.C. (1965) 'Transport of the human young', in B.M. Foss (ed.), *Determinants of Infant Behaviour Vol. III*, pp. 87–110, London: Methuen.

Rice, M. (1980), *Cognition to Language: Categories, word meanings, and training*, Baltimore, MD: University Park Press.

Richards, M.P.M. and Bernal, J.F. (1972) 'An observational study of mother–infant interaction', in N.G. Blurton Jones (ed.), *Ethological Studies of Child Behaviour*, pp. 175–97, London & New York: Cambridge University Press.

Richer, J. (1976) 'The social-avoidance behaviour of autistic children', *Animal Behaviour*, 24, 898–906.

Richer, J. (1979) 'Human ethology and psychiatry', in H.M. van Praag, M.H. Lader, O.J. Rafaelsen and E.J. Sachar (eds.), *Textbook of Biological Psychiatry*, pp. 163–93, New York: M. Dekker Inc.

Richer, J. (1983) 'Development of social avoidance in autistic children', in A. Oliverio and M. Zappella (eds.), *The Behavior of Human Infants*, pp. 241–66, New York: Plenum.

Richer, J. (1988) 'Ethology and disturbed behaviour in children', *Human Ethology Newsletter*, 5 (issue 7), 2–6.

Richer, J. and Coss, R.G. (1976) 'Gaze aversion in autistic and normal children', *Acta Psychiatrica Scandinava*, 53, 193–210.

Richer, J. and Zappella, M. (1989) 'Changing social behaviour. The place of holding', *Communication*, 23, 35–9.

Richman, N. (1976) 'Depression in mothers of preschool children', *Journal of Child Psychology and Psychiatry*, 17, 75–8.

Ristau, C.A. (1986) 'Do animals think?', in R.J. Hoage and L. Goldman (eds.), *Animal Intelligence: insights into the animal mind*, pp. 165–85, Washington, D.C. & London: Smithsonian Institution Press.

Ristau, C.A. (1991) 'Cognitive psychology: an overview', in C.A. Ristau (ed.), *Cognitive Ethology: The minds of other animals. Essays in honor of Donald R. Griffin*, pp. 291–313, Hillsdale, NJ: Lawrence Erlbaum.

Ritchey, R.L. and Hennessy, M.B. (1987) 'Cortisol and behavioral responses to separation in mother and infant guinea pigs', *Behavioral and Neural Biology*, 48, 1–12.

Röell, A. (1978) 'Social behaviour of the jackdaw, *Corvus monedula*, in relation to its niche', *Behaviour*, 64, 1–124.

Rohwer, S. and Ewald, P.W. (1981) 'The cost of dominance and advantage of subordination in a badge signalling system', *Evolution*, 35, 441–54.

Rosaldo, M.Z. (1974) 'Women, culture and society: A theoretical overview', in M.Z. Rosaldo and L. Lamphere (eds.), *Women, Culture and Society*, pp. 16–42, Stanford, CA: Stanford University Press.

Rose, S., Kamin, L.J. and Lewontin, R.C. (1984) *Not in our Genes*, Harmondsworth: Penguin Books.

Rowell, T.E. (1966), 'Hierarchy in the organization of a captive baboon group', *Animal Behaviour*, 14, 430–43.

Rowell, T.E. (1974) 'The concept of social dominance', *Behavioral Biology*, 11, 131–54.

Rushton, J.P. (1985) 'Differential K theory: The sociobiology of individual and group differences', *Personality and Individual Differences*, 6, 441–52.

Rushton, J.P. (1988) 'Race differences in behavior', *Personality and Individual Differences*, 9, 1009–24.

Rushton, J.P. and Erdle, S. (1987) 'Evidence for an aggressive (and delinquent) personality', *British Journal of Social Psychology*, 26, 87–9.

Rutter, M. (1978) 'Diagnosis and definition', in M. Rutter and E. Schopler (eds.), *Autism – a reappraisal of concepts and treatments*, pp. 1–25, New York: Plenum.

Rutter, M. (1979a) *Maternal Deprivation Reassessed* (2nd edn), Harmondsworth: Penguin Books.

Rutter, M. (1979b) 'Maternal deprivation, 1972–1978: new findings, new concepts, new approaches', *Child Development*, 50, 283–305.

Sachser, N. and Lick, C. (1991) 'Social experience, behavior, and stress in guinea pigs', *Physiology and Behavior*, 50, 83–90.

Sackin, S. and Thelen, E. (1984) 'An ethological study of peaceful associative outcomes of conflict in preschool children', *Child Development*, 55, 1098–102.

Salzen, E.A. and Meyer, C.C. (1967) 'Imprinting: reversal of a preference established during the critical period', *Nature*, 215, 785–6.

Sants, J. (1980) 'The child in psychology', in J. Sants (ed.), *Developmental Psychology and Society*, pp. 15–45, London & Basingstoke: Macmillan.

Savage-Rumbaugh, E.S. (1986) *Ape Language: From conditioned response to signal*, Oxford: Oxford University Press; New York: Columbia University Press.

Savin-Williams, R.C. (1976) 'An ethological study of dominance formation and maintenance in a group of human adolescents', *Child Development*, 47, 972–9.

Savin-Williams, R.C. (1977) 'Dominance in a human adolescent group', *Animal Behaviour*, 25, 400–6.

Savin-Williams, R.C. (1980a) 'Dominance and submission among early adolescent boys', in D.R. Omark, F.F. Strayer and D.G. Freedman (eds.), *Dominance Relations: An ethological view of human conflict and social interaction*, pp. 217–29, New York & London: Garland STPM Press.

Savin-Williams, R.C. (1980b) 'Social interactions of adolescent females in natural groups', in H.C. Foot, A.J. Chapman and J.R. Smith (eds.), *Friendship and Social Relations in Children*, pp. 343–64, Chichester & New York: Wiley.

Scarr, S. and McCartney, K. (1983) 'How people make their own environments. A theory of genotype→environment effects', *Child Development*, 54, 424–35.

Schaffer, H.R. (1977) 'Early interactive development', in H.R. Schaffer (ed.), *Studies in Mother–Infant Interaction*, pp. 3–16, London & New York: Academic Press.

Schenkl, R. (1956) 'Zur Deutung der Phasianidenbalz', *Der Ornithologische Beobachter*, 53, 182–201.

Schjelderup-Ebbe, T. (1922), 'Beiträge zur Socialpsychologie des Haushuhns', *Zeitschrift für Psychologie*, 88, 225–52.

Schleidt, W.M. (1974) 'How "fixed" is the fixed action pattern?', *Zeitschrift für Tierpsychologie*, 36, 184–211.

Schneirla, T.C. (1959) 'An evolutionary and developmental theory of biphasic processes underlying approach and withdrawal', in M.R. Jones (ed.), *Nebraska Symposium on Motivation, Vol. 7*, pp. 1–42, Lincoln: University of Nebraska Press.

Scott, J.P. (1944) 'Social behavior, range and territoriality in domestic mice', *Proceedings of the Indiana Academy of Sciences*, 53, 415–20.

Scott, J.P. (1946) 'Incomplete adjustment caused by frustration of untrained fighting mice', *Journal of Comparative Psychology*, 39, 379–90.

Scott, J.P. (1962) 'Critical periods in behavioral development', *Science*, 138, 949–58.

Scott, J.P. and Fredericson, E. (1951) 'The causes of fighting in mice and rats', *Physiological Zoology*, *24*, 273–309.

Scott, J.P. and Marston, M.V. (1950) 'Critical periods affecting the development of normal and maladjusted social behavior of puppies', *Journal of Genetic Psychology*, *77*, 25–60.

Searle, J.R. (1980) 'Minds, brains and programs', *The Behavioral and Brain Sciences*, *3*, 417–57 (including commentaries).

Seay, B., Hansen, E. and Harlow, H.F. (1962) 'Mother–infant separation in monkeys', *Journal of Child Psychology and Psychiatry*, *3*, 123–32.

Senar, J.C., Camerino, M. and Metcalfe, N.B. (1989) 'Agonistic interactions in siskin flocks: Why are dominants sometimes subordinate?', *Behavioral Ecology and Sociobiology*, *25*, 141–5.

Seyfarth, R.M., Cheney, D.L. and Marler, P. (1980) 'Monkey responses to three different alarm calls: evidence of predator classification and semantic communication', *Science*, *210*, 801–3.

Shaffer, D.R. (1989) *Developmental Psychology: Childhood and adolescence* (2nd edn), Pacific Grove, CA: Brooks/Cole.

Shepher, J. (1971) 'Mate selection among second generation Kibbutz adolescents and adults: incest avoidance and negative imprinting', *Archives of Sexual Behavior*, *1*, 293–307.

Short, R. and Horn, J. (1984), 'Some notes on factor analysis of behavioral data', *Behaviour*, *90*, 203–14.

Short, R.V. (1980) 'The origins of sexuality', in C.R. Austin and R.V. Short (eds.), *Reproduction in Mammals, vol. 8: Human sexuality*, pp. 1–33, Cambridge: Cambridge University Press.

Simon, T. and Smith, P.K. (1983) 'The study of play and problem solving in preschool children: Have experimenter effects been responsible for previous results?', *British Journal of Developmental Psychology*, *1*, 289–97.

Simon, T. and Smith, P.K. (1985) 'Play and problem solving: A paradigm questioned', *Merrill Palmer Quarterly*, *31*, 256–77.

Simpson, M.J.A. (1968) 'The display of the Siamese fighting fish *Betta splendens*', *Animal Behaviour Monographs*, *1*, 1–73.

Singer, J.L. (1973) *The Child's World of Make-believe: Experimental studies of imaginative play*, New York & London: Academic Press.

Singer, P. (1976) *Animal Liberation: Towards an end to man's inhumanity to animals*, London: Jonathan Cape.

Slater, P.J.B. (1973) 'Describing sequences of behavior', in P.P.G. Bateson and P.H. Klopfer (eds.), *Perspectives in Ethology*, pp. 131–53, New York: Plenum.

Slater, P.J.B. (1978) 'Data collection', in P.W. Colgan (ed.), *Quantitative Ethology*, pp. 8–28, New York & London: Wiley.

Slater, P.J.B (1983) 'The development of individual behaviour', in T.R. Halliday and P.J.B. Slater (eds.), *Animal Behaviour, 3: Genes, development and learning*, pp. 82–113, Oxford: Blackwell Scientific.

Slater, P.J.B. (1986) 'Individual differences and dominance hierarchies', *Animal Behaviour*, *34*, 1264–5.

Slocum, S. (1975) 'Woman the gatherer: Male bias in anthropology', in R. Reiter (ed.), *Toward an Anthropology of Women*, pp. 36–50, New York & London: Monthly Review Press.

Sluckin, A.M. and Smith, P.K. (1977) 'Two approaches to the concept of dominance in preschool children', *Child Development, 48,* 917–23.

Sluckin, W. (1968), 'Imprinting in guinea pigs', *Nature, 220,* 1148.

Sluckin, W. (1972) *Imprinting and Early Learning* (2nd edn), London: Methuen.

Sluckin, W., Herbert, M. and Sluckin, A. (1983) *Maternal Bonding,* Oxford: Blackwell.

Smith, P.K. (1974) 'Aggression in a preschool playgroup: effects of varying physical resources', in J. DeWit and W.W. Hartup (eds.), *Determinants and Origins of Aggressive Behaviour,* 97–105, The Hague: Mouton.

Smith, P.K. (1978) 'A longitudinal study of social participation in preschool children: solitary and parallel play re-examined', *Developmental Psychology, 14,* 517–23.

Smith, P.K. (1979) 'How many people can a young child feel secure with?', *New Society, 48,* 504–6.

Smith, P.K. (1980) 'Shared care of young children: alternative models to monotropism', *Merrill Palmer Quarterly, 26,* 371–89.

Smith, P.K. (1982) 'Does play matter: Functional and evolutionary costs of animal and human play', *The Behavioral and Brain Sciences, 5,* 139–84 (including commentaries).

Smith, P.K. (1988) 'Children's play and its role in early development: A re-evaluation of the "play ethos" ', in A.D. Pellegrini (ed.), *Psychological Bases of Early Education,* pp. 207–26, New York & London: Wiley.

Smith, P.K. (1989) 'Ethological approaches to the study of aggression in children', in J. Archer and K. Browne (eds.), *Human Aggression: Naturalistic approaches,* pp. 65–93, London & New York: Routledge.

Smith, P.K. and Boulton, M. (1990) 'Rough-and-tumble play, aggression and dominance: Perception and behavior in children's encounters', *Human Development, 33,* 271–82.

Smith, P.K. and Connolly, K.J. (1972) 'Patterns of play and social interaction in pre-school children', in N. Blurton Jones (ed.), *Ethological Studies of Child Behaviour,* pp. 65–95, London: Cambridge University Press.

Smith, P.K. and Connolly, K.J. (1977) 'Social and aggressive behaviour in preschool children as a function of crowding', *Social Science Information, 16,* 601–20.

Smith, P.K. and Connolly, K.J. (1980) *The Ecology of Preschool Behaviour,* Cambridge: Cambridge University Press.

Smith, P.K. and Cowie, H. (1988) *Understanding Children's Development,* Oxford: Blackwell.

Smith, P.K. and Lewis, K. (1985) 'Rough-and-tumble play, fighting, and chasing in nursery school children', *Ethology and Sociobiology, 6,* 175–81.

Smith, W.J. (1965) 'Message, meaning and context in ethology', *American Naturalist, 99,* 405–9.

Sodian, B. (1991) 'The development of deception in young children', *British Journal of Developmental Psychology, 9,* 173–88.

Sodian, B., Taylor, C., Harris, P. and Perner, J. (1991) 'Early deception and the child's theory of mind: false trails and genuine markers', *Child Development, 62,* 468–83.

Sparks, J. (1982) *The Discovery of Animal Behaviour,* London: Collins/BBC.

Spencer-Booth, Y. and Hinde, R.A. (1971a) 'Effects of 6 days' separation from mother on 18- to 32-week old rhesus monkeys', *Animal Behaviour, 19,* 174–91.

Spencer-Booth, Y. and Hinde, R.A. (1971b) 'The effects of 13 days' maternal separation on infant rhesus monkeys compared to those of shorter and repeated separations', *Animal Behaviour, 19,* 595–605.

Spinozzi, G. and Natale, F. (1989) 'Early sensorimotor development in gorilla', in F. Antinucci (ed.), *Cognitive Structure and Development in Nonhuman Primates*, pp. 21–38, Hillsdale, NJ: Lawrence Erlbaum.

Sroufe, L.A. (1988) 'The role of infant–caregiver attachment in development', in J. Belsky and T. Nezworski (eds.), *Clinical Implications of Attachment*, pp. 18–38, Hillsdale, NJ and London: Lawrence Erlbaum.

Sroufe, L.A. and Waters, E. (1977) 'Attachment as an organizational construct', *Child Development*, 48, 1184–99.

Sternglanz, S.H., Gray, J.L. and Murakami, M. (1977) 'Adult preferences for infantile facial features: An ethological approach', *Animal Behaviour*, 25, 108–15.

Stokes, A.W. (1962) 'Agonistic behaviour among blue tits at a winter feeding station', *Behaviour*, 19, 118–38.

Strayer, F.F. (1980a) 'Current problems in the study of human dominance', in D.R. Omark, F.F. Strayer and D.G. Freedman (eds.), *Dominance Relations: An ethological view of human conflict and social interaction*, pp. 443–52, New York & London: Garland STPM Press.

Strayer, F.F. (1980b) 'Child ethology and the study of preschool social relations', in H.C. Foot, A.J. Chapman and J.R. Smith (eds.), *Friendship and Social Relations in Children*, pp. 235–65, New York & Chichester: Wiley.

Strayer, F.F. (1989) 'Coalitions and redirected aggression in the preschool peer group', presented at the British Psychological Society Developmental Section Annual Conference, University of Surrey, 9 September.

Strayer, F.F. and Noel, J.M. (1986) 'The prosocial and antisocial functions of preschool aggression: An ethological study of triadic conflict among young children', in C. Zahn-Waxler, E.M. Cummings and R. Iannotti (eds.), *Altruism and Aggression: Biological and social origins*, pp. 107–31, Cambridge & New York: Cambridge University Press.

Strayer F.F. and Strayer, J. (1976) 'An ethological analysis of social agonism and dominance relations among preschool children', *Child Development*, 47, 980–9.

Strayer, F.F. and Trudel, M. (1984) 'Developmental changes in the nature and function of social dominance among young children', *Ethology and Sociobiology*, 5, 279–95.

Studdert-Kennedy, M. (1981) 'The beginnings of speech', in K. Immelmann, G.W. Barlow, L. Petrinovich and M. Main (eds.), *Behavioral Development: The Bielefeld interdisciplinary project*, pp. 533–61, Cambridge & New York: Cambridge University Press.

Sullivan, K. and Winner, E. (1991) 'When 3-year-olds understand ignorance, false beliefs and representational change,' *British Journal of Developmental Psychology*, 9, 159–71.

Suomi, S.J. (1989) 'Genetic and environmental factors shaping individual differences in rhesus monkey behavioural development,' presented at the 21st International Ethological Conference, Utrecht, 9–17 August.

Sutton-Smith, B. and Kelly-Byrne, D. (1984) 'The idealization of play', in P.K. Smith (ed.),*Play in Animals and Humans*, pp. 306–21, Oxford: Blackwell.

Sylva, K. and Lunt, I. (1981) *Child Development: a first course*, Oxford: Blackwell.

Sylva, K., Roy, C. and Painter, M. (1980) *Child Watching at Playgroup and Nursery School*, London: Grant McIntyre.

Symons, D. (1979) *The Evolution of Human Sexuality*, New York & Oxford: Oxford University Press.

Tanner, J.M. (1970) 'Physical growth', in P.H. Mussen (ed.), *Carmichael's Manual of Child Psychology Vol. 1* (3rd edn), New York: Wiley.

Taylor, G.T. (1980) 'Fighting in juvenile rats and the ontogeny of agonistic behavior', *Journal of Comparative and Physiological Psychology*, *94*, 953–61.

ten Cate, C. (1989) 'Behavioural development: toward understanding processes', in P.P.G. Bateson and P.H. Klopfer (eds.), *Perspectives in Ethology 8*, pp. 243–69, New York: Plenum.

Thelen, E. (1979) 'Rhythmical stereotypies in normal human infants', *Animal Behaviour*, *27*, 699–715.

Thelen, E. (1981) 'Kicking, rocking, and waving: contextual analyses of rhythmical stereotypies in normal human infants', *Animal Behaviour*, *29*, 3–11.

Thomas, A., Chess, S. and Birch, H.G. (1970) 'Origins of personality', *Scientific American*, *223*, 102–9.

Thor, D.H. and Holloway, W.R. Jr (1983) 'Play-solicitation behavior in juvenile male and female rats', *Animal Learning and Behavior*, *11*, 173–8.

Thorpe, W.H. (1951) 'The learning abilities of birds', *The Ibis*, *93*, 252–96.

Thorpe, W.H. (1954) 'The process of song-learning in the chaffinch as studied by means of the sound spectrograph', *Nature*, *173*, 465–9.

Thorpe, W.H. (1956) *Learning and Instinct in Animals*, London: Methuen.

Thorpe, W.H. (1958) 'The learning of song patterns by birds with special reference to the song of the chaffinch, *Fringilla coelebs*', *The Ibis*, *100*, 535–70.

Thorpe, W.H. (1961) *Bird Song*, Cambridge: Cambridge University Press.

Thorpe, W.H. (1979) *The Origins and Rise of Ethology*, London: Heinemann; New York: Praeger.

Tinbergen, N. (1942) 'An objectivistic study of the innate behaviour of animals', *Bibliotheca Biotheoretica*, *1*, (2), 39–98.

Tinbergen, N. (1950) 'The hierarchical organization of nervous mechanisms underlying instinctive behaviour', *Symposium of the Society for Experimental Biology*, *4*, 305–12.

Tinbergen, N. (1951) *The Study of Instinct*, London: Oxford University Press.

Tinbergen, N. (1952a) 'Derived activities, their causation, biological significance, origin, and emancipation during evolution', *Quarterly Review of Biology*, *27*, 1–32.

Tinbergen, N. (1952b) 'A note on the origin of threat displays', *The Ibis*, *94*, 160–2.

Tinbergen, N. (1953) *Social Behaviour in Animals*, London: Methuen.

Tinbergen, N. (1959) 'Comparative studies of the behaviour of gulls (Laridae): A progress report', *Behaviour*, *15*, 1–70.

Tinbergen, N. (1963) 'On the aims and methods of ethology', *Zeitschrift für Tierpsychologie*, *20*, 410–33.

Tinbergen, N. and Tinbergen, E.A. (1983) *'Autistic' children: new hope for a cure*, London: Allen & Unwin.

Tinbergen, N. and van Iersel, J.J.A. (1948) ' "Displacement reactions" in the three-spined stickleback', *Behaviour*, *1*, 56–63.

Townshend, T.J. and Wootton, R.J. (1985) 'Variation in the mating system of a biparental cichlid fish, *Cichlasoma panamense*', *Behaviour*, *95*, 181–97.

Trevarthen, C. (1977) 'Descriptive analyses of infant communicative behavior', in

H.R. Schaffer (ed.), *Studies in Mother–Infant Interaction*, pp. 227–70, London & New York: Academic Press.

Trivers, R.L. (1971) 'The evolution of reciprocal altruism', *Quarterly Review of Biology*, *46*, 35–57.

Trivers, R.L. (1972) 'Parental investment and sexual selection', in B. Campbell (ed.), *Sexual Selection and the Descent of Man*, Chicago: Aldine.

Trivers, R.L. (1974) 'Parent–offspring conflict', *American Zoologist*, *14*, 249–64.

Tyler, S. (1979) 'Time-sampling: a matter of convention', *Animal Behaviour*, *27*, 801–10.

Uhrich, J. (1938) 'The social hierarchy in albino mice', *Journal of Comparative Psychology*, *25*, 373–413.

Umbertson, D. (1986) 'Sociobiology: a valid explanation of child abuse?', *Social Biology*, *33*, 131–7.

Unwin, D.M. and Martin, P. (1987) 'Recording behaviour using a portable microcomputer', *Behaviour*, *101*, 87–100.

Uzgiris, I.C. and Hunt, J. (1975), *Assessment in Infancy: Ordinal scales of psychological development*, Champaign, IL: University of Illinois Press.

van den Bercken, J.H.L. and Cools, A.R. (1980) 'Information-statistical analysis of factors determining ongoing behaviour and social interaction in Java monkeys (*macaca fascicularis*)', *Animal Behaviour*, *28*, 189–200.

van de Rijt-Plooij, H.H.C. and Plooij, F.X. (1987) 'Growing independence, conflict and learning in mother–infant relations in free-living chimpanzees', *Behaviour*, *101*, 1–86.

van der Heijden, P.G.M., de Vries, H. and van Hooff, J.A.R.A.M. (1990) 'Correspondence analysis of transition matrices, with special attention to missing entries and asymmetry', *Animal Behaviour*, *40*, 49–64.

van Engeland, H., Bodnar, F.A. and Bolhuis, G. (1985) 'Some qualitative aspects of the social behaviour of autistic children: An ethological approach', *Journal of Child Psychology and Psychiatry*, *26*, 879–93.

van Hooff, J.A.R.A.M. (1967) 'The facial displays of the Catarrhine monkeys and apes', in D. Morris (ed.), *Primate Ethology*, pp. 7–68, London: Weidenfeld & Nicolson.

van Hooff, J.A.R.A.M. (1972) 'A comparative approach to the phylogyny of laughter and smiling', in R.A. Hinde (ed.), *Non-verbal Communication*, pp. 209–41, Cambridge: Cambridge University Press.

van Lawick-Goodall, J. (1967) 'Mother–offspring relationships in free-ranging chimpanzees', in D. Morris (ed.), *Primate Ethology*, pp. 286–346, London: Weidenfeld & Nicolson.

van Lawick-Goodall, J. (1970) 'Tool-using in primates and other vertebrates', *Advances in the Study of Behavior*, *3*, 195–249.

van Wyk, P.H. and Geist, C.S. (1984) 'Psychosocial development of heterosexual, bisexual, and homosexual behavior', *Archives of Sexual Behavior*, *13*, 505–44.

Vaughn, B.E. and Waters, B. (1980) 'Social organization among preschool peers: Dominance, attention and sociometric correlates', in D.R. Omark, F.F Strayer and D.G. Freedman (eds.), *Dominance Relations: An ethological view of human conflict and social interaction*, pp. 359–79, New York & London: Garland STPM Press.

Vodegel, N. (1978) 'A causal analysis of the behaviour of Pseudotropheus zebra (Boulenger) (Pisces, Cichlidae)', PhD thesis, Rijksuniversiteit Groningen.

Voland, E. and Engel, C. (1990) 'Female choice in humans: A conditional mate selection strategy of Krummhorn women (Germany, 1720–1873)', *Ethology*, *84*, 144–54.

von Cranach, M., Foppa, K., Lepenies, W. and Ploog, D. (1979) 'Introduction', in M. von Cranach, K. Foppa, W. Lepenies, and D. Ploog (eds.), *Human Ethology*, pp. xiii–xix, Cambridge & New York: Cambridge University Press.

von Cranach, M. and Vine, I. (1973) 'Introduction', in M. von Cranach and I. Vine (eds.), *Social Communication and Movement: Studies of interaction and expression in man and chimpanzee*, London & New York: Academic Press.

von Frisch, K. (1967) *The Dance Language And Orientation of Bees*, Cambridge, MA: Belknap Press of Harvard University Press.

von Uexküll, J. (1934) 'Streifzüge durch die Umwelten von Tieren und Menschen', Berlin: Springer, translated as 'A stroll through the worlds of animals and man', in C.H. Schiller (ed.), *Instinctive Behaviour: The development of a modern concept* (1957), London: Methuen.

Waddington, C.H. (1957) *The Strategy of Genes*, London: Allen & Unwin.

Waters, E. (1978) 'The reliability and stability of individual differences in infant–mother attachment', *Child Development*, *49*, 483–94.

Weisfeld, G.E. (1980) 'Social dominance and human motivation', in D.R. Omark, F.F. Strayer and D.G. Freedman (eds.), *Dominance Relations: An ethological view of human conflict and social interaction*, pp. 273–86, New York & London: Garland STPM Press.

Weisfeld, G.E., Muczenski, D.M., Weisfeld, C.C. and Omark, D.R. (1987) 'Stability of boys' social success among peers over an eleven-year period', in J.M. Meacham (ed.), *Interpersonal Relations: Family, peers, friends*, pp. 58–80, Basel & New York: Karger.

Weisfeld, G.E., Omark, D.R. and Cronin, C.L. (1980) 'A longitudinal and cross-sectional study of dominance in boys', in D.R. Omark, F.F. Strayer and D.G. Freedman (eds.), *Dominance Relations: An ethological view of human conflict and social interaction*, pp. 205–16, New York & London: Garland STPM Press.

West, M.J., King, A.P. and Duff, M.A. (1990) 'Communicating about communicating: When innate is not enough', *Developmental Psychobiology*, *23*, 585–98.

Westermarck, E. (1891) *The History of Human Marriage*, London: Macmillan.

Westermarck, E. (1922) *The History of Human Marriage* (5th edn), New York: Allerton Book Company.

Whitam, F.L. and Zent, M. (1984) 'A cross-cultural assessment of early cross-gender behavior and familial factors in male homosexuality', *Archives of Sexual Behavior*, *13*, 427–39.

White, B.L. (1969) 'Child development research: An edifice without a foundation', *Merrill Palmer Quarterly*, *15*, 49–78.

Whiten, A. and Byrne, R.W. (1988) 'Tactical deception in primates', *The Behavioral and Brain Sciences*, *11*, 233–73 (including commentaries).

Whiting, B.B. and Edwards, C.P. (1988) *Children of Different Social Worlds: The formation of social behavior*, Cambridge, MA & London: Harvard University Press.

Wickler, W. (1967) 'Socio-sexual signals and their intra-specific imitation among primates', in D. Morris (ed.), *Primate Ethology*, pp. 69–147, London: Weidenfeld & Nicolson.

Wiepkema, P.R. (1961) 'An ethological analysis of the reproductive behaviour of the bitterling (Rhodeus amarus Bloch)', *Archives Neerlandaises de Zoologie, 14*, 103–99.

Wiepkema, P.R. (1977) 'Agressief gedrag als regalsysteem', in P.R. Wiepkema and J.A.R.A.M. van Hooff (eds.), *Agressief Gedrag: Oorzaken en functies*, pp. 69–78, Utrecht: Bohn, Scheltema en Holkema.

Wilkinson, S. (1986) 'Sighting possibilities: Diversity and commonality in feminist research', in S. Wilkinson (ed.), *Feminist Social Psychology: Developing Theory and Practice*, pp. 7–24, Milton Keynes & Philadelphia: Open University Press.

Wilson, E.O. (1975) *Sociobiology: The new synthesis*, Cambridge, MA: Harvard University Press.

Wilson, E.O. (1977) 'Animal and human sociobiology', in C.E. Goulden (ed.), *The Changing Scenes in the Natural Sciences 1776–1976*, pp. 273–81, Philadelphia, PA: Philadelphia Academy of Natural Sciences.

Wimmer, H. and Perner, J. (1983) 'Beliefs about beliefs: Representation and constraining function of wrong beliefs in young children's understanding of deception', *Cognition, 13*, 103–28.

Winter, J.S.D., Hughes, I.A., Reyes, F.I. and Faiman, C. (1976) 'Pituitary-gonadal relations in infancy: 2. Patterns of serum gonadal steroid concentrations in man from birth to two years of age', *Journal of Clinical Endocrinology and Metabolism, 42*, 679–86.

Woodruff, G. and Premack, D. (1979) 'Intentional communication in the chimpanzee: The development of deception, *Cognition, 7*, 333–62.

Wright, A.A., Shyan, M.R. and Jitsumori, M. (1990) 'Auditory *same/different* concept learning by monkeys', *Animal Learning and Behavior, 18*, 287–94.

Wynne Edwards, V.C. (1962) *Animal Dispersion in Relation to Social Behaviour*, Edinburgh: Oliver & Boyd.

Yarczower, M. and Hazlett, L. (1977) 'Evolutionary scales and anagenesis', *Psychological Bulletin, 84*, 1088–97.

Yoerg, S.I. and Kamil, T.C. (1991) 'Integrating cognitive ethology with cognitive psychology', in C. Ristau (ed.), *Cognitive Ethology: The minds of other animals. Essays in honor of Donald R. Griffin*, pp. 273–89, Hillsdale, NJ: Lawrence Erlbaum.

Zuckerman, S. (1932) *The Social Life of Monkeys and Apes*, London & Boston: Routledge & Kegan Paul.

Name index

Abbott, D., 124
Abramovitch, R., 20, 143
Ainsworth, M.D.S., 37, 49, 50, 53–4, 105, 117
Albon, S.D., 199
Alcock, J., 161
Aldis, O., 162–4, 170
Allee, W.C., 128, 130, 132
Alley, T.R., 85
Altmann, J., 21, 22, 161
Altmann, S.A., 6, 31, 195, 196
Ambrose, J.A., 91, 150, 178, 181
Anastasi, A., 58, 60, 61
Anderson, J.R., 216
Andrew, R.J., 181–4, 190, 192, 194, 200
Apatow, K., 88–9
Appleby, M.C., 133, 134–7, 139
Archer, J., 6, 23–4, 30, 46, 47, 55, 63, 66, 71, 75, 85, 100, 106, 107, 114, 115, 120, 122, 124, 126, 133, 140, 165, 167, 188, 195, 196–9
Ardrey, R., 155
Astington, J.W., 219, 224
Attili, G., 82, 106–9
Atz, J.W., 152

Baerends, G.P., 3, 4, 9, 38, 81, 82, 93, 94, 95–7, 109, 122, 187, 189
Baerends-van Roon, J.M., 4
Bakeman, R., 14–15, 18, 22, 24, 25, 26, 31
Bandura, A., 35–6
Baptista, L.F., 67, 172
Barash, D.P., 10, 114, 116, 160
Barber, N., 162, 169
Barden, L.A., 86–8, 126
Barlow, G.W., 5, 62, 91, 178
Barnard, C.J., 129, 132
Baron-Cohen, S., 104–5, 219
Barrett, J., 124
Barrett, P., 166

Bateman, A.J., 113, 115
Bateson, P.P.G., 12, 14, 20–2, 24, 25, 26, 37, 49, 53, 58–67, 69–70, 72–3, 75, 77, 78, 116, 121–2, 125, 166, 178
Beach, F.A., 116, 150, 151, 161
Beer, C.G., 204, 212, 213, 214, 225
Bekoff, M., 162–3
Belsky, J., 118, 119
Bennett, J., 213, 220
Bernal, J.F., 10, 14, 26
Bernstein, I.S., 131, 138, 140
Berry, D.S., 88–90
Berry, T.D., 1, 158
Bertenthal, B.I., 216, 218
Bickerton, D., 208
Bischof, H-J., 69, 72
Bishop, D.T., 197, 198
Blanchard, D.C., 107
Blanchard, R.J., 107
Blest, D., 180
Block, N., 178
Blurton Jones, N., 9–10, 15, 18–19, 25, 26, 30, 33–6, 82, 100–1, 106, 108, 109, 125, 131, 165, 170, 176–7, 179, 186, 190–2, 194, 200
Boakes, R., 3, 150
Bolles, R.C., 178
Borgerhoff Mulder, M., 125
Bornstein, M.H., 67, 72
Borsutzky, D., 143
Boulton, M.J., 35, 36, 82, 100, 165, 166
Bowlby, J., 1, 4, 8–9, 39–43, 45–8, 55, 68, 82, 91–2, 93–5, 98–100, 109, 117, 122, 124, 178
Bradshaw, J.L., 174
Brannigan, C., 15, 17, 19, 20, 30, 177, 179, 189, 200
Bronfenbrenner, U., 34, 38
Brooks-Gunn, J., 213, 216
Brown, A.L., 208, 211

264

Subject index